50p

Modern Construction Management

Modern Construction Management

Second Edition

Frank Harris
and
Ronald McCaffer

COLLINS
8 Grafton Street, London W1

Collins Professional & Technical Books
William Collins Sons & Co. Ltd
8 Grafton Street, London W1X 3LA

First published in Great Britain 1977 by Granada Publishing Limited
in Crosby Lockwood Staples (0 258 97064 2 hk)
Reprinted in paperback 1979 (0 258 97164 9)
Reprinted 1981 by Granada Publishing (0 246 11712 5)
Second edition 1983 (0 246 11818 0)
Reprinted 1984
Reprinted with minor updates 1985 by Collins Professional & Technical Books

Copyright © Frank Harris and Ronald McCaffer 1977, 1983

British Library Cataloguing in Publication Data
Harris, Frank
    Modern construction management. – 2nd ed.
    1. Construction industry – Management
    I. Title   II. McCaffer, Ronald
    624′.068   HD9715.A2

ISBN 0 00 383198 1

Printed in Great Britain by
Richard Clay (The Chaucer Press) Ltd, Bungay, Suffolk

CONTENTS

ACKNOWLEDGEMENTS

The book has benefited from the generosity of the many colleagues who read and criticised the original script in part or in total and those who assisted in the preparation of some of the diagrams, drafting and typing, particularly Vera Cole.

Thanks are due to J. B. Evans who helped write some of the computer programs and to Keith Lawson, construction plant consultant, for his helpful comments.

The authors also thank E. G. Trimble for his advice on the manuscript of the first edition.

Finally, thanks are extended to Loughborough University of Technology for permission to use past examination questions.

PREFACE

This book is aimed at aspiring construction industry executives and students of civil engineering, building and quantity surveying. Like the first edition published in 1977 this edition is divided into three sections. The first two sections reflect distinct phases in a successful construction industry executive's career, namely site experience followed by head office activities. The third section contains computer-based training games to aid the understanding of the techniques featured in the first two sections and, in particular, to provide a means of training that exposes the learner to uncertainty. For example, while it is relatively easy to understand planning techniques it is much more difficult to plan, monitor and re-plan continually in an uncertain environment.

The second edition has been extended in response to the demands of course tutors at home and overseas in the Universities, Polytechnics, Scottish Central Institutions and Technical Colleges who have adopted the book as a teaching text and to reflect industry's interest in the authors' research in work study and computer-aided estimating. The second edition has also provided the opportunity to make revisions in response to changes in some aspects of financial legislation and taxation, and to deal more fully with the effects of inflation which has become deeply rooted in recent years. Specifically, the chapter on financial management has been updated to include the recommendations of the accountancy profession in dealing with inflation in the profit and loss statement and balance sheet. The chapter on plant selection has been enlarged to reflect the growing need for more efficient management of plant fleets in the construction enterprise and covers purchasing, selection, maintenance, organisation and control of equipment. The chapter on economic assessments has been extended to include explanations of how inflation can be incorporated into such assessments and the chapter on cash flow now includes fuller explanations of the variables that control capital lock-up in a project and the effects of inflation and price adjustment formulae.

Two completely new chapters have been introduced, one on work study which illustrates comprehensively the modern methods used for monitoring and improving construction productivity. The other, on estimating and tendering, deals with the processes employed to produce estimates and tenders, the calculations involved and the modern computer aids available.

Because the authors have intended this book to reflect the career patterns of young managers from site control to general management the logic of the presentation needs to be understood and it is recommended that Chapter 1, which sets out the contents, is read first.

INTRODUCTION

This book is divided into three sections:

Section 1   deals with management techniques relating to production planning and cost control of projects including work study and plant management.

Section 2   deals with broader aspects of management and with techniques relating to company organisation and control.

Section 3   presents some simulations and management games, or exercises, that can be used as part of in-house training or as part of a course in a university or college. The simulations and games demonstrate the applications and implications of some of the more important techniques described in sections 1 and 2.

The reasons for this particular presentation are:

1. The successful construction industry executive has two distinct phases in his career. One phase is the first 10 to 20 years which are spent on site, the other is the remainder of his career which involves him in head office activities. Sections 1 and 2 are intended to cater for these two phases.

2. The construction industry is inherently an uncertain industry. This uncertainty arises from the nature of the industry itself – the competitive tendering process, the company's turnover, site production rates and the weather are all variable. Construction industry executives must learn to cope with this. The management techniques described in sections 1 and 2 help to reduce variability, for example with proper planning the duration of a project is not just an experienced guess. The inevitable residual variability in even the best-run company needs to be controlled by:

    (a) Planning and setting targets
    (b) Choosing methods to achieve such plans and targets
    (c) Monitoring progress
    (d) Taking corrective action when necessary.

This continual monitoring and revision is ultimately the only way to cope with uncertainty and variability. The simulations presented in section 3 offer this experience in a training environment.

Objectives and contents

Each chapter deals with a specific topic. (Each topic dealt with could, if exhaustively treated, form the basis of a whole book; suggestions for further reading appear at the ends of chapters.) The level of detail aimed at is that which will provide the reader with a basic working knowledge of the topic, rather than with specialist expertise. For example, the planning section of the book explains the major techniques available for planning both repetitive and non-repetitive works in sufficient detail to allow the intelligent engineer to apply them; it should enable him to understand and talk sensibly to a specialist support group such as a planning department. Engineers and builders need enough knowledge to enable them to understand, appreciate and, where necessary, question the work of specialist support staff such as accountants, cost clerks, planners and plant managers. A grasp of the techniques described in sections 1 and 2 helps in achieving this skill. Participation in the exercises and simulations in section 3 provides a deeper and better understanding of the implications of the various techniques.

This book largely covers the numerically based techniques which assist in resource management. It does not deal with the management of human resources as considered from a psychological or sociological standpoint, which is a subject beyond its scope.

A number of topics are covered, and it has been assumed that the reader from industry has some experience which will act as a reference or framework for each. The student can, of course, turn to his tutor for discussion relating to the context in which the various techniques are used.

The contents are:

Section 1

Section 1 relates to project planning, cost control, work study and plant management as follows:

Chapter 2: Planning techniques deals with the principles of the techniques used in planning repetitive or non-repetitive construction work. Described are bar charts, linked bar charts, network analysis and line of balance scheduling.

Chapter 3: Work study covers the techniques of method study, time study, delay surveys, and time-lapse photography.

Chapter 4: Activity sampling describes a method of checking productivity without either waiting to the end of a section of work or continuously monitoring the operations.

Chapter 5: Incentives links the use of bonus schemes to motivation theory.

Chapter 6: Cost control gives guidance on the various cost control methods available.

Chapter 7: Plant management considers the financing of plant and gives guidance on plant selection. Calculating a hire rate and maintenance procedures are also covered.

Most chapters also provide exercises which are useful in testing whether the newly acquired knowledge is fully understood. In particular, the planning exercise at the end of Chapter 2 forms the basis of the planning and resource decision simulation described in Chapter 17; also, the principles of line of balance described in Chapter 2 are applied in the 'Roadway Game' in Chapter 18, which again involves planning and resource decisions. Both of the games reflect the variability of output experienced in real life and require the participant to take account of this variability. There is evidence that people who are introduced to planning techniques in short courses or in company training seminars, while they may enjoy the exercise, do not implement their new-found knowledge because the classroom example was simple and contrived, unlike their real job. Equally, real jobs used as examples result in very long training courses! A compromise is to let the new user of a technique experience some of the difficulties of real-world application through simulation exercises. Chapters 17 and 18 are examples of such exercises.

Section 2

Section 2 relates to company organisation and control. It is hoped that the information in this section will help project-based staff to understand and appreciate the company's attitudes and activities, and it is also hoped that this section will ease the transition from site to head office. The topics described are:

Chapter 8: Company organisation, a brief description and discussion of company structure and managerial responsibilities.

Chapter 9: Market planning, a description of a marketing approach to construction and of the benefits likely to be derived.

Chapter 10: Estimating and tendering, a description of the parties involved in the estimating and tendering process and a description of the process, including the decisions and calculations involved and the use of computers in estimating.

Chapter 11: Competitive bidding, an examination of the effect of estimating accuracy which implies the need for more resources in the estimating department, and a review of how to interpret the various available items of data relating to competitors' behaviour.

Chapter 12: Cash flow forecasting, a case for company cash flow forecasting and some guidance on how to do this type of forecasting.

Chapter 13: Economic assessments, a description of the principles employed in economic comparisons and in measuring rates of return.

Chapter 14: Financial management, a description of the sources and means of acquiring capital funds and the use of balance sheets and profit and loss accounts.

Again, where appropriate, some chapters contain exercises to test understanding of the techniques. The contractors' management game, in Chapter 15 (section 3), relies on an understanding of competitive bidding, cash flow forecasting and financial management. The game has been used successfully to demonstrate how the uncertainty of the bidding process leads to a fluctuating turnover with consequential difficulties in recovering overheads and making adequate cash provisions. Chapter 16, the investment appraisal exercise, shows that DCF (discounted cash flow) yield is a good measure of a project's profitability.

Section 3

Section 3 presents simulations or games that highlight some of the techniques described in the earlier chapters. The simulations or games are further used to introduce to otherwise 'static' exercises the real-life condition of variability: e.g. estimates are subject to error, productivity is subject to varying output rates. The participant can thus experience, in a training environment, the effect of such variability on his own plans and targets. All these games were specifically designed for the construction industry.

Chapter 15. Contractors' management game illustrates the relationships between estimating accuracy, mark-up, bidding success, overhead recovery, company cash flow and profit. A simpler bidding game is also presented. Chapter 15 relies on material discussed in Chapters 10, 11, 12 and 14.

Chapter 16: Investment appraisal exercise demonstrates that the use of DCF yield to discriminate between alternative projects leads to the fastest capital recovery and hence company growth. Chapter 16 relies on material discussed in Chapter 13.

Chapter 17: A labour-scheduling game for construction work is a planning and resource allocation exercise for non-repetitive work which has to take account of variations in productivity. Chapter 17 relies on material discussed in Chapter 2.

Chapter 18: Roadway game is a planning and resource allocation exercise for repetitive work which has to take account of variations in productivity. Chapter 18 relies on material discussed in Chapter 2.

The simulations or games in Chapters 15, 17 and 18 are presented complete with the listing of the original computer programs. These programs have been written in Fortran for an ICL 1904A computer, and can quite easily be used on a similar machine, with no program rewriting. Use on a different machine may require some rewriting but this will be a small chore in comparison to developing the programs from scratch. Assistance by someone with experience in computers and in Fortran will be necessary to set up and run these programs successfully.

The research reported in Chapter 11 relating to the effect of estimating accuracy and interpreting competitors' behaviour, and the work on the estimating system referred to in Chapter 10, and cash flow forecasting system in Chapter 12 were carried out in the Department of Civil Engineering, Loughborough University. The management games and exercises in section 3 of the book have also been developed within the same department.

SECTION ONE

CHAPTER 2

PLANNING TECHNIQUES

Summary

Bar charts, linked bar charts, activity on the arrow networks, precedence diagrams and line of balance schedules.

Who Plans?

A number of people require plans – proposed programmes of work – of varying complexity for varying purposes: the estimating department requires a project plan of work around which to develop proposed construction methods, and hence estimates: the site manager, at the start of the project, needs plans or work programmes to determine his resource requirements; the site manager, during the execution of the project, needs plans to assist him to direct his resources, to monitor progress and to evaluate the effect of the changes that may be imposed by varying productivity, by mistakes, by the weather or by the client; the section engineer needs a detailed plan of the week's work.

In some companies planning is provided as a service, by a central planning department, for estimators and site engineers; in others, they must rely on their own planning skills. It is sometimes considered that centralised planning results in the imposition of a plan of operation, whereas site staff have a sense of commitment to plans they have drawn up themselves. In all companies, however, the person in charge of the individual section of work, i.e. the section engineer, must plan that work or suffer the resulting uncertainty.

Planning Techniques

The most common and widely used techniques available for planning are: (1) bar charts and linked bar charts; (2) network analysis, either activity on the arrow or on the node; and (3) line of balance, for repetitive construction work.

1. Bar Charts and Linked Bar Charts

Bar charts are the easiest to understand and the most widely used form of planning tool. Even when the more sophisticated techniques like network analysis are used the eventual schedule of work is usually presented in bar chart form.

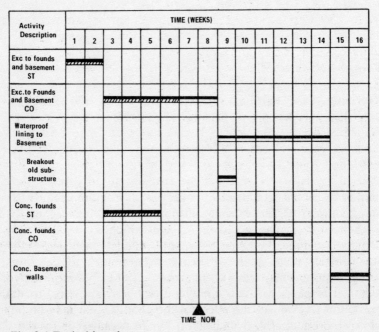

Fig. 2.1 Typical bar chart.

The bar chart in Fig. 2.1 shows the typical form: a list of activities with the start, duration and finish of each activity shown as a 'bar' plotted to a time scale. The level of detail of the activities depends on the intended use of the plan. The site manager may be content with an activity as broad as 'Construct foundations'. The section engineer will break this into a finer level of detail, say 'Excavate', 'Blind', 'Fix reinforcement', 'Erect side shutters', 'Concrete', 'Strike shutters', 'Cure' and

'Backfill'. Similarly the time scale will be chosen to suit the user's purpose. The site manager may use weeks while the section engineer may use days or half days.

Figure 2.1 also shows the bar chart being used as a progress control chart. The bars are in two sections, the upper section showing the planned time, the lower section left blank for recording progress. At the end of each time period the amount of work done in each activity is recorded by shading the lower section. Figure 2.1 shows time now as being end of week 7, the shading on the chart shows activities 'Exc. to founds and basement ST' and 'Conc. founds ST' are 100% complete. Activity 'Exc. to founds and basement CO' is shown as being four-sixths or 67% complete whereas, to be on programme, it should be 83% complete. This means that this activity is unlikely to finish at the end of week 8 as planned. The lower section could be extended to show the new time of finishing. The effect on the other activities would need to be calculated. This effect would be more easily studied by using an extension to the simple bar chart such as the linked bar chart.

The linked bar chart, as in Fig. 2.2, shows the links between an activity and the preceding activities which have to be complete before this activity can start. Similarly the links are shown between the activity and the succeeding activities which are dependent on the activity being completed. This illustration of dependency between activities has the advantage that the effect of delays in any activity are easily seen. The time available for each activity is also displayed: for example, in Fig. 2.2 activity 'Conc. founds ST' is shown as starting on week 3 and finishing on week 5, but it can be seen that the absolute deadline before it interferes with the next succeeding activity, 'Conc. founds CO', is end of week 9. This activity has some 'float' or extra time available before any delay affects other activities. Activity 'Exc. to founds and basement CO' for example, has no float and must be completed by week 8; this is usually called a critical activity.

The bar chart is also useful for calculating the resources required for the project. To add the resources, say labourers, to each activity and total them as in Fig. 2.2 is called resource aggregation. An aggregation chart similar to the one produced in Fig. 2.2 for labourers can also be done separately for other resource types such as carpenters or steelfixers, or cranes.

The bar chart and the resource aggregation charts are useful for estimating the work content in terms of manhours or machine hours. Similar calculations done on site may be used to check the work content implied by the estimate, so as to determine whether the chosen construction methods will result in a profit or loss. Cost control is more effectively based on such assessment of construction method than on simple historical cost checks.

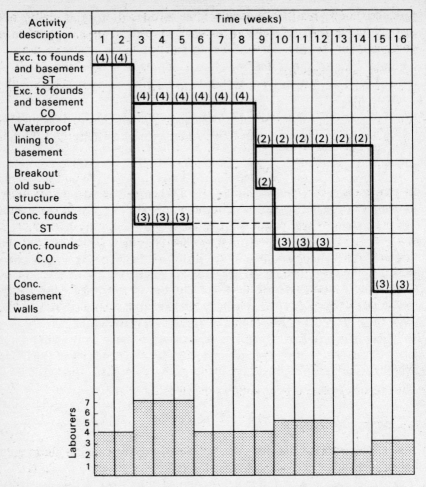

Fig. 2.2 A linked bar chart and resource aggregation chart. The vertical links indicate dependency between activities, the broken lines indicate 'float'. Labourers required shown in brackets.

Bar charts as means of communication between engineers and foreman are particularly useful and can be improved by colour coding the activities, for example blue for carpenters, yellow for steelfixers etc.

2. Network Analysis

Network analysis offers little more than a linked bar chart, but its protagonists claim, with some justification, that the smaller, self-contained steps of a network are more applicable to complex operations than is the bar chart, and that the greater rigour imposed by the logic diagram produces more realistic models of the proposed work. Finally, only through some form of network analysis is there a possibility of using computers for the calculations. The steps in producing a network are:

(*a*) Listing the activities
(*b*) Producing a network showing the logical relationship between activities
(*c*) Assessing the duration of each activity, producing a schedule, and determining the start and finish times of each activity and the float available
(*d*) Assessing the resources required

In producing a bar chart (*b*) and (*c*) are taken in one step and therefore in complex projects the various alternatives are unlikely to be considered.

There are now two popular forms of network analysis, activity on the arrow and activity on the node, the latter now usually called a precedence diagram. Each of these approaches offers virtually the same facilities and it seems largely a matter of preference which is used. Enthusiasts of precedence diagrams claim that the technique is more easily understood by the uninitiated. 'Activity on the arrows' will be described first and the differences with 'precedence diagrams' will be highlighted.

Activity on the Arrow ·

The preparing of a network follows the steps listed above.

(a) *Listing the activities*

The comments regarding the level of detail are the same as those given for bar charts.

(b) *Producing a logical network of activities*

Network logic   In this system of planning, the activity is represented by an arrow. Unless the network is being drawn to a time scale the length of the arrow is irrelevant. Even if the ultimate network will be drawn to a time scale it is not recommended that it be so drawn in the first instance.

The arrows are joined together in a logical relationship, and as each arrow is included in the network three questions should be asked in order to check that correct logic is being maintained. The questions are:

Which activities must be complete before this activity starts?
Which activities cannot start until this activity is complete?
Which activities have no logical relationship with this activity and can therefore take place at the same time?

Ignoring the restraints that will be placed upon the sequence of activities by resources, either labour or plant, the network that satisfies the above questions will show the logical relationship of all activities. It may be necessary to introduce *dummy* arrows, drawn as broken lines, which do not represent any activity but are simply a logical link. For example, if activity C was dependent on only A and B being completed and activity D was dependent only on B being completed, the network would require a *dummy* arrow to represent the logic as shown in Fig. 2.3.

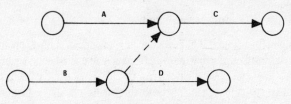

Fig. 2.3 A dummy arrow to maintain correct logic.

Identifying the activities   The points where arrows start or finish are called *events*. The numbering of these events provides a method of identification. As an example the 'Conc. founds CO' activity in Fig. 2.4 would be called activity ④–⑤. Excepting that each event must have a unique number there are no special rules to observe. Most practitioners begin numbering at the start of the network and progress through the events in numerical order until the end event is reached, ensuring that the number at the tail of an arrow is always smaller than that at the head of the arrow. There may be situations where two arrows leave the same event and arrive together at another event. In this case the activities would have the same identification numbers. To avoid this, a *dummy* is used and an extra event introduced thus ensuring that each activity has a unique identification. Figure 2.5 gives an example.

(c) *Producing a Schedule*

Durations and time analysis   The time required for each activity needs to be estimated; the estimate of duration will be based on knowledge of the work, experience, records and work study. Once estimated, the duration of each activity is marked against the arrow in the logic network. The earliest possible time of each event is then calculated and written in the left-hand square alongside each event. This has determined the earliest possible start time of each activity.

The calculations are shown in Fig. 2.4. For example, the earliest time of event ① is 0, the earliest time of event ② is $0 + 2 = 2$, the earliest time of event ③ is $2 + 6 = 8$ and so on. The point to watch is that where two paths or chains of activities merge, as for example at event ④, the

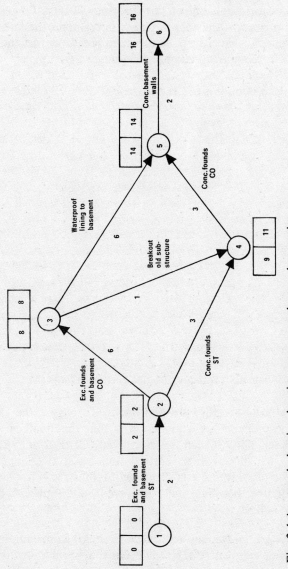

Fig. 2.4 A network showing durations, event numbers and event times.

longest path determines the earliest possible time of the event. At event ④ the path via event ③ produces an earliest time of $8 + 1 = 9$ which is greater than the path direct from ② which produces an earliest time of $2 + 3 = 5$. Therefore 9 is the earliest time of event ④. The calculation of the earliest event times is known as the forward pass.

The reverse process, the backward pass, determines the latest possible time for the event, that is the latest possible time for each activity finishing without delaying the completion date of the project. The latest event time is calculated and written in the right-hand square alongside each event. The calculations are shown in Fig. 2.4. The latest time of the finish event, event ⑥, is taken as 16 weeks; the latest time of event ⑤ is $16 - 2 = 14$; and of event ④ it is $14 - 3 = 11$. Event ③ has two activities leaving it, and the latest time of event ③ is determined by the earlier or smaller calculated latest time, i.e. one calculation for event ③ from event ④ is $14 - 6 = 8$ and the other is $11 - 1 = 10$, therefore the latest time of event ③ is 8. If event ③ was any later than 8 the time to complete activities ③–⑤ and ⑤–⑥ would extend beyond the project end date of 16.

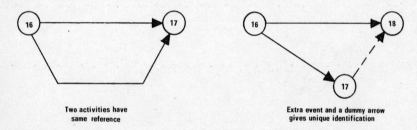

Two activities have
same reference

Extra event and a dummy arrow
gives unique identification

Fig. 2.5 Use of dummies for unique identification of activities.

Having completed the forward and backward passes, the earliest and latest times of each event are known. From this, the 'float' or spare time available for each activity can be calculated. Critical activities, which have no float, are those whose earliest and latest time of start event coincide, whose earliest and latest time of finish event coincide and the time difference between the start event and finish event equals duration of the activity.

Float Figure 2.6 shows an activity extracted from the network in Fig. 2.4. The times shown refer to the event times and have the following meanings. *The earliest time of start event* is the earliest possible time the activity can start. *The latest time of finish event* is the latest time the activity can finish without delaying the completion of the project. The *latest time of start event* is the latest time a preceding activity may finish, and the *earliest time of finish event* is the earliest time that a succeeding activity may start. Knowing these times, the float can be calculated; Fig. 2.6 shows the calculation of total float and free float.

Total float is the total amount of time by which the activity could be extended or delayed and still not interfere with the project end date. Total float is the total time available for the activity less the duration, i.e. the latest time of the finish event less the earliest time of the start event less the duration.

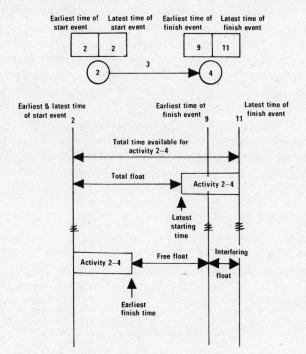

Fig. 2.6 Calculation of float.

If the total float for one activity is completely used up by the activity then some of the total float of the succeeding activity is also used. Free float, however, is the amount of time by which an activity could be extended or delayed without interfering with the succeeding activity. Free float is calculated by the earliest time of the finish event less the earliest time of the start event less the duration. Free float assumes both the preceding and succeeding activities start as early as possible.

Using the example in Fig. 2.6 the total float of activity ②–④ is $11 - 2 - 3 = 6$, and the free float is $9 - 2 - 3 = 4$.

The difference between total float and free float is sometimes referred to as interfering float, as shown in Fig. 2.6. It is the amount of total float shared by the succeeding activity. Interfering float is rarely used in any subsequent calculations.

(d) *Assessing resources*

In estimating the duration of an activity, the resources required for that activity will have to be considered. The resources can be written alongside each arrow in the network. For example, an activity with a work content of 20 carpenter days requires two carpenters for 10 days. The first and most widely used assessment of resources is the aggregation chart. Figure 2.2 is an example of a resource aggregation chart for labourers. In many cases a more elaborate approach is not justified. The resource aggregation chart is useful in assessing work content for estimates and can be used in conjunction with the linked bar chart (Fig. 2.2); a visual assessment of the float available within activities (shown as a broken line) allows the distribution of peaks of resource demand. In many practical situations this is sufficient resource manipulation.

Beyond the use of resource aggregation there are two approaches to assessing resources required. They are: (1) the time-limited problem, the project must be completed by a specific date; and (2) the resource-limited problem, in which the project must be completed with the limited resources available even if this means extending the project deadline.

Time-limited resource considerations   Time analysis will provide the minimum time possible for completing the project. If this minimum is taken as the time limit, adjustments in the timing of any activity that may affect resource requirements must be undertaken within the float available. The steps in assessing the resources required in a time-limited situation are:

 (i) Prepare a list of activities ranked in order of their earliest start dates.
 (ii) Produce a resource aggregation chart as in Fig. 2.7, based on this list of activities in earliest start order and the resources required as shown in Fig. 2.7. This gives the resources required assuming all activities start as early as possible.
(iii) Produce a list of activities ranked in order of latest start dates. (*Note*: The latest start date of an activity is the latest time of the finish event less the duration.)
(iv) Produce a resource aggregation chart as in Fig. 2.7 based on this list of activities in latest start order, and starting at these latest start times. This is the resources required when all activities start as late as possible.
 (v) Compare the resource aggregation charts from (ii) and (iv). This provides the two extremes of resource requirements, all activities starting as early and as late as possible. Between these extremes a compromise to produce acceptable resource requirements can be

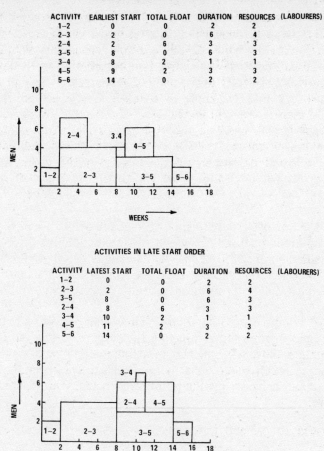

ACTIVITIES IN EARLY START ORDER

ACTIVITY	EARLIEST START	TOTAL FLOAT	DURATION	RESOURCES (LABOURERS)
1–2	0	0	2	2
2–3	2	0	6	4
2–4	2	6	3	3
3–5	8	0	6	3
3–4	8	2	1	1
4–5	9	2	3	3
5–6	14	0	2	2

ACTIVITIES IN LATE START ORDER

ACTIVITY	LATEST START	TOTAL FLOAT	DURATION	RESOURCES (LABOURERS)
1–2	0	0	2	2
2–3	2	0	6	4
3–5	8	0	6	3
2–4	8	6	3	3
3–4	10	2	1	1
4–5	11	2	3	3
5–6	14	0	2	2

Fig. 2.7 Resource aggregation charts for activities starting as
early and as late as possible (based on network in Fig. 2.4).

sought by visual inspection and manipulation of activities within the
two extremes.

Resource-limited resource considerations   The production of a resource-
limited aggregation chart is similar to that of the unlimited resource
aggregation, except that if the total resource demand of an activity
exceeds the specified limit then that activity must be delayed. To produce
reasonable results, and so that earlier activities are allocated their
resources first, the activities must be arranged according to a system of
priorities or 'decision rules'.

The decision rule is a device whereby activities are ranked in the order in which their resource demand is added to the resource aggregation chart. Each activity is thus given its appropriate priority in the queue for resources. It is possible that not all activities can receive the resources they require at the earliest time they require them. Consequently some activities will be delayed until the resources are available. The ordering according to a chosen priority or decision rule ensures that activities high in the priority list receive their resources first. Activities low in the priority list may get delayed.

The ranking in a priority order is known as sorting, and one of the more common sorts or decision rules is to sort in order of 'early start time'. For activities with the same early start time a second sort is required and this could be in order of total float. The upper part of Fig. 2.7 gives the activities for the network shown in Fig. 2.4 ranked in order of early start as the first or major sort and in total float order as the second or minor sort. This ranking has been used in preparing the resource aggregation chart shown in Fig. 2.8. This example shows that

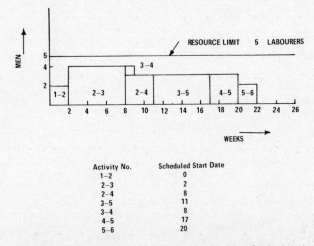

Activity No.	Scheduled Start Date
1–2	0
2–3	2
2–4	8
3–5	11
3–4	8
4–5	17
5–6	20

Fig. 2.8 Resource-limited histogram and table of scheduled start dates.

activity ②–④ is the first to exceed the resource limit and is therefore delayed from starting on week 2 to starting on week 8. When the resources for all the activities have been entered in the resource aggregation chart a list of scheduled start dates can be extracted as in the table shown in Fig. 2.8; Fig. 2.9 gives similar examples for two types of resource, for demonstration purposes the decision rule or priority sort used in this case are early start as the major sort and largest duration as the minor sort. The choice of decision rule or sort is left to the user

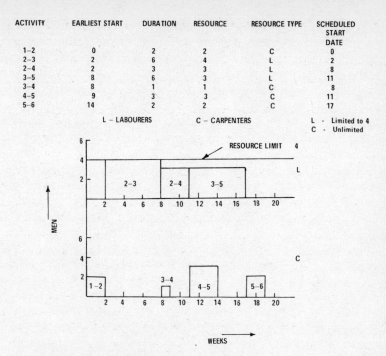

ACTIVITY	EARLIEST START	DURATION	RESOURCE	RESOURCE TYPE	SCHEDULED START DATE
1–2	0	2	2	C	0
2–3	2	6	4	L	2
2–4	2	3	3	L	8
3–5	8	6	3	L	11
3–4	8	1	1	C	8
4–5	9	3	3	C	11
5–6	14	2	2	C	17

L – LABOURERS   C – CARPENTERS   L - Limited to 4   C - Unlimited

Fig. 2.9 Resource allocation for two resource types.

of these techniques. The decision rules in common use are Early start–total float, Late start–total float, and since each type of decision rule may load the resources into the aggregation chart in a different order the resulting resource aggregation chart will be different. The priority list guides the user towards an acceptable solution.

Use of computers

Where network analysis is used the possibility of using computers to do the calculations exists. The input data required by such computer programs for each activity are start event number, end event number, activity description, activity duration and the level of resources required for each resource type. For example three resource types may be specified, say carpenters, labourers and steelfixers. The activity may require three carpenters, four labourers and no steelfixers. These data would be entered on a form, one line for each activity and these would be subsequently punched on to cards for computer processing.

In addition to the data required for each activity the available resources are also needed if resource allocation is required.

The output from such programs are a time analysis, that is a listing of the activities in some order such as earliest start date with the start and finish times and the float calculated for each activity. The output is often

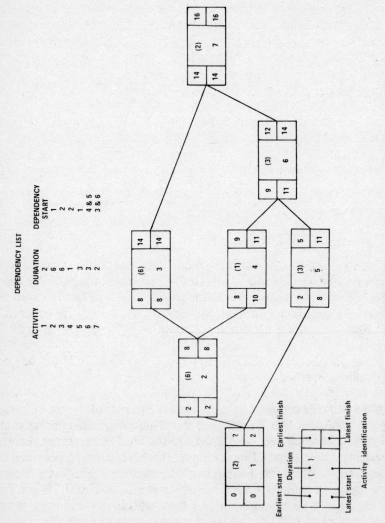

Fig. 2.10 Precedence list and precedence diagram showing the same network as in Fig. 2.4.

also produced in bar chart form printed by the computer. If resource analysis is done then the resource aggregation charts are also produced. Staffurth and Walton (ref. 2) reviews the computer packages available as at 1974 and describes the facilities offered by each package.

Early commercial computer packages developed in the United Kingdom for network analysis calculations offered only activity on the arrow systems. Campbell (ref. 1) covered only on arrow packages in his 1968 report on network analysis. Staffurth and Walton (ref. 2) in updating Campbell's work published their report in 1974 and presented both arrow and precedence packages.

Precedence Diagrams

Network analysis by precedence diagram follows the same logical steps as the arrow diagram. The differences in the application are as follows.

(a) Listing the activities

The activity list can be extended to show the dependency between activities, as shown in Fig. 2.10.

(b) Producing a logical Network

Logic   In precedence diagrams the 'node' represents the activity and the link or arrow represents only the logical relationship. Figure 2.10 shows the precedence network and the list of activities on which it is based. No dummies are needed to maintain correct logic or for unique numbering of activities.

Identifying the activities   Each node representing an activity can be given a single unique number.

Durations and time analysis   As for arrows, the duration of each activity is estimated and the forward and backward passes are done and the earliest and latest start and finish times of each activity are entered as shown in Fig. 2.10. These times calculated refer to the activity whereas the calculations for arrows referred to event times. This is claimed by some to be an advantage of the precedence diagram over the arrow diagram. Float can be calculated as before, for example the total float of activity No. 5 is latest finishing time less earliest starting time less duration, that is $11 - 2 - 3 = 6$.

Relationships between activities

The major advantage offered by precedence diagrams and the available computer packages are that the number of relationships that can exist between activities is more than the simple finish–start relationship offered by arrow networks. The finish–start limitation means that if an activity is to start before the completion of a preceding activity upon which the activity is dependent then the preceding activity must be divided into

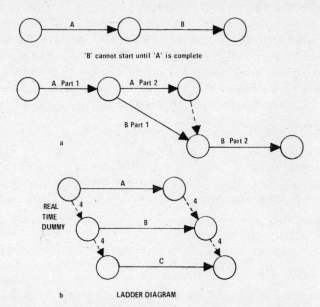

Fig. 2.11 Adjustments to arrow networks to produce overlaps between activities.

smaller parts, as in Fig. 2.11(a); otherwise, dummies with a time allowance as in Fig. 2.11(b) must be used to produce overlaps between activities.

In precedence diagrams a number of different relationships exist between activities, for example:

> Finish – start
> Finish – finish
> Start – start
> Part complete – start
> Part complete – finish
> Finish – part complete

The particular selection of relationships which exist depend on the computer package chosen and reference should be made to Staffurth and Walton's (ref. 2) review of packages available. This survey also revealed at least one arrow package which offered 'transit times' between activities. Transit times which can be either positive or negative have the effect of overlapping or separating activities thus providing the multiple relationships available in most precedence packages.

In practice the use of many different relationships between activities has proved in some cases to be a disadvantage. The reason is that the user finds the alternatives too complicated. Also there is now some evidence that when extensive overlapping of activities is used in planning, the project duration tends to be underestimated. This results from a zealous use of the overlap facility in order to meet a predetermined target date.

The main differences between precedence diagrams and activity on the arrow systems are that precedence diagrams have no dummies, no change of reference number when additional activities are added, and complex relationships. The case as to which system to use is not as yet sufficiently clear and remains largely a matter of preference in most construction type projects.

3. Line of Balance

Line of balance is a planning technique for repetitive work, the principles employed are taken from the planning and control of manufacturing processes greatly modified by E. G. Trimble when he was joint chief executive of the NBA (ref. 6). The basis of the technique is to find the required resources for each stage or operation so that the following stages are not interfered with and the target output can be achieved. The technique

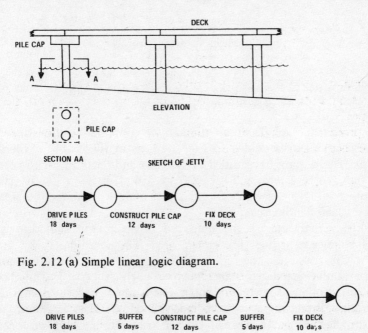

Fig. 2.12 (a) Simple linear logic diagram.

Fig. 2.12 (b) Logic diagram with buffers.

has been applied in construction work mainly to house building and to a lesser extent to jetty work and in conjunction with networks to roadworks.

Consider a simplified example of the construction of a jetty which is represented by three operations – say, Drive piles, Construct pile cap, Fix deck – and that this sequence had to be repeated ten times to finish the jetty.

The inter-relationship of the three basic operations can be shown in a simple logic diagram, as in Fig. 2.12(a). To provide for a margin of error in the time taken to complete each of these operations, a time buffer is usually placed between each operation, as in Fig. 2.12(b). This construction plan shows that a total time of 50 days is needed to complete one sequence of operations. The target output of the project can be expressed in terms of the completion rate of these sequences. For example it may be that the jetty comprising 10 sections has to be completed in 20 weeks, or 100 days. Thus if a target rate of completion of one section per week was chosen, the total time taken for 10 sections would be 19

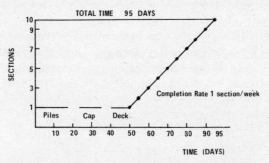

Fig. 2.13 Time for completion of ten repetitive sequences at the rate of one per week.

weeks, as in Fig. 2.13. The logic diagram or construction plan for section 1 in Fig. 2.12 can be added to Fig. 2.13, as in Fig. 2.14 for the other sections. The sloping lines added to the start and finish of each operation allow dates to be established for each section. This is the line of balance schedule if sufficient resources are made available to maintain the production represented in the schedule.

It must be made clear at this point that this is *not* the method by which line of balance schedules are constructed. The schedule shown in Fig. 2.14 is only possible if the required number of teams of men is available to start at the scheduled start dates on each section. The method of construction of a proper line of balance schedule is described later under the heading 'Preparing a line of balance schedule'. The basic approach is to determine the resources available and calculate the rates of construction that can be achieved. This example is produced only for demonstration purposes.

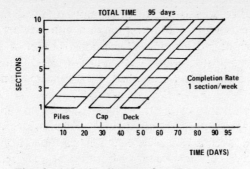

Fig. 2.14 Logic diagram for each section added to the completion schedule.

If for example operation 'Pile cap' required a team of six men to construct the pile cap in 12 days and two teams of six men were employed, the output of that gang of two teams would be 0·83 sections per 5-day week and not the one section per week required by the target. This is because if two teams were employed team 'a' would start on section 1 on day 23 and finish on day 35 (from schedule Fig. 2.14) and team 'b' would start on section 2 on day 28 and finish on day 40 (from schedule Fig. 2.14). Section 3, according to the schedule, is due to start on day 33, but team 'a' is not available until day 35. Therefore the rate of completion of the operation 'Pile cap' would be less than 1·0 section per 5-day week; calculations show this rate to be 0·83 and Fig. 2.15 shows the delay to the project.

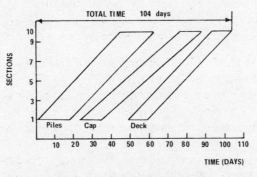

Fig. 2.15 Effect of scheduling operation 'Pile cap' at a completion rate of 0·83 per week.

If three teams were employed on operation 'Pile cap' the output would be 1·25 sections per week. This is because team 'a' completes the first section on day 35 and moves to section 4, which is not due to start until day 38. Figure 2.16 shows that the project completion date is in fact later than the original despite the speeding up of operation 'Pile cap'.

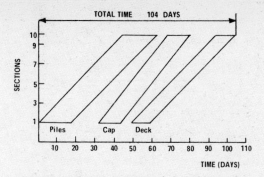

Fig. 2.16 Effect of scheduling operation 'Pile. cap' at a completion rate of 1·25 per week.

This is because operation 'Pile cap' is no longer in 'balance' with its preceding and succeeding operations.

Preparing a line of balance schedule
1. Prepare a logic diagram as in Fig. 2.12.
2. Estimate the manhours required to complete each operation.
3. Choose buffer times which will guard against the risk of interference between operations.
4. Calculate the required output target in order to meet a given project completion date.
5. Complete the table as shown in Table 2.1.

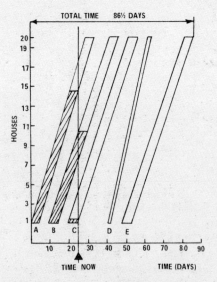

Fig. 2.17 Line of balance schedule drawn from data in Table 2.1.

1 Activity or operation	2 Manhours per activity	3 Men per activity	4 Theoretical gang size at the chosen output rate of R	5 Actual gang size	6 Actual rate of output	7 Time in days for one activity	8 Time from start on first section to start on last section	9 Minimum buffer time
A Substructure	110	3	8·25	9	3·27	4·58	29·05	5
B Superstructure	320	8	24·00	24	3·0	5·00	31·67	5
C Joinery	365	9	27·38	27	2·96	5·07	32·09	5
D Plumbing	35	2	2·63	4	4·56	2·19	20·83	5
E Finishes	210	5	15·75	15	2·86	5·25	33·22	5

Note: Operations are sequential. Total no. of houses = 20. Target rate of build (or completions) R = 3 per week (1 week comprises five 8-hour days).

The columns in the foregoing table are:

[1] Activity description and identification.

[2] The estimated manhours for each activity.

[3] The optimum number of men for each activity, this is the number of men in one team.

[4] The theoretical gang size required to maintain the output rate R given by

$$\frac{R \times (\text{manhours per activity})}{\text{Number of working hours per week}}$$

R would be the number of sections to be completed each week.

[5] The actual gang size would be chosen as a number which would be a multiple of the men required for one team[3] near to the theoretical gang size. If the actual gang size is greater than the theoretical gang size the rate of output will be more than the target rate, and if the actual is less than the theoretical the actual rate of output will be less than the target rate.

[6] The actual rate of output is given by

$$\frac{\text{Actual gang size}}{\text{Theoretical gang size}} \times \text{target rate}$$

[7] Time taken for one activity in days is given by

$$\frac{\text{Manhours for activity}}{\text{No. of men in one team} \times \text{no. of hours in a working day}}$$

[8] The time in days from start on first section to start on last section is given by

$$\frac{(\text{No. of sections} - 1) \times \text{no. of working days per week}}{\text{Actual rate of build}}$$

This is useful in plotting the schedule.

[9] Minimum buffer time is assessed from knowledge of the likely variability of the preceding activity.

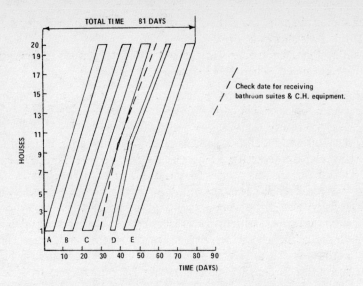

Fig. 2.18 Line of balance schedule based on Table 2.1 except that operation D has a gang of four men for houses 1 to 10 and a gang of two thereafter.

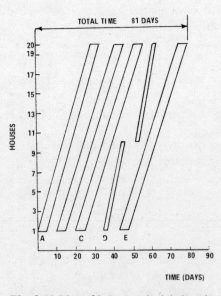

Fig. 2.19 Line of balance schedule based on Table 2.1 except that operation D suspended for 7 days after completing house 10.

6. Draw the schedule, from the information calculated in Table 2.1. The example is as shown in Fig. 2.17.
7. Examine the schedule and assess possible alternatives to bring about a more 'balanced' schedule which might include:

   (i) Changing the rate of output of one activity by reducing (or increasing) the gang size partway through the project; an example is given in Fig. 2.18.

   (ii) Lay-off and recall one gang; an example is given in Fig. 2.19.

   (iii) Overlap some activities, i.e. have a non-sequential logic diagram, which means that the schedules shown as sloping lines on the diagrams would be superimposed. Such schedules become difficult to read and this severely reduces the effectiveness as a means of communication with operational staff such as foremen and gangers.

   (iv) Or schedule every activity to work at the same rate. This is known as 'parallel scheduling' and involves employing enough resources to ensure that the rate of output required can be achieved. In the example in Table 2.1, if activities C and E had actual gang sizes one team more than shown then all activities could proceed at a rate of 3·0 per week. However, this means that most gangs of men are working at less than their natural rate. The parallel schedule would have a shorter overall duration. Before employing parallel scheduling, examination would be needed as to whether the savings in overall duration and hence indirect overheads offset the extra costs in overmanning.

Using the schedule

The completed schedule is based on chosen resources, therefore the rates of construction calculated have taken account of these resources. This is different to the network calculations, which separated logic and resource allocations.

The schedule and the start and finish dates of the various teams on each operation can be used to monitor progress. Figure 2.17 shows time now as day 25 and the completions of operations A and B marked by shading. The situation portrayed is operation A on schedule and operation B ahead of schedule. The danger from this is that B may run out of work because it is progressing at a faster rate than A. Action is needed either to speed up A or slow down B.

Updating a line of balance schedule once the project has started, and if the rates of construction prove to be different from those calculated, can be difficult. This difficulty arises from the fact that the resources, that is teams of men with different skills, are already on site.

Another use for the line of balance schedule is checking material orders or deliveries. If a deadline for ordering and/or receiving materials is marked on the schedule, as shown in Fig. 2.18 for plumbing supplies, then a simple check can be made in good time.

Other applications of line of balance schedules are described in *Programming House Building by Line of Balance* published by the National Building Agency (ref. 6).

References and Bibliography

1. Campbell, J. Y. Network analysis. *Computer User Report No. 5.* Department of Civil Engineering, Loughborough University of Technology, 1968.

2. Staffurth, C. & Walton, H. *Programs for Network Analysis.* National Computer Centre, 1974.

3. Lockyer, K. G. *An Introduction to Critical Path Analysis.* Pitman, 1969.

4. Holden, I. & McIlroy, P. K. *Network Planning in Management Control Systems.* Hutchinson Educational, 1970.

5. O'Brien, J. *CPM in Construction Management.* McGraw-Hill, 1965.

6. National Building Agency. *Programming House Building by Line of Balance.* NBA, 1968.

7. Lumsden, P. *The Line of Balance Method.* Pergamon, 1968.

8. Harris, F. C. & McCaffer, R. Costing the Effects of Bad Weather, DOE *Construction* Vol. 17, March 1976.

9. Thompson, P. *Organisation and Economics of Construction.* McGraw-Hill, London, 1981.

10. Harris, F. and McCaffer, R. *Worked Examples in Construction Management.* Granada, 1978.

11. Madubike, E. and Harris, F. C. Planning for Materials on Remote Projects. *D.O.E. Construction.* June, 1977.

PLANNING EXERCISES

Network Planning Exercise

Your company is preparing a tender for a sewage works, details of which are shown on drawings No. 51910 and No. 51911 (Chapter 17). You are asked by the estimator to prepare the following information:

1. A critical path diagram showing the sequence of operations, the earliest and latest times and the total float of each activity, assuming that there are no resource restraints. (Table 2.2 lists the activities and the start and finish event numbers of each activity.)

Approach 1 Use the activities and the event numbers given in Table 2.2 to produce the network.
Approach 2 Use the activities given in Table 2.2, but not the event numbers, to produce the network.
Approach 3 Do not use the information given in Table 2.2, but create your own list of activities from the drawings given.

Each of these three approaches to the exercise is more demanding than the previous one. Approach 3 is nearest to the real-life situation; however, Approaches 1 and 2 are useful as training steps.

2. The type and cost of craneage necessary to carry out the work, taking into account the limitations set out in the data below. The activities in Table 2.2 should be used and the network should be redrawn as a linked bar chart, so that craneage usage can be analysed to produce a chart of the number and type of cranes required against time.

Table 2.2 Event numbers, activity descriptions, durations and craneage requirements

Start event	End event	Activity description	Duration (weeks)	Scheduled start	Crane usage[1]
1,2		Start on site and clear	4	starts wk. 1	
2,3		Pile Testing	3		
3,4		Pile Heater House	1		
4,5		Start Exc. Heater House Founds	4		
5,6		Dummy	—		
6,7		Complete Exc. Heater House Founds	4		
5,8		Dummy	—		
8,9		Construct H. House Founds	16		1 day/wk.
9,10		Dummy	—		
10,11		Complete H. House Founds	8		1 day/wk.
7,10		Dummy	—		
11,12		Construct H. House Superstructure	18		
12,13[2]		Install Plant, Test and Commission	22		
13,56		Dummy	—		

Table 2.2 – *continued*

Start event	End event	Activity description	Duration (weeks)	Scheduled start	Crane usage[1]
14,15		Sheet Pile Sludge Well	3	starts wk. 20	
15,16		Exc. and Construct Sludge Well	20		30%
16,17		Remove Sheet Piling	2		
17,18		Construct Valve Chamber	15		30%
18,56		Dummy	—		
3,19		Dummy	—		
19,20		Pile Consol Tanks	1		
20,21		Construct Consol Chambers $\frac{1}{2}$ Duct B	11		
21,22		Start Consol Tank Bases	3		1 day/wk.
22,23		Dummy	—		
23,24		Complete Consol Tank Bases	5		1 day/wk.
22,25		Dummy	—		
25,26		Start Consol Tank Walls	10		50%
26,27		Dummy	—		
24,27		Dummy	—		
27,28		Complete Consol Tank Walls	10		50%
28,29		Test and Commission Consol Tanks	6		
29,56		Dummy	—		
3,30		Dummy	—		
30,31		Pile Tanks P_1 and S_1	3		
31,32		Exc. and Blind P_1 and S_1	2		
32,33		Dummy	—		
33,34		Complete Exc. and Blind P_1 and S_1	2		
33,35		Dummy	—		
35,36		Construct Bases P_1 and S_1	4		1 day/wk.
34,37		Dummy	—		
36,37		Dummy	—		
37,38		Complete Bases P_1 and S_1	2		1 day/wk.
38,39		Construct Walls P_1 and S_1	15		50%
39,40		Construct Roof P_1	8		2 days (first and last day)
40,41[2]		Install Plant, Test and Commission	4		
41,56		Dummy	—		
3,42		Dummy	—		
42,43		Pile Tanks P_2 and S_2	3		
43,44		Exc. and Blind P_2 and S_2	2		
44,45		Dummy	—		
45,46		Complete Exc. and Blind P_2 and S_2	2		
44,47		Dummy	—		

Table 2.2 – *continued*

Start event	End event	Activity description	Duration (weeks)	Scheduled start	Crane usage[1]
47,48		Construct Bases P_2 and S_2	4		1 day/wk.
48,49		Dummy	—		
49,50		Complete Bases P_2 and S_2	2		1 day/wk.
46,49		Dummy	—		
50,51		Construct Walls P_2 and S_2	15		50%
51,52		Construct Roof P_2	8		2 days (first and last day)
52,53[2]		Install Plant, Test and Commission	4		
53,56		Dummy	—		
2,54		Dummy	—		
54,55		Construct Duct A	6		
55,56		Dummy	—		
56,57		Clean Site	2		

[1] (a) The percentage figure given for the crane usage refers to the percentage of the duration for which a crane is required. This time is uniformly spread throughout the duration. If two activities take place at the same time, one requiring a crane for 40% and the other for 30% of the duration, the total crane usage is 70% and one crane is sufficient. If the usage totals more than 100%, more than one crane is needed.

(b) When the crane requirement is quoted as one day per week it may be taken that the crane is required for the complete day on the first day, sixth day, eleventh day, etc. (assuming a five-day week).

(c) When the usage is given as a specific number of days, the days for which crane is required are specified.

[2] The plant contract provides only one installation gang which must complete all the work in one visit.

Data

1. Craneage will mainly be required for handling formwork ànd reinforcement and for placing concrete. The estimated craneage requirement of each activity is given in Table 2.2.
2. The contract must be completed in 78 weeks.
3. Ready-mixed concrete will be used throughout.
4. Purpose-made formwork will be used for the following elements in the structure:

(i) Digestion tank walls: one set of panels to be used for all tanks, comprising formwork for a full-circle pour $\frac{1}{3}$ of total wall height. Max. panel weight $1\frac{3}{4}$ tonnes.

(ii) Consolidation tank walls: one set of panels to be used for all tanks, comprising formwork for a full-circle pour $\frac{1}{3}$ of total wall height. Max. panel weight $\frac{3}{4}$ tonnes.

(iii) Digestion tank bases: one set of panels to be used for all tanks. All panels can be manhandled.

(iv) Digestion tank roofs: one set of panels to be used on both tanks. All panels can be manhandled.

5. Formwork for all other structures will be Acrow 'U' forms.
6. Max. concrete pour (digestion tank walls) $= 80 \text{ m}^3$.
7. Rate at which concrete can be poured using a crane and skip:

$$\frac{1}{2} \text{ yd}^3 \text{ skip} \quad 6 \text{ m}^3/\text{h}$$
$$1 \text{ yd}^3 \text{ skip} \quad 10 \text{ m}^3/\text{h}$$

8. Ground conditions on site are as follows:

Ground–1·0 m	soft to firm silty clay
1·0 m–1·6 m	soft peat
1·6 m–3·5 m	compact sandy gravel
Below 3·5 m	hard red marl

Line of Balance Exercise 1

Your company has been awarded a contract to erect 124 pylons for the electricity board.

Table 2.3 shows the sequential operations involved in the construction of each pylon together with the estimated manhours and optimum number of men for each operation.

Table 2.3 Data for line of balance exercise No. 1

	Operation	Manhours	Optimum no. of men
A	Excavate	55	4
B	Concrete foundations	64	4
C	Erect tower	145	8
D	Fix cantilever cable arms	90	8
E	Fix insulators	25	5

The handover rate specified is six pylons per week and this can be taken as the target rate of build. Prepare a line of balance schedule assuming that each gang works at its natural rate. State clearly the contract duration. Assume a 5-day working week, 8 hours per day, and a minimum buffer time of two days.

Line of Balance Exercise 2

Prepare a line of balance schedule for a small contract of 15 houses based on a rate of building of three per week assuming five 8-hour days per week. A minimum buffer of 5 days should be assumed. Table 2.4 shows the operations together with the estimated manhours and optimum number of men for each operation.

The sequence of operations is shown in Fig. 2.20.

Make two suggestions as to how the overall duration of the project could be reduced.

Table 2.4 Data for line of balance exercise No. 2

Operation		Manhours	Optimum number of men per operation
A	Substructure	180	6
B	Brickwork	320	4
C	Joiner, first fix	200	4
D	Tilers	60	2
E	Glazing	40	2
F	Joiner, second fix	120	3
G	Electrician	80	2
H	Plumber	100	2
I	Painter	40	3

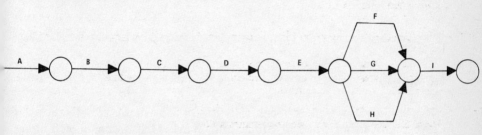

Fig. 2.20 Logic diagram for line of balance exercise No. 2.

CHAPTER 3

WORK STUDY

Summary

Work Study is presented specifically to suit construction applications. A case study using Method Study and Work Measurement techniques illustrates a logical approach to production improvements. Supplementary methods are described with particular emphasis given to production surveys and time lapse photography.

Introduction

The British Standard Glossary of terms in Work Study BS 3138:1969 defines work study as:

> 'A measurement service based on those techniques, particularly method study and work measurement, which are used in the examination of human work in all its contexts, and which lead to the systematic investigation of all the resources and factors which affect the efficiency and economy of the situation being reviewed, in order to effect improvement.'

More specifically, *method study* is the technique used to record work procedures, to provide systems of analysis and to develop improvements. Applications of the methodology can assist in project planning, design of temporary works, distributing plant and other resources at the work place, and re-planning and progressing of production.

Work measurement, sometimes called *time study* is the measurement of the time required to perform a task so that an output standard of

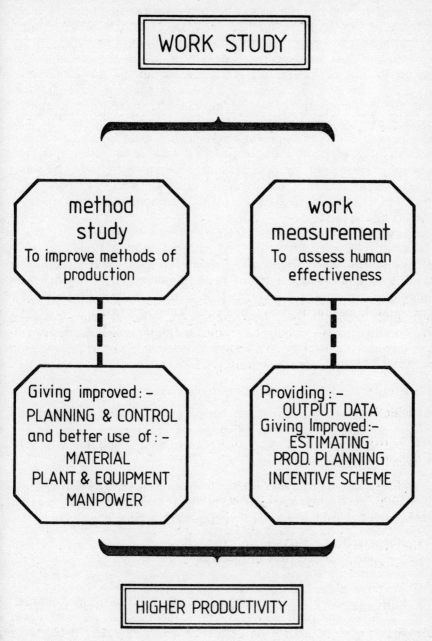

Fig. 3.1 Work Study.

production for a worker and/or machine may be established. Such information is required in the estimating process, in setting financial incentives, as part of the data in method study, and can also be used to monitor actual production performance against the standard expected.

Both methods have gained wide acceptance in the manufacturing industry, and are increasingly finding favour in the construction industry. However, problems have arisen in applying the techniques, due to the temporary nature of most construction projects and the associated need to perform almost unique tasks in each project, thereby causing difficulties in acquiring data which can readily and reliably be used in future planning and control. In addition, construction operations are subject to many variables such as weather, bad ground, dispersed locations, high labour turnover, sub-contract works on site, design divorced from construction, etc. which compound the problems of recording the facts.

Notwithstanding these difficulties, however, work study can play a valuable role in construction and, in particular, the method study technique provides a disciplined procedure for recording information and its subsequent analysis. The badly organised environment all too often found on construction projects leads to inefficiency which could be reduced and productivity and competitiveness improved.

Method Study

British Standard 3138:1969 defines method study as:

'The systematic recording and critical examination of the factors and resources involved in existing and proposed ways of doing work, as a means of developing and applying easier and more effective methods and reducing costs.'

Many situations arise in construction work which can be identified and improved by the introduction of method study and might manifest themselves typically in the following symptoms:

1. Recourse to excessive labour overtime.
2. Bottlenecks in the flow of materials.
3. High materials wastage.
4. Frequent plant breakdowns.
5. Fatiguing work.
6. Late programme.
7. Poor quality and workmanship.
8. Delays to and by sub-contractors.
9. Excessive errors and mistakes.
10. Shortages of resources.

11. Insufficient information.
12. Site congestion.
13. Bad working conditions.
14. Cost overrun.
15. High labour turnover.
16. Poor design of temporary works.
17. Poor site layout.

The method study procedure is used to analyse and reduce the incidence of such problems in a series of steps which may be summarised as:

 (i) Defining the problem.
 (ii) Recording the facts.
(iii) Analysing the data.
(iv) Proposing a course of action.
 (v) Putting the proposals into effect.
(vi) Monitoring the consequences.

Step 1: Define the Problem

The nature of construction work lends itself to methods improvement, since in many cases the pre-planning has been hurried and ill-conceived. The major difficulty in deciding whether to carry out a method study exercise is judging the benefits to be expected compared to the cost and effort in pursuing them. Quite often revised working procedures quickly degenerate because of the constantly changing situation of the construction site. However, the problems listed above are usually good starting points for selection.

Step 2: Record

The next step in the procedure after selecting the work for study is to record the facts. For basic tasks, simply writing down the process may be sufficient, but for many complex situations the separate elements involved become too numerous and other means are required. For example, the main areas of inefficiency for an individual or group of workers can often be revealed and quantified by use of 'activity sampling' or 'foreman delay' surveys. Activities which take place in a sequence of events are sometimes best recorded on charts and diagrams similar to those used in network planning. Others which require the sequence of tasks to be recorded on a time scale, so that interactions may be studied, are suited to bar plans and multiple activity charts. Situations illustrating applications of the recording methods are described more fully at the end of the chapter.

Step 3: Analyse the Present Method and Develop Alternatives

Careful study of the sampling statistics, diagrams or charts is the starting point in the design of a more efficient model. The process of analysis requires a critical examination of each recorded operation in the form of a question and answer technique as shown below.

The Questioning Technique (ref. 14)

What...?	Why...?	Could it be...?	Should it be...?
purpose is achieved?	is that necessary?	what else?	what?
place is occupied?	that place?	where else?	where?
sequence is followed?	that time?	when else?	when?
person is involved?	that person?	who else?	who?
means used?	that way?	how else?	how?

In this way a simpler method of working, a reduction of delays, transport, time for operations etc., may be devised so resulting in improved efficiency.

Step 4: Instal and Maintain

After the improved method has been designed, existing work practices must be replaced and persuasion and discussion with those personnel both directly and indirectly involved will be most important if the new method is to be accepted. Some form of financial incentive may be necessary as an encouragement, but in a well-prepared scheme one would usually expect these costs to be recovered by the increased productivity. In addition, those requirements indirectly associated with the new proposals should not be overlooked, such as extra temporary works, better materials scheduling, improved plant maintenance, more supervision required by management, etc. Finally, the revised method must be monitored and compared with the expectations and revised if necessary.

Recording Techniques

Example 1: Illustrating the Use of Flow Charts and Diagrams to Study Cranage Activity

A sewage works (see drawings 51910 and 51911 in Chapter 17) involves the simultaneous construction of various structures. They include:

(i) Digestion tanks.
(ii) Consolidation tanks.
(iii) Heater house.
(iv) Ducts.

The structures are constructed in reinforced concrete and the tanks' walls are formed in 1 m high lifts, the shutters being raised manually into position. The heater house comprises reinforced concrete foundations and a ground slab and the ducts are also of concrete.

The existing plan chosen by the contracting firm adopts a crawler crane with a concrete skip attachment to place the concrete. To achieve the required levels of production, the crane must travel from structure to structure as each pour of concrete is completed. The objective is to work on each structure during the day and return to the plant compound overnight. However, the sequence is interrupted, in particular by the Resident Engineer insisting on checking all the work after the concrete placing and before allowing the crane to move on. Also the crane experiences severe delays *en route* caused by the soft ground. Consequently the required number of concrete pours cannot be achieved every day and the project programme begins to fall behind schedule. The

A.S.M.E. SYMBOLS

SYMBOL	ACTIVITY
◯	OPERATION
▢	INSPECTION
⇨	TRANSPORT
▽	STORAGE
D	DELAY

Fig. 3.2 ASME Symbols.

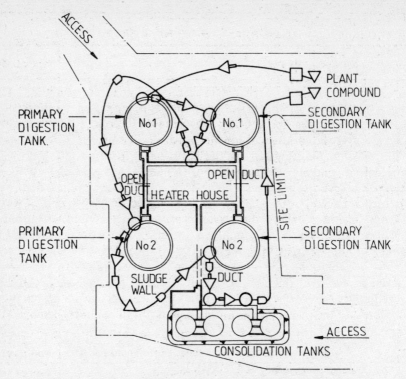

Fig. 3.3 Flow Diagram for Bogtown Sewage Works Site Layout.

site manager therefore decides to reconsider the existing work procedure and chooses method study techniques to record and analyse the current work practices of the crane as follows.

(a) *Flow diagram*
The flow diagram records activities on a plan of the area and for construction work this method is usually very appropriate. A set of symbols is used to record the sequence of events and assists in the visualisation of the processes under study. The accepted symbols are shown in Fig. 3.2, and are known as the ASME symbols after the originators – the American Society of Mechanical Engineers.

This technique illustrates clearly and simply the work done, such as the path of travel of the crane on the work site (Fig. 3.3) and allows each event to be considered with a view to making improvements.

(b) *Process chart*
Sometimes it is inappropriate to use flow diagrams: for instance, the sequence of movements adopted by a bricklayer, or maintenance performed on a piece of equipment would congest a drawing. A more

			FLOW PROCESS CHART FOR A CRANE.	
Time	Dis-tance	Symbol	Activity	Type of activity
		▽	Crane in plant compound	Non-productive
		☐1	Crane inspected for service	Non-productive
	60m	⟶▷	Travel to Primary Digestion Tank No. 1	Non-productive
90 mins		①	Pick up skips and pour concrete in shutters	Productive
		⊃1	Delay while engineer checks work	Non-productive
	20m	⟶▷	Travel to Secondary Digestion Tank No. 1	Non-productive
60 mins		②	Pick up skips and pour concrete in shutters	Productive
		⊃2	Delay while engineer checks work	Non-productive
		⟶▷	Travel to heater house	Non-productive
20 mins	20m	③	Pick up skips and pour concrete	Productive
		⊃3	Delay while engineer checks work	Non-productive
	40m	⟶▷	Travel and turn	Non-productive
		⊃4	Delay as crane manoeuvres on the soft ground	Non-productive
	40m	⟶▷	Travel to Primary Digestion Tank No. 2	Non-productive
		⊃5	Delay as crane negotiates obstructions	Non-productive
	10m	⟶▷	Complete travel to digestion tank	Non-productive
60 mins		④	Pick up skips and pour concrete	Productive
		⊃6	Delay while engineer checks work	Non-productive
	20m	⟶▷	Travel to Secondary Digestion Tank No. 2	Non-productive
		⊃7	Delay as crane meets soft ground	Non-productive
	20m	⟶▷	Travel and turn to tank	Non-productive
		⊃8	Further delay on soft ground	Non-productive
	20m	⟶▷	Complete travel to tank	Non-productive
60 mins		⑤	Pick up skips and pour concrete	Productive
		⊃9	Delay while engineer checks work	Non-productive
	20m	⟶▷	Travel to consolidation tanks	Non-productive
20 mins		⑥	Pick up skips and pour concrete in first two tanks	Productive
	10m	⟶▷	Travel to next two tanks	Non-productive
20 mins		⑦	Pick up skips and pour concrete in final two tanks	Productive
		⊃10	Delay while engineer checks work	Non-productive
	100m	⟶▷	Travel back to plant compound	Non-productive
		☐2	Inspect crane after day's work	Non-productive
		▽	Store crane in compound	Non-productive

Fig. 3.4 Process Chart for a crane.

practical solution is to represent the sequence of activities by symbols only. Such charts may take two forms:

(a) Man/machine type to record what happens to the machine or operator;

(b) Material type to record what happens to the materials handled by the operator.

The method of presentation for each type is similar, except that only the relevant aspects are recorded for the subject. Like the flow diagram ASME symbols are used, but a plan of the area is not required. A machine type process chart for the sewage works covering the cranage activities is shown in Fig. 3.4. The results are summarised in Table 3.1. (Note that, because the process chart is directed towards the plant, inspection of the concrete represents a delay. Had a material type chart been adopted to study the flow of concrete, then this probably would be represented by an inspection symbol.)

Table 3.1 Summary of cranage activity of a daily cycle.

Summary of cranage activity of a daily cycle				
◯	☐	⇨	▽	D
7	2	12	2	10
5½hrs.		380 m		

Clearly, the chart has highlighted the excessive travel and delays experienced by the crane, together with a record of where the main problems are occurring. The next stage is therefore to consider more efficient methods of working.

It can be seen from the flow process chart that concreting time at the Primary Digestion Tank No. 1 was rather prolonged, a further detailed concrete *material process chart* involving all the events, including the mixing of the concrete, its transport, the movements of the crane, and activities of the concrete gang, may reveal the reasons. For studies made at this level of detail, it is advisable initially to prepare only an *outline process diagram*, which gives an overall view and from which a decision with respect to a further and more detailed study can be taken. The outline process diagram technique uses only two symbols, operation and inspection, and is not concerned with who or what performs the task. An example of the sequence of operations in placing concrete at Primary Digestion Tank No. 1 is shown in Fig. 3.5. It can be seen that the outline process chart reveals a cyclical *interaction* between the crane, dumper and concrete mixer and a more suitable technique for analysing the time relationships is the *multiple activity chart*.

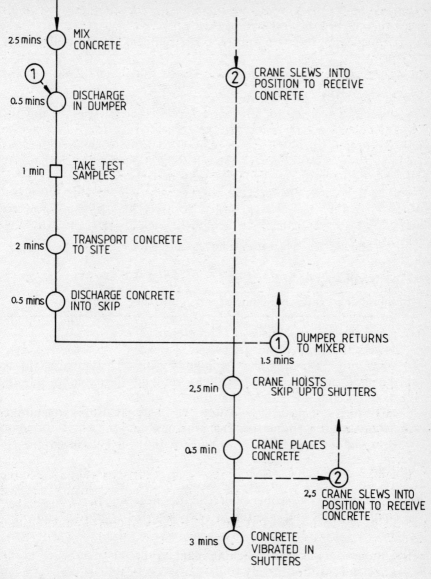

Fig. 3.5 Outline Process Diagram.

Example 2: Illustrating a Multiple Activity Chart

Observation of the activities performed by the concrete mixer, dumpers, and crane when placing concrete at Primary Digestion Tank No. 1 reveals the following operations.

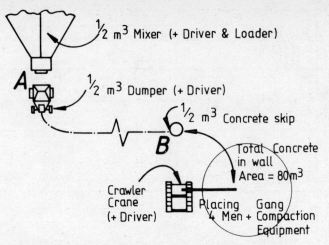

Fig. 3.6 Site layout at Primary Digestion Tank No. 1.

Concrete batching plant

(i) Sand, aggregate, cement, are loaded into the hopper	2 standard minutes
(ii) After completion of task (i), the mixer driver lowers the hopper and discharges the contents into the mixing drum and adds water	0.5 standard minutes
(iii) The hopper is then raised ready for refilling	0.5 standard minutes
(iv) The materials are mixed immediately after task (ii) is complete	2 standard minutes
(v) The concrete is discharged from the mixing drum into dumpers	0.5 standard minutes

Concrete placing

Immediately after discharging the concrete into the dumper the mixing cycle is restarted. The sequence of activities in getting the concrete from the batching plant and into the formwork of the Digestion Tank is as follows.

(i) Dumper travels from batching plant to the tank and positions ready to discharge concrete into skip	2 standard minutes
(ii) Dumper discharges concrete into skip and driver attaches to crane hook	0.5 standard minutes
(iii) Dumper returns to batching plant	1.5 standard minutes
(iv) Crane lifts full skip, travels, slews and discharges concrete from skip into shutters	3 standard minutes
(v) Crane lifts empty skips, slews and travels back to position	2.5 standard minutes

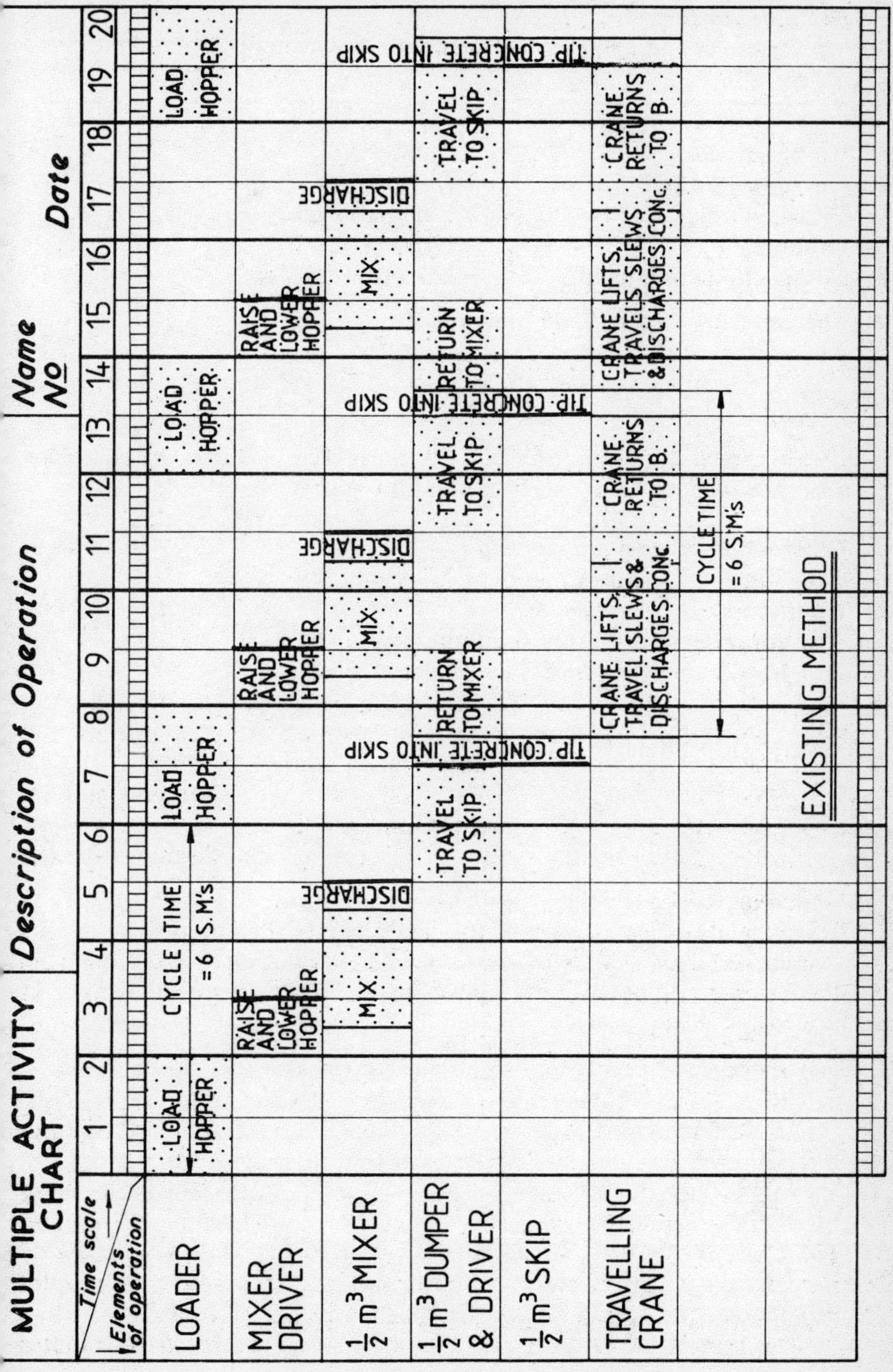

MULTIPLE ACTIVITY CHART | Description of Operation | Name Nº | Date

Time scale →

Elements of operation

LOADER	LOAD HOPPER
MIXER DRIVER	RAISE AND LOWER HOPPER
½ m³ MIXER	MIX / DISCHARGE
½ m³ DUMPER & DRIVER	TRAVEL TO SKIP / RETURN TO MIXER
½ m³ SKIP	TIP CONCRETE INTO SKIP
TRAVELLING CRANE	CRANE LIFTS, TRAVELS SLEWS & DISCHARGES CONC. / CRANE RETURNS TO B.

CYCLE TIME = 6 S.M.s

EXISTING METHOD

Fig. 3.7 Multiple Activity Chart for existing method.

Notes to the study
The resources and plant requirements are shown on Fig. 3.7 and the costs are as follows.

$\frac{1}{2}m^3$ concrete batching plant	£120 per week
$\frac{1}{2}m^3$ dumper	£40per week
$\frac{1}{2}m^3$ concrete skip	£8 per week
Crawler crane	£400 per week
Labourer	£2.50 per hour
Compaction equipment	£12 per week

The site works a 5 day, 40 hour week.

Present method

It is observed in the multiple activity chart (Fig. 3.7) that the complete sequence of operations has a minimum 6 minute cycle time.

Concrete production and placing
Cycle time = 6 minutes
Hours worked per day = 8
$\frac{1}{2}m^3$ concrete placed every 6 minutes
Output per day $= \dfrac{60 \times 8}{6} \times 0.5 = 40m^3$

Time to place $80m^3$ = 2 days.

Costs

$\frac{1}{2}m^3$ batch	$0.4 \times 120 =$	£48
$\frac{1}{2}m^3$ dumper	$0.4 \times 40 =$	£16
$\frac{1}{2}m^3$ skip	$0.4 \times 8 =$	£3.2
Crane	$0.4 \times 400 =$	£160
Labour	$16 \times 8 \times 2.5 =$	£320
Compaction equipment	$0.4 \times 12 =$	£4.8
Total costs		£552.0

Labour

Mixer loader and driver	= 2
Dumper driver	= 1
Concrete gang	= 4
Crane driver	= 1
Total labour	8 men

Therefore cost of placing concrete $= \dfrac{552}{80} = £6.9$ per m^3

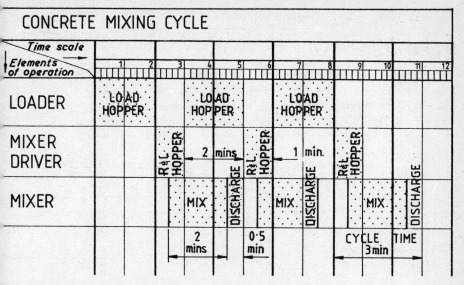

Fig. 3.8 Multiple Activity Chart for concrete batching plant.

Proposed Solution

It can be seen from Fig. 3.8 that the batching plant could easily produce a batch of concrete every 3 minutes. A possible improved solution would be to use 2 skips of 1m³ capacity and to increase the number of ½m³ dumpers to two as shown in Fig. 3.9.

Revised concrete production and placing
1m³ concrete placed every 6 mins.

Output per day $= \dfrac{60 \times 8}{6} = 80\text{m}^3$

Time to place 80m³ = 1 day.

Costs

½m³ mixer	0.2 × 120 =	£24
2 × ½m³ dumpers	2 × 0.2 × 40 =	£16
2 × 1m³ concrete skips	2 × 0.2 × 12 =	£4.8
Travelling crane	0.2 × 400 =	£80
Labour	8 × 10 × 2.5 =	£200
Construction equipment	0.2 × 12 =	£2.4
Total costs		£327.2

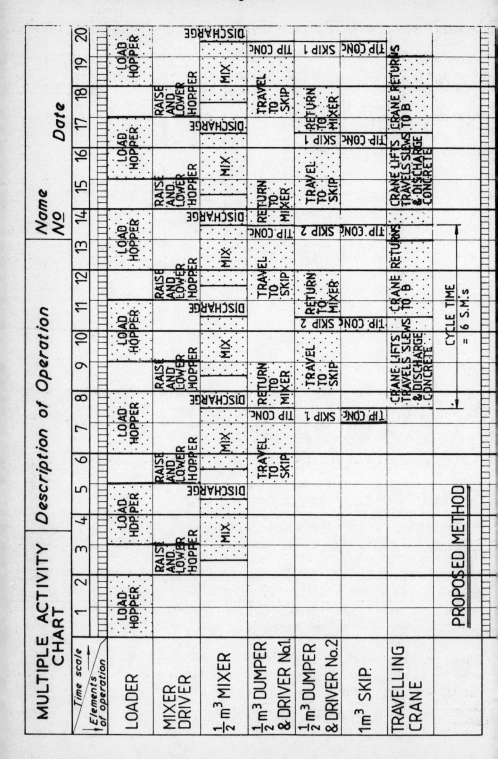

MULTIPLE ACTIVITY CHART

Description of Operation

Name
No
Date

Elements of operation	1	2	3	4	5	6	7	8	9	10	11	12	13	14	15	16	17	18	19	20
LOADER	LOAD HOPPER			LOAD HOPPER			LOAD HOPPER			LOAD HOPPER			LOAD HOPPER			LOAD HOPPER			LOAD HOPPER	
MIXER DRIVER		RAISE AND LOWER HOPPER			DISCHARGE		RAISE AND LOWER HOPPER			MIX			DISCHARGE		RAISE AND LOWER HOPPER			MIX			DISCHARGE
½m³ MIXER			MIX				TRAVEL TO SKIP	RETURN TO MIXER		MIX			TRAVEL TO SKIP	RETURN TO MIXER		MIX			TRAVEL TO SKIP	
½m³ DUMPER & DRIVER No1.											TIP CONC SKIP 2	RETURN TO MIXER			TIP CONC SKIP 1		RETURN TO MIXER		
½m³ DUMPER & DRIVER No.2							TIP CONC SKIP 1			TIP CONC SKIP 2			TIP CONC SKIP 2			TIP CONC SKIP 1			TIP CONC SKIP 1	
1m³ SKIP.																				
TRAVELLING CRANE									CRANE LIFTS TRAVELS SLEWS & DISCHARGE CONCRETE			CRANE RETURNS TO B			CRANE LIFTS TRAVELS SLEWS & DISCHARGE CONCRETE		CRANE RETURNS TO B			CRANE RETURNS

PROPOSED METHOD

CYCLE TIME = 6 S.M.'s

Labour

Mixer loader and driver	2
Dumper drivers	2
Concrete gang	5 (extra man)
Crane driver	1
Total labour	10 men

Proposed cost of placing concrete $= \dfrac{325.6}{80} = $ £4.09 / m³

Utilisation factor

The utilisation factor for each resource is calculated by extracting the working time of the resource and dividing by the cycle time. In this way alternative schemes can be compared immediately.

Summary of Utilisation Factors of Multiple Activity Charts

Activity		Present Work	Present Idle	Proposed Work	Proposed Idle	Difference Work	Difference Idle
Loader	Time	2	4	4	2	+2	−2
	%	33%	67%	67%	33%	+34%	−34%
Mixer driver	Time	1	5	2	4	+1	−1
	%	17%	83%	33%	67%	+16%	−16%
Mixer	Time	2.5	3.5	5	1	+2.5	−2.5
	%	42%	58%	83%	17%	+41%	−41%
Dumper 1	Time	4	2	4	2	0	0
	%	67%	33%	67%	33%	0%	0%
Dumper 2	Time			4	2		
	%			67%	33%		
Crane	Time	5.5	0.5	5.5	0.5	0	0
	%	92%	8%	92%	8%	0%	0%

Other Alternative Solutions

The reader should now examine other possible solutions before deciding on the most economic alternative. For example:

Alternative 3	2 × ½m³ dumpers
	2 × ½m³ skips
Alternative 4	1 × 1m³ dumper
	1 × 1m³ skip
Alternative 5	3 × ½m³ skips
	1m³ skip + ½m³ skip

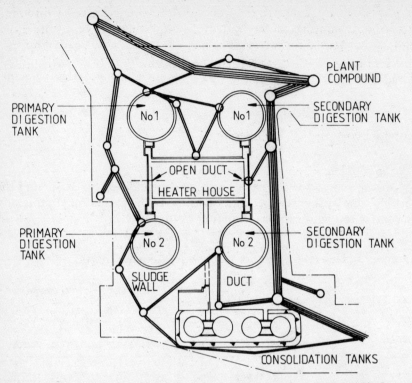

PLANT
COMPOUND

PRIMARY
DIGESTION
TANK

No 1

No 1

SECONDARY
DIGESTION TANK

OPEN DUCT

HEATER HOUSE

PRIMARY
DIGESTION
TANK

No 2

No 2

SECONDARY
DIGESTION TANK

SLUDGE
WALL

DUCT

CONSOLIDATION TANKS

Fig. 3.10 String diagram of transport movements on Bogtown Sewage Works Site Layout.

Example 3: Illustrating a String Diagram

On many construction sites the positioning of materials and the layout of temporary roads, scaffolds, access points, etc. often develop haphazardly as work proceeds, and frequently leads to delays, wastage and inconvenience generally. The string diagram is an effective technique in picturing the transport and distribution situation in such cases. The method requires a scale drawing of the construction site firmly mounted on a hard base of hardboard or similar. The observer then proceeeds to count the movements of the worker, machine, material, etc. or even all the movements on the site depending upon the scale of the study. The length of time needed for observation depends upon the judgement of the observer but all journeys, say, during a typical work day should be captured.

At the close of the study pins are driven into the scale drawing and a length of thread is led from the starting points of movement and around all the other points of call, in the order noted.

The result emphasises the relative volumes of movement between the pin positions. By using several colours the movements of different workers, or machines, can be compared easily. Indeed, by measuring the length of string used for each the distances travelled may be determined.

Fig. 3.10 illustrates the application of the technique in plotting the travel paths of vehicles and other equipment entering or used on the

<u>FOREMAN DELAY SURVEY</u>

SECTION OF CONTRACT _____

NAME OF FOREMAN _____   TRADE _____

(Date) DAILY EVALUATION _____   NUMBER IN GANG _____

PROBLEMS CAUSING DELAY

	Number of hours	x	Number of men	= Manhours
			Manhours lost	
1.a) Waiting for materials (On site)	_____		_____	_____
b) Waiting for materials (Outside delivery)	_____		_____	_____
2. Waiting for tools and equipment	_____		_____	_____
3. Lack of access	_____		_____	_____
4. Plant breakdowns	_____		_____	_____
5. Changes/Redoing work (a) Design errors	_____		_____	_____
(b) Site errors	_____		_____	_____
6. Move to other work area	_____		_____	_____
7. Waiting for information	_____		_____	_____
8. Lack of continuity	_____		_____	_____
9. Overcrowded working areas	_____		_____	_____
10. Inclement weather	_____		_____	_____
11. Other	_____		_____	_____
_____	_____			
_____	_____			

COMMENTS: _____

Fig. 3.11 Foreman Delay Survey form.

sewage-works construction site. It is observed that quite heavy flows of traffic occur between the access points to the site and the stores compound. This is particularly apparent on the east side of the site, and for other material stocks located around the site perimeter. Further analysis may bring forward a more efficient distribution arrangement and so reduce the transport distances.

Example 4: Illustrating Foreman Delay Surveys

Borcherding (ref. 2) and Tucker (ref. 4) in the USA and subsequently Easton (ref. 3) in Australia recognised that quite often the best means of acquiring information about production problems is by asking the workmen themselves. The method adopted by these two investigators was to approach the foremen, who are then asked to identify and estimate time losses and causes at the end of the working day. These types of study have revealed areas of inefficiency caused by factors other than those due to the performance of the workforce, such as badly scheduled material deliveries, lack of information, equipment, etc. Thus the Foreman Delay Survey is aimed at determining the administrative items which are outside the foreman's control, but which nonetheless affect the performance of the work group. A sample survey form as used by Tucker is shown in Fig. 3.11 and typical results obtained by Easton are illustrated in Fig. 3.12. By diligent application of the recommended method study procedures improvements can be effected. Subsequent use of the Foreman Delay Survey, would indicate whether the revisions were proving effective by the reducing percentage of delays. An example illustrating improvement is shown in Fig. 3.13. Clearly the Foreman Delay Survey (FDS) is a cost effective technique which is particularly useful for evaluating administratively related problems. The FDS has the following features:

1. It provides a link between management and foremen and facilitates discussion of problems and means of solution.
2. Delays to particular groups of workers are immediately highlighted.
3. Information is provided on particular aspects, such as materials, subcontract interference, drawing information, plant availability, etc.
4. The whole project can be readily monitored.
5. The survey is inexpensive to carry out, can be done regularly and by untrained personnel.
6. The information is current.

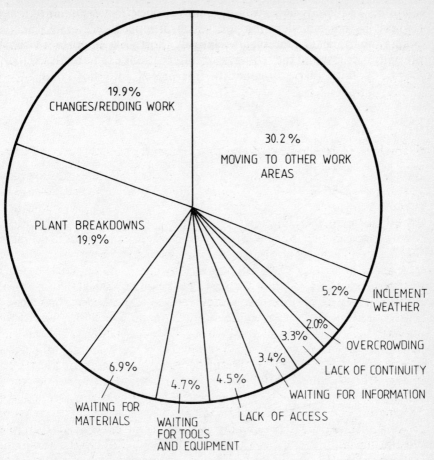

Fig. 3.12 Pie diagram of Foreman Delay Survey results.

Example 5: Illustrating Time-lapse Film

Both time and method study require visual observation, and data can only be recorded as the work proceeds, which is time-consuming. An alternative approach to stop-watch time and motion studies is to record activities performed by an item of plant, an individual or group of workers as a motion picture. The recording is made on photographic film or video tape at a slow speed taking one frame at pre-selected intervals. Investigators in the USA (refs. 1, 5) and Australia (ref. 3) have demonstrated that for most construction operations an interval of 4 seconds between frames is acceptable using a photographic camera. The film is then played back at faster speeds. For example, with 8 mm film the normal running speed is 18 frames per second, and several hours of recording can thereby be viewed in minutes. The effect is similar to that produced by the old silent movies, which produce a jerky movement. Because the frame time interval is relatively short, little important visual information is lost and the sequence of observations can be analysed like time study data and subsequently interpreted into flow diagrams,

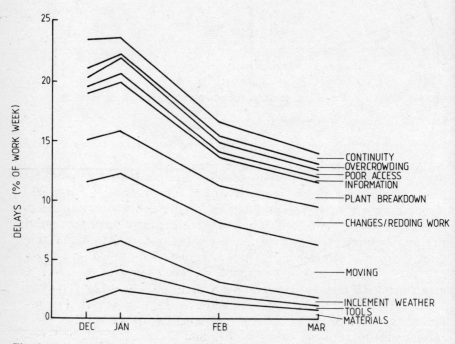

Fig. 3.13 Results of regular Foreman Delay Surveys.

multiple activity charts and even used for activity sampling. This is made possible by either including a clock in the picture itself, or using more modern methods by digitising the actual time on each frame.

Equipment Specifications

Motion film
Early studies adopted 16 mm film but the equipment was too bulky for the portability needed for speedy applications on construction projects, and today most practitioners select an 8 mm time-lapse camera such as a

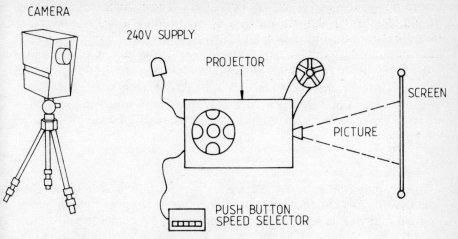

Fig. 3.14 Time-lapse photographic equipment.

Standard Super-8 or equivalent camera. Equipped with a time delay device, the camera can be set to record pictures between 0.5 and 99.5 second intervals, in 0.5 second intervals, or alternatively filming can be made at 18 frames per second, which is the normal motion picture speed. In addition, more expensive versions are able to record digitally the time of exposure on each frame of film. The camera is mounted on a tripod and for outside use a detachable weather protective cover is recommended. Power is supplied from a rechargeable 6 or 12 volt battery.

The camera requires a zoom lens, with variable focal length. For an 8 mm camera, 5 mm up to 75 mm focal length is recommended which corresponds to a magnification of 1:15 and allows scenes to be filmed with a field width varying from 50° to 30°. The lens should be equipped with an automatic exposure control, together with a manual override, because during, say, a day's filming the light intensity is likely to fluctuate.

The camera is usually loaded with about 50 ft (15 m) of 8 mm film

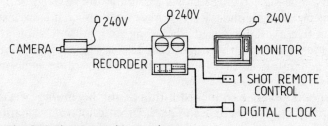

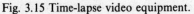

Fig. 3.15 Time-lapse video equipment.

(either colour or black and white is acceptable) which will take 3 600 frames. Thus at 1 frame per 4 seconds the filming will last 4 hours.

After developing, the film is shown on a screen with a projector. This is similar to a standard movie projector except that the play-back speed may be varied at 1, 2, 3, 6, 9 and 18 frames per second. Thus, a film recorded at 1 frame per 4 seconds and played back at the commonly preferred speed of 3 frames per second represents a time compression of 12 to 1. The projector also requires a zoom lens and 240 v supply for U.K. operation.

Video recordings

Photographic film suffers the disadvantge that film is expensive to buy and develop and can be used once only. Video recorders allow film to be re-used many times and modern equipment now includes the time-lapse facility. The equipment comprises a T.V. camera with a cable link to the video recorder and T.V. monitor. The obvious difference with photography is that all units must be present at the site of recording and generally all require 120 v or 240 v power supply. The camera is usually mounted on a tripod, and protected by a detachable weather proof cover. The lens should have a zoom capability, giving at least 1:10 magnification, with an automatic exposure control. The video recorder receives signals from the camera and records the information on magnetic tape, which may be observed simultaneously on a T.V. monitor. It is necesary for the recorder and monitor to be set up in a well-protected environment, such as a nearby building or shed. Consequently both the power and signal cables for the camera may require careful positioning to avoid damage when operating on a construction site. With a powerful zoom lens, however, the camera placing frequently can be set well away from the site of study without a significant loss of definition.

The recorder itself is usually loaded with a reel of tape of one hour's duration when run at normal speed. For time-lapse work, however, the recording speed may be reduced to $\frac{1}{80}$, $\frac{1}{40}$, $\frac{1}{20}$, $\frac{1}{10}$ of normal and normal itself. Thus, in effect, images are recorded at time intervals: for example, $\frac{1}{80}$ speed played back at normal is almost equivalent to 1 frame per 4 seconds played back at 18 frames per second in the movie system. In addition, a one-shot device allows an image to be recorded with an interval of up to 14 seconds. Recordings may be played back instantly at any of the five available speeds including manual 'one shot' at a time. Like the movie camera, the video recorder may be equipped with a time and date generator, so that the exact time of recording each image will appear on the monitor.

It is a good practice to record a title at the beginning of each work situation, and should include the date, filming interval, location and a sketch of the camera placement. The camera can be used to film almost

Table 3.2 Comparison between film and video time-lapse systems

Feature	Video	Film	Comments
Recording time.	About 1 hour at normal.	About 3⅓ mins on a 50 ft (15 m) roll at normal speed (18 frames per second).	Video produces 'noise' or visual interference, as recordings at slow speeds are condensed between shots, when played back at normal speed.
Playback.	Immediate.	Delay for developing negative.	Video tape can be erased and photographic film is permanent.
Editing.	Possible, but requires care.	Simple.	Video requires editing by transfer of recorded parts to another recorder. Film requires only a splicer.
Resolution.	Fair.	Good.	Picture definition is sharper with film than video.
Colour.	Not available.	Available.	Only black and white is presently available with video time-lapse equipment.
Choice of intervals.	Limited to 4 or 5.	Many.	Video time-lapse presently offer ⅟₈₀, ⅟₄₀, ⅟₂₀, ⅟₁₀ normal and normal speed. Film offers intervals of 0.5 to 99.5 seconds in 0.5 second increments. The projector has playback at 1, 2, 3, 6, 9 and 18 frames per second.
Compatibility.	Limited.	Interchange-able.	8 mm or 16 mm film is standard and can be used on most cameras and projectors. Video tape is not yet standard and even same width tapes often are not mountable on competitor's recorders.
Portability.	Cumbersome.	Light.	Film requires only a camera mounting. Viewing takes place separately after film developing. Video requires camera, recorder and monitor at the site.
Outdoor mounting.	Cover.	Cover not required.	Both cameras require detachable weather proof covers, but video recorder and monitor must be in the dry.
Power.	120 v–240 v supply.	6 volt battery.	Video camera, recorder and monitor must be interconnected by leads, and each connected to 120 v–240 v power supply. Film

Table 3.2 – *continued*

Feature	Video	Film	Comments
			camera can be operated with a self-contained battery.
Cost of equipment.	£4 000 (1981).	£3 000 (1981).	Video only in black and white.
Cost of film.	£15 (for 1 hour).	£10 for 50 ft (15 m) roll (3½ minutes).	Film cost includes developing and is permanent. Video is reusable.

any construction scene. For close study, such as a gang of bricklayers, the camera should be a few feet above the area being recorded. A high camera placement is necessary to capture a complete construction site and a nearby hill might suffice. However, there are no hard and fast rules since virtually all situations can be accommodated with modern zoom lenses capable of up to 15:1 magnification. Once the camera has been set for focus and exposure, it may be left to record unmanned.

Viewing procedure
The purpose of viewing recorded work is to analyse what is happening, design a revised method and implement it. The film is viewed four or five times at about six to nine frames per second to develop a general understanding, followed by viewing at three to four frames per second and finally several times at two to three frames per second, looking specifically at each item of equipment, worker or group of workers. At this stage it may be beneficial to show the film informally to the work gang: this can act as a very useful brainstorming session, with faults and suggested improvements coming spontaneously from the men. The information should then be transferred to more traditional forms using bar charts, flow diagrams and multiple activity charts for subsequent method study analysis.

A sensible approach is to review the film from one standpoint at a time, for example:

1. Flow of men and materials.
2. Equipment utilisation and balance.
3. Safety and working conditions.
4. Comparison with the time sheet or foreman's record.
5. Comparison with the existing plan or programme.
6. Activity sampling.

Work Measurement or Time Study

Introduction

BS 3138 defines Work Measurement as:

'The application of techniques designed to establish the time for a qualified worker to carry out a specified job at a defined level of performance.'

The aim of the technique is the evaluation of human work and provides a fundamental part of the recording procedures described earlier under Method Study. However, the applications of work measurement data are extensive and can be used in:

1. Determining suitable manning levels on construction activities.
2. Setting standards of machine utilisation and labour performance.
3. Providing the basis for sound financial incentive targets.
4. Providing a basis for cost control by fixing standard performance targets.
5. Determining the most economic from alternative methods.

Accurate time data is indispensable to estimators and planners in contracting organisations, but for such data to be of value it must have been measured in a planned environment, and not obtained from a disorganised site with inefficient working practices. For instance, the time for excavating a foundation of given dimensions with a backhoe is likely to be quite different to that required for digging with some ill-chosen method. Furthermore the observed time will be affected by the skill of the worker and the condition of the equipment used, etc. The time study method attempts to quantify these latter factors which interfere with standard conditions in order to establish the 'proper' time for the job.

Work Measurement (Time Study) Procedure

The work to be observed should be broken down into elements, to facilitate subsequent synthesis. For example, a tower crane can be used for lifting formwork and reinforcement, pouring concrete, etc. Therefore records of lifting, slewing and moving times at different heights would be valuable in assembling activity times for, say, placing concrete in a high-rise building. In this way, direct observation could in principle be avoided when the data bank has developed to include most construction tasks or elements.

The equipment required to measure and record output information consists of a stop watch, study board and pre-prepared time study sheets, supplemented by a hand calculator, tape measure, micrometer, etc. depending upon the type of work.

The stop watch may take several forms. The popular type shown in Fig. 3.16 has a large hand which completes one minute per revolution and is graduated in hundredths of a minute while the small hand records cumulative time up to 30 minutes in one minute graduations. A fly-back mechanism on the large hand allows the timing of elements to start at zero for each element without affecting the elapsed time shown on the small hand. Before the study begins it is important to approach the

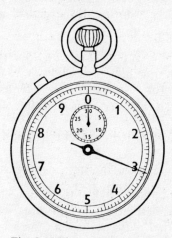

Fig. 3.16 Time study stop watch.

workers to be observed and their foreman and explain the purpose of the exercise. In most cases workers are willing to co-operate, if the final result is to be increased earnings or less fatiguing work. Where time study is new to the workforce then it is good policy to enter into discussions with the union representatives on site and to answer all questions quite frankly.

When these problems are sorted out, the observation can commence. It is advisable to make a sketch of the work and to record general details such as weather and site conditions, date, time, name of workers under study, notes about access to the site of work, proximity of material supplies, and tools and equipment to be used, etc. – the more information the better for later applications of the data. The actual time observed for each element is recorded with the stop watch and examples of observed time are shown later in Fig. 3.21.

However, because the objective of the study is to obtain a realistic time for the element, the time study observer must additionally make a judgement on the effective rate of working of the subject under observation since the elapsed time observed for one worker may be different from another doing an identical task. The procedure is known as 'rating'.

Rating

BS 3138 defines Standard Rating as:

'The rating corresponding to the averge rate at which qualified workers will naturally work at a job, provided they adhere to the specified method and provided they are motivated to apply themselves to their work. If the Standard Rating is maintained and the appropriate relaxation is taken, a worker will achieve Standard Performance over the working day or shift.'

The time study practitioner must have a concept in his mind of standard rating, which comes only from experience in judging different speeds of movement, effort, consistency and dexterity. Thus the practitioner must be able to differentiate between fast, slow or medium rates of doing work. The B.S. rating scale provides a suitable description for varying levels of worker performance achieved over a short period of time. The scale is divided in 5 point graduations with 100 representing standard rating. Thus:

125: Very quick; high skill; highly motivated.
100: Brisk; qualified skill; motivated.
75: Not fast; average skill; disinterested.
50: Very slow; unskilled; unmotivated.

As a guide, a man of average build and a regular walker, is said to achieve standard rating when walking at about 4 mph (6.43 kph) along a straight road without a load and with adequate rest periods.

Calculation of basic time

The basic or normal time for a job = observed time $\times \dfrac{\text{assessed rating}}{\text{standard rating}}$

The basic or normal time is therefore the time for a *qualified* worker to carry out a specific job at a defined level of working. In practice, the the worker could not be expected to achieve this level of rating over the working day without rest and relaxation.

Factors affecting the rating

(a) The observer should guard against malpractices, whereby workers being timed, for example, to set standards for a bonus incentive scheme, may try to give the impression of working at standard rating while hoping that disguised inefficiencies will go unnoticed by the time study observer.

(b) While the observer must be aware of such practices, he must also try to assess the true effort required for the task. For example, the same rating could be assessed for light and heavy tasks, which would normally be carried out at different speeds even by a qualified and motivated worker.

(c) Factors which can influence the observed time but not necessarily the rating include:

  (i) Quality of tools used.
 (ii) Type and quality of material worked on.
(iii) Working conditions.
 (iv) Learning period required before task becomes familiar.
  (v) Interruption of supply of materials.
 (vi) Quality of working drawings.
(vii) Supervision.
(viii) Quality specification.

These factors are difficult to assess and are best included by taking a large number of studies to give a representative sample.

(d) Factors attributable to the worker which affect the observed time and therefore should be removed in the rating assessment include:

  (i) Intelligence and education.
 (ii) Attitude and motivation.
(iii) Skill and training.
 (iv) Personal discipline and organisation.
  (v) Health.
 (vi) Level of fatigue.

The Required Number of Observations

If the time study practitioner possessed perfect judgement and could accurately assess the correct rating irrespective of the worker under observation and take full account for the effort required then the basic time for a task would be the same for any multiple of observed time and rating. This is unlikely to occur and in practice the basic times calculated for a number of observations would be distributed on either side of a mean value. In these circumstances the mean basic time is usually selected as the Basic Time for the task.

A simpler method which does not require the observed times to be reduced to basic times, uses a graphical presentation as typified in Fig. 3.17. The observer records the time against the assessed rating and the best straight line fit through the points is drawn . The basic time is simply read off at 100 rating. The method will also indicate the amount of under- or over-rating included inadvertently by the observer. The true rating line should pass through the origin, since in theory infinite rating should take

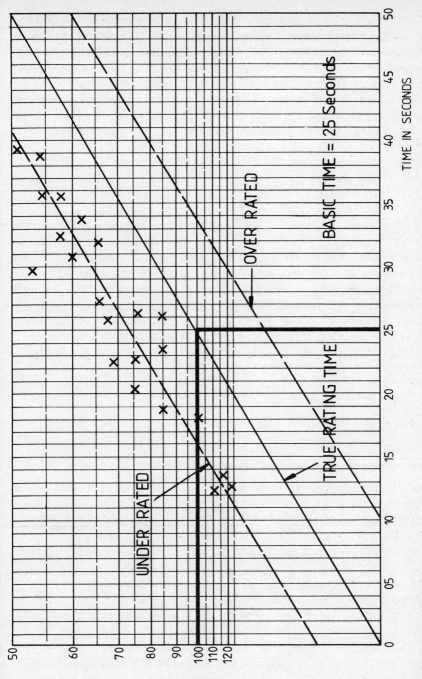

Fig. 3.17 Rating graph.

zero time and infinite time corresponds to zero rating. The method also highlights unrepresentative ratings due either to faulty rating or fraudulent performance by the worker. Such data can be removed from the diagram.

The correct size of sample is difficult to determine but certainly enough observations should be taken to cover the likely changes over a working day, such as starting up and finishing periods, weather, etc. The simplest method is to plot the cumulative average basic time against the number of observations as demonstrated in Fig. 3.18. When the line begins to stabilise, sufficient observations have probably been taken. Unfortunately, as far as construction work is concerned elements often are insufficiently repetitive for enough observations to be made. However, with well-trained staff the intangibles caused by changes in the work place can be taken into consideration, to permit the inclusion of data of similar elements observed at different sites. Indeed, the observer of construction work is frequently faced with variable elements and tasks: for example, the time for placing of concrete by crane will vary with several factors such as size of the concrete skip, the size of the opening in the shuttering, the quantity of concrete poured and so on. By plotting the basic times obtained against changes in a variable or combination of variables a line of best fit quite often can be drawn. In this way the basic times, for example, of placing concrete per cubic metre, with a range of skips or sizes of pour, etc. could be ascertained, as demonstrated in Fig. 3.19.

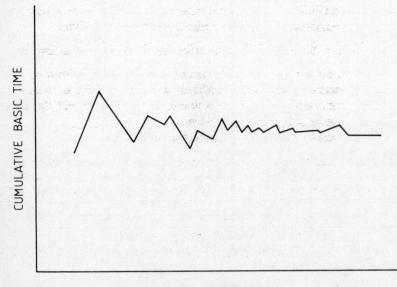

Fig. 3.18 Cumulative mean basic time.

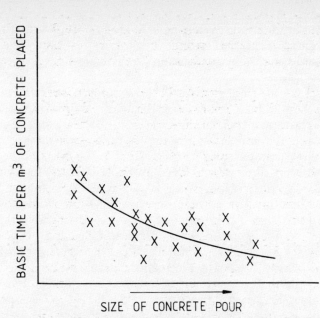

Fig. 3.19 Basic times plotted against volume of concrete.

Standard Time

The need for workers to have rest periods over a working shift of several hours has been ignored until now in calculating the Basic Time for an element. To establish the standard time it is therefore necessary to include some relaxation allowances plus a contingency. Thus:

Standard time = Basic time + relaxation allowances + contingency

The units will either be *standard hours* or *standard minutes*, and represent the 'proper' time for a qualified worker working at standard rating to execute a task or element of work. If this is obtained then the worker will achieve *standard performance*.

BS 3138 defines standard performance as follows:

'The rate of output which qualified workers will naturally achieve without over-exertion as an average over the working day or shift provided they are motivated to apply themselves to their work.'

Clearly the concept of performance encompasses both the standard rating achieved over short durations and the allowances which must be included if the standard rating is to be maintained over a longer period.

Because construction work is so variable, the difference between standard time and basic time for a job can be quite large and as a consequence, most records or data banks of output times are kept as basic times, with the user applying suitable contingencies as necessary.

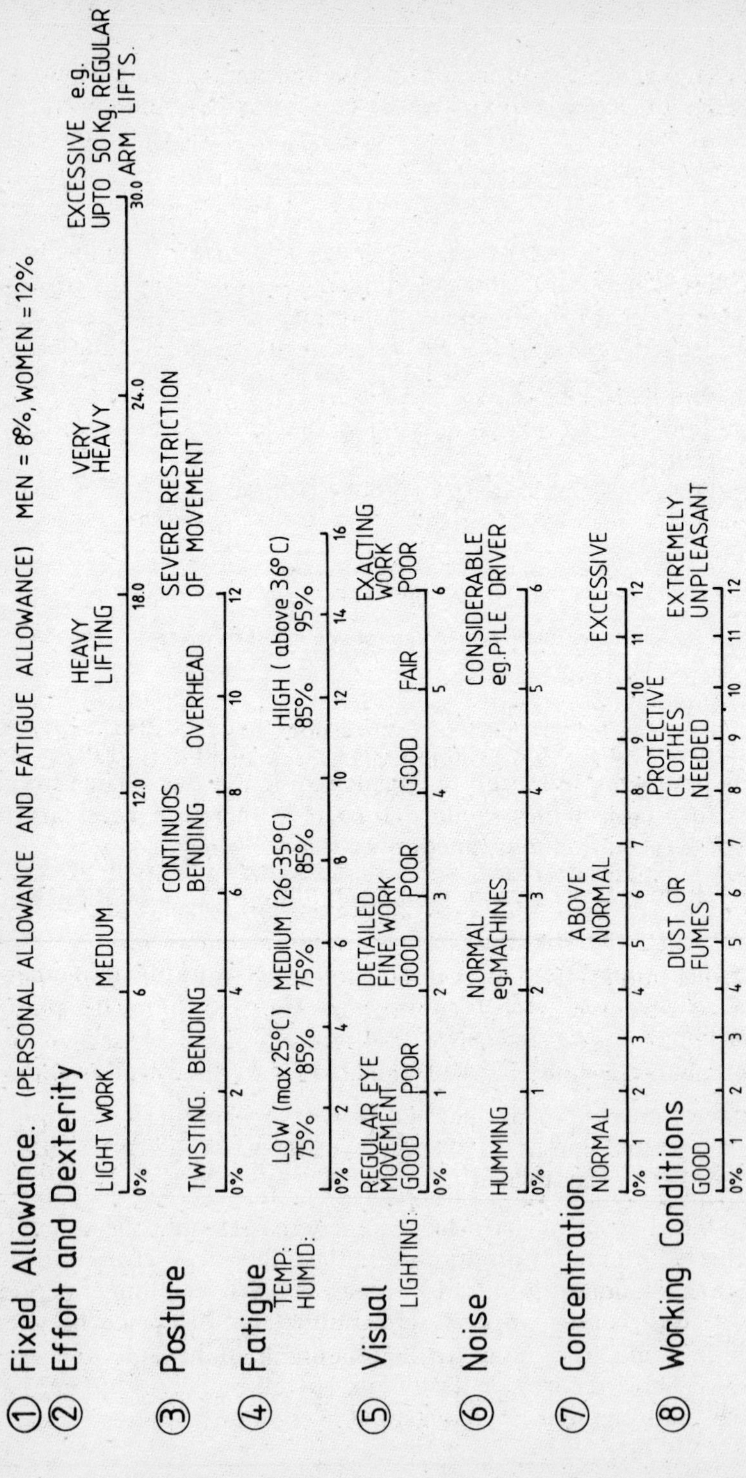

① **Fixed Allowance.** (PERSONAL ALLOWANCE AND FATIGUE ALLOWANCE)   MEN = 8%, WOMEN = 12%

② **Effort and Dexterity**

LIGHT WORK	MEDIUM	HEAVY LIFTING	VERY HEAVY	EXCESSIVE e.g. UPTO 50 Kg. REGULAR ARM LIFTS.
0%	6	12.0	18.0	24.0	30.0

③ **Posture**

TWISTING. BENDING   CONTINUOS BENDING   OVERHEAD   SEVERE RESTRICTION OF MOVEMENT

0%   2   4   6   8   10   12

④ **Fatigue**
TEMP: LOW (max 25°C)   MEDIUM (26-35°C)   HIGH (above 36°C)
HUMID: 75%   85%   75%   85%   85%   95%

0%   2   4   6   8   10   12   14   16

⑤ **Visual**
REGULAR EYE MOVEMENT   DETAILED FINE WORK   EXACTING WORK
LIGHTING: GOOD   POOR   GOOD   POOR   GOOD   FAIR   POOR

0%   1   2   3   4   5   6

⑥ **Noise**
HUMMING   NORMAL eg.MACHINES   CONSIDERABLE eg.PILE DRIVER

0%   1   2   3   4   5   6

⑦ **Concentration**
NORMAL   ABOVE NORMAL   EXCESSIVE

0%   1   2   3   4   5   6   7   8   9   10   11   12

⑧ **Working Conditions**
GOOD   DUST OR FUMES   PROTECTIVE CLOTHES NEEDED   EXTREMELY UNPLEASANT

0%   1   2   3   4   5   6   7   8   9   10   11   12

Fig. 3.20 Typical relaxation allowances.

Allowances

Allowances are extremely difficult to assess and for construction work there appears to be no rational basis as yet for determining such. Relaxation allowances are given as percentages of basic time and Fig. 3.20 illustrates examples which may be considered.

Contingencies

To obtain the final standard time it is usually prudent to include additional time which cannot be determined accurately but which will almost certainly occur. The following contingencies are typical and can either be added as a percentage to the basic time or as absolute time itself.

(a) Adjustment and maintenance of tools.
(b) Waiting time caused by subcontractors, machine breakdowns, lack of materials, etc.
(c) Unexpected site conditions, e.g. bad ground, high winds, bad weather.
(d) Learning time.
(e) One-off tasks.
(f) Design changes.

Performance Comparison

Once standard times for elements are established, they provide a basis for estimating, planning and controlling work. In particular standard time estimates may be used for comparison with the actual time spent on the task. Thus:

$$\text{Performance} = \frac{\text{Total standard time for all measured and estimated work}}{\text{Man minutes or hours of work time available}}$$

Example

A small project calls for the excavation of column base foundations. The contractor's programme provides for a $\frac{1}{2}m^3$ backhoe to do the work. Basic time for the task is estimated at 4 minutes per m^3, based on an expected rating of 100 and 50% is to be added for relaxation allowances and contingencies.

100 m^3 of excavation had been completed at the end of the second day. If an 8 hour day were worked, what level of performance by the machine and its operator would have been achieved?

Solution

$$\text{Standard time} = (1 + 0.5) \times 4 = 6 \text{ standard minutes.}$$

$$\text{Machine performance} = \frac{\text{standard minutes produced} \times 100}{\text{available minutes worked}}$$

$$= \frac{100 \times 6}{2 \times 8 \times 60} \times 100 = 62.5P$$

CONTRACT: BOGTOWN SEWAGE WORKS	STUDY NO: 41
OPERATION: Place concrete to walls of Primary Digestion Tank No. 1.	REFERENCE: TC/WS/704
	DATE: 12 September 1981
(A study of 24 skip placings)	TIME STARTED: 8.00 a.m.
OPERATIVES: Concrete gang – 4 labourers	TIME FINISHED: 10.18 a.m.
MACHINES: Crane driver, dumper driver	ELAPSED TIME: 138 mins
OBSERVER: P L Sirnam	TOTAL O.T. 700 man mins
	T.OT ex idle time: 350 man mins

CONDITIONS	NOTES
15°C, light breeze, cloudy and dull no rain, dry ground	Poorly prepared temporary roads between batching plant and digestion tank.

R = Rating: O.T. = Observed Time: CT = Clock Time: BT = Basic Time: IT = Idle Time

ELEMENTS	R	O.T.	C.T.	B.T.	ELEMENTS	R	O.T.	C.T.	B.T.
A) Crane driver					B) Fills $\frac{1}{2}$m^3 skip	75	0.30		0.23
B) Dumper driver (Note: Only included when transferring concrete into skip)					B) Attaches hook to crane	75	0.30		0.23
C)									
D) Concrete					A) Waits	IT	(0.6)		
E) Labourers									
F)					CD)EF) Waits	IT	(2.4)		
Start time			0800.0					0807.0	
B) Fills $\frac{1}{2}$m^3 skip	110	0.2		0.22					
B) Attaches hook to crane	110	0.2		0.22	A) Lifts, travels, slews	75	2.7		2.0
A) Waits	IT	(0.4)			CD)EF) Wait	IT	(10.8)		
					CD) Discharge EF) concrete	85	2.0	0809.7	1.7
CD)EF) Wait	IT	(1.6)			A) Waits	IT	(0.5)		
			0800.4					0810.2	
					A) Returns to B)	60	3.4	0810.2	2.0
A) Lifts, travels, slews	80	2.4		1.9	CD) Vibrate EF) concrete	90	8.8		7.9
CD)EF) Wait	IT	(9.6)							
CD) Discharge EF) concrete	70	2.4	0802.8	1.7	CD)EF) Wait	IT	(4.8)		
A) Wait	IT	(0.6)						0813.6	
			0803.4						
A) Returns to B)	70	3.0		2.1	(etc.	–	–	–	
CD) Vibrate EF) concrete	100	8.0		8.0	(etc.	–	–	–	
CD)EF) Wait	IT	(4.0)	0806.4		(etc. up to 24 skips	–	–	1018.0	
					TOTAL		O.T.	C.T.	B.T.

Fig. 3.21 Time study observation sheet.

TIME STUDY ABSTRACT SHEET (24 observation rounds only are shown)																									STUDY NO.			
																									REF, NO.			
																									DATE			
ELEMENTS	BASIC TIMES (mins)																								TOTAL B.Ts (mins)	FREQUENCY PER	QTY	UNIT BASIC TIMES
Fill $\frac{1}{2}m^3$ concrete skip from $\frac{1}{2}m^3$ dumper	0.2	0.2	0.3	0.1	0.2	0.3	0.3	0.2	0.2	0.2	0.2	0.1	0.1	0.2	0.4	0.2	0.2	0.2	0.2	0.1	0.1	0.3	0.3	0.2	5.0	SKIP	24	0.21 BM/SKIP
Attach/detach skip to/from crane hook	0.2	0.2	0.1	0.2	0.2	0.3	0.3	0.2	0.1	0.1	0.2	0.2	0.2	0.2	0.2	0.3	0.3	0.1	0.1	0.2	0.2	0.2	0.2	0.2	4.7	SKIP	24	0.20 BM/SKIP
Crane lifts, slews, travels	1.9	2.0	1.9	2.0	2.2	1.8	1.7	1.9	1.9	2.0	2.9	2.1	2.1	2.0	1.9	1.8	1.7	1.9	1.8	2.0	2.0	2.1	2.0	1.9	46.6	SKIP	24	1.94 BM/SKIP
Concrete gang, vibrates concrete	8.0	7.9	8.9	7.4	8.1	8.1	8.2	8.0	8.0	8.0	8.2	7.9	8.0	8.1	8.2	8.2	8.1	8.0	8.0	8.0	7.9	7.9	8.1	8.0	192.3	SKIP	24	8.01 BM/SKIP
Crane returns to position	2.1	2.0	2.1	2.1	1.9	1.8	1.9	2.0	2.0	2.0	2.3	2.3	1.8	1.8	2.1	2.1	2.0	2.0	2.0	2.1	2.1	2.1	2.0	2.0	48.6	SKIP	24	2.02 BM/SKIP
Discharge concrete	1.7	1.7	1.6	1.6	1.4	1.5	1.8	1.9	1.5	1.3	1.7	1.7	1.7	1.7	1.8	1.8	1.6	1.6	1.9	1.5	1.7	1.7	1.7	1.7	39.8	SKIP	24	1.66 BM/SKIP

Fig. 3.22 Time study abstract sheet.

<u>SUMMARY SHEET</u>

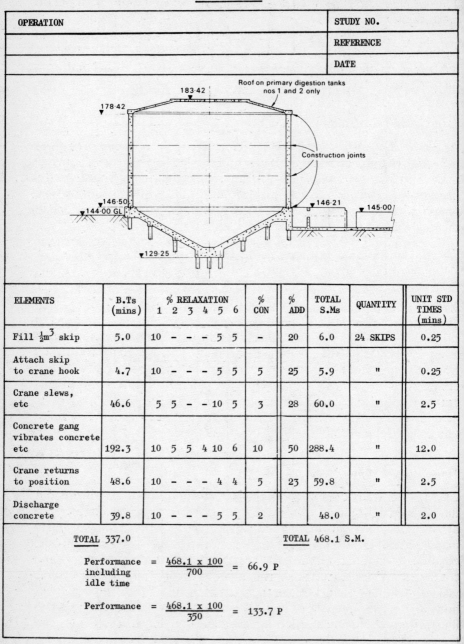

OPERATION		STUDY NO.
		REFERENCE
		DATE

ELEMENTS	B.Ts (mins)	% RELAXATION 1 2 3 4 5 6	% CON	% ADD	TOTAL S.Ms	QUANTITY	UNIT STD TIMES (mins)
Fill $\frac{1}{2}m^3$ skip	5.0	10 - - - 5 5	-	20	6.0	24 SKIPS	0.25
Attach skip to crane hook	4.7	10 - - - 5 5	5	25	5.9	"	0.25
Crane slews, etc	46.6	5 5 - - 10 5	3	28	60.0	"	2.5
Concrete gang vibrates concrete etc	192.3	10 5 5 4 10 6	10	50	288.4	"	12.0
Crane returns to position	48.6	10 - - - 4 4	5	23	59.8	"	2.5
Discharge concrete	39.8	10 - - - 5 5	2		48.0	"	2.0

TOTAL 337.0   TOTAL 468.1 S.M.

$$\text{Performance including idle time} = \frac{468.1 \times 100}{700} = 66.9 \text{ P}$$

$$\text{Performance} = \frac{468.1 \times 100}{350} = 133.7 \text{ P}$$

Fig. 3.23 Time study summary sheet.

The result would be expressed as 62.5P where 100P is standard performance.

The machine was working well below the expected standard level of performance, and either the estimate was misjudged or the driver is inefficient, or the allowances were not enough to cover the conditions met on site.

Example of Time Study Procedure

As part of the previous method study exercise on the sewage works it was necessary to obtain the standard times for mixing and placing of concrete in the walls of the primary digestion tank. Work measurement using a fly-back stop watch was selected to carry out the study. Observations were separately taken, at the batching plant, of the dumper truck route and at the digestion tank itself.

Recordings of two complete cycles of operations at the digestion tank are shown in elemental form on the time study sheet in Fig. 3.21, beginning at 8.00 a.m. in the morning. Fig. 3.22 is an abstract sheet and shows subsequent records of the elements for twenty-four cycles. Fig. 3.23 is the summary shet on which the basic times and assessed allowances are collected against the measured quantity of work done. It can be seen from the summary sheet that the performance data indicates a low level of activity if idle time is included. With reference to Fig. 3.7 where the standard times are used to establish a multiple activity chart, a cycle time of 6 minutes is required to place $\frac{1}{2}$m^3 of concrete, so producing 5m^3 per hour. The potential output can be considerably improved as demonstrated in Fig. 3.9, where it should be noted that the same standard times have been adopted in the revised method.

Time Study Data in Practice

Clearly time study data will be expensive to collect because it is obvious that only practitioners with experience in work study techniques can perform the investigations. The data cannot be assembled quickly and in many situations, especially civil engineering, the variables on site complicate the interpretation of the information as the allowances and contingencies needed often considerably exceed the basic time for the task. For building work and other activities of a more stable nature, however, basic times are useful in estimating and planning, and illustrations of methods of storing the data on computer disc files and their subsequent application can be seen in Chapter 10.

These methods in essence can be described as Synthetical and Analytical estimating.

Synthetical Estimating

Many tasks in construction work are not truly repetitive. Different projects have different site foundations, in different ground conditions, for example, and to establish estimating data a separate time study would be needed each time foundation formwork was erected. The records would therefore be useful only if a subsequent and identical foundation were available. To overcome this disadvantage the technique of

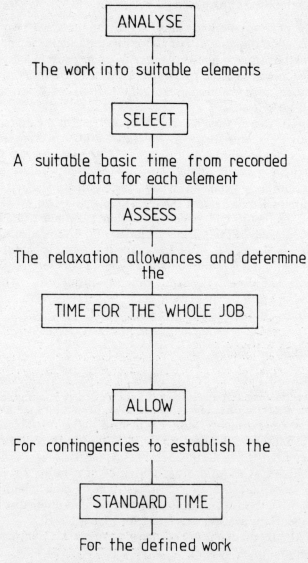

Fig. 3.24 Synthetical estimating.

Synthesis was developed. A careful study of work measurement data indicates that there is an underlying base of repetitive elements in many construction activities. The smaller the size of the elements the easier it becomes to *build up* the time for the whole series of tasks in the job. Thus, from experience, the work content of a job, e.g. the foundation formwork mentioned above and the method by which it can be carried out, may be predetermined and broken down into elements. The basic time for each element is selected from established *Basic Data* and the synthesis of these elements plus allowances gives the standard time for the work at standard performance.

The technique can be incorporated into the unit rate or operational estimating methods currently used by estimators in construction companies (see Multiple Activity Chart earlier in this chapter), and no doubt as data banks are developed and improved by individual concerns, the use of standard data will increase the accuracy of estimating.

EXERCISES

Exercise 1
A truck delivers a load of structural steelwork beams to a construction site. Before each item is unloaded, a labourer checks and notes any defects, scratches etc., and then attaches the lifting sling. A crane raises the load clear of the truck and the banksman directs the item to an appropriate stock pile and unhooks the load. The crane then returns to position in readiness for the next beam. Using A.S.M.E. symbols, draw (i) a flow diagram, (ii) a process diagram and (iii) a process chart to illustrate the sequence of actions.

Exercise 2
The work study engineer for a construction company is invited to a construction site to study the present method of transporting concrete in the expectation that productivity improvements can be suggested.

The present method observed involves a mono-rail concrete delivery system, beginning with direct discharge of concrete into a mono-rail car from the batching plant, transport to the placing point, discharge into shuttering and return back along the line to the concrete mixer. The system is operated with two concrete-cars and starting and stopping is performed by a workman at each end of the line. Both cars presently travel in tandem and a single batch of concrete is sufficient to fill both cars.

From time study, the following standard times for various activities have been established.

Travel up	180 secs
Travel down	120 secs
Fill one car with concrete	30 secs
Discharge concrete and reposition car	60 secs
Mix one batch of concrete	120 secs.

(a) Construct a Multiple Activity Chart for the present method.
(b) Calculate the hourly delivery rate of concrete in cars per hour.

(c) Determine the utilisation factors of start and stop operators of the cars, and the cars themselves.
(d) Devise improvements.

Exercise 3
(a) An estimator expects bricks to be laid requiring 66 SM's per m². If there are 5 bricklayers (excluding labourers) in a gang, and the men work at 75 Performance over a 480 minute day, how long will it take to lay 150 m² of brickwork?
(b) What performance level is required if the men are to finish the task in 4 days?
(c) If this level of performance cannot be obtained, what size of gang is required to finish in 4 days at the original 75P level?
Assume 10% relaxation allowances are available in the estimators' standard times.

References and Bibliography

1. Howell, G. A. *Construction Productivity Improvement.* Time Laps Inc., California, U.S.A., 1980.
2. Borcherding. J. D. What is the construction foreman really like? *Journal of the A.S.C.E. (Construction Division)*, U.S.A., March, 1977.
3. Easton, G. R. and Woodhead, R. W. *A survey of motivation and productivity on Australian construction sites.* Report prepared for the Australian Project Managers' Forum, School of Civil Engineering, University of New South Wales, Australia, 1981.
4. Tucker, R. L. Methods to measure productivity in construction. *Proceedings of the Mexican Roads Association Conference*, Mexico City, July 1980.
5. Parker, H. W. and Oglesby, C. H. *Methods in Improvement for Construction Managers.* McGraw-Hill, U.S.A., 1972.
6. International Labour Office. *Introduction to Work Study.* (3rd Edition), ILO, Geneva, 1979.
7. British Standards Institution. *BS 3138: Glossary of Terms used in Work Study.* London, 1969.
8. Taylor, F. W. *Principles of Scientific Management.* Harper, N.Y., U.S.A., 1911.
9. Blain, B. C. R. Work Study as an aid to Estimating. *Chartered Institute of Building*, No. 30, Autumn 1978.
10. Whitmore, D. A. *Measurement and Control of Indirect Work.* Heinemann, London, 1971.
11. Currie, R. M. *Work Study.* Pitman, 1977.
12. Geary, R. *Work Study applied to Building.* Godwin, 1972.
13. Winstanley, W. P. Use of Work Study in Europe and its effect on Productivity. Institute of Building. Occasional Paper No. 4, 1973.
14. Calvert, R. E. *Introduction to Building Management.* Newnes-Butterworths, London, 1970.

CHAPTER 4

ACTIVITY SAMPLING

Summary

Recording the efficiency of the production process on construction sites is time-consuming and unreliable when either work study or cost control methods are adopted. A simple method, by means of which unskilled practitioners can monitor productive efficiency, is explained and supported by worked examples.

Introduction

Construction work involves the employment of many different kinds of tradesmen working in a multitude of different situations. To record the level of productivity in these conditions is not easily achieved, because rarely are conditions stable enough for the correct clerical procedures to take place. In comparison, the output of a worker in manufacturing industry in many instances can be determined in detail, by means of time study methods. Such techniques are not easily applied to a construction worker, whose output may vary over a wide margin, because of bad weather conditions, machine breakdowns, poor communications, poor continuity of work and many other problems. But the project manager needs to know at all times if the site is working efficiently. Cost control methods do play a part. However, the time between observation and report is usually too long to pick up inefficient sections of work quickly enough for corrective action to be taken. The technique known as Activity Sampling is a method which provides the project manager with a fairly sensitive management tool to do a similar job to time study methods without many of its disadvantages when applied to construction work. The fundamentals of the technique are apparent in the following observations of a passerby seeing a group of construction workers (J. Carney, ref. 4). The passerby was so distressed about what he saw that he sent the following letter to the local newspaper:

Sir,

I would like to make known to you a record I recently made of an exhibition of slow motion around a hole, which I have passed by on the last six occasions on my way to work each morning.

First occasion—   Eight men talking near the hole.

Second occasion—   The hole was deserted.

Third occasion—   Four men watching, one man priming some kind of pump, and one man holding a pneumatic drill (not working).

Fourth occasion—   Four men motionless, and sitting in various attitudes around the hole.

Fifth occasion—   Six men watching, one man working.

Sixth occasion—   Seven men watching, one man at work. (One of the seven was in the hole.)

After this experience, I gave up in despair and made no further records. Although I must add that the hole did get very large and deep. It has subsequently been filled in again!!

Clearly, this is not typical of construction work, and unfortunately the observer was observing a gang of men early in the morning before they had settled into the day's work. But the observer did make a sample study of what was happening. If the number of observations is increased and the time of the study is randomly chosen, then by the application of simple statistics the results will be valid.

Field Count

A field count provides preliminary information before carrying out a full activity sampling exercise. For example, the project manager may feel that the overall level of efficiency of the workers on the construction site is poor. To test this possibility quickly, the manager simply takes a walk round the site and casually records those men working and those not working.

$$\text{Activity rating} = \frac{\text{Number observed active}}{\text{Total number observed}} \times 100\%$$

Obviously if the rating causes concern, further investigation may be warranted. Figures 4.1 and 4.2 demonstrate possible results for a daily

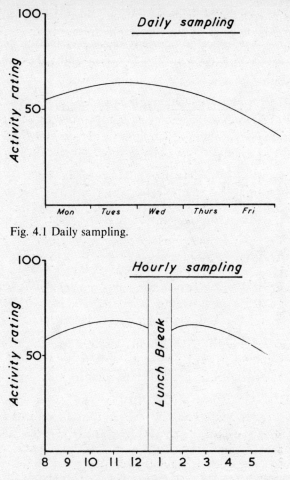

Fig. 4.1 Daily sampling.

Fig. 4.2 Hourly sampling.

and an hourly check. The total number of men observed should be between 75–80% of the total employed workforce. Clearly the field count technique can only provide a guide since the number of observations is so few. The following example illustrates the use of statistics in turning the method into something more meaningful.

The Theory of Activity Sampling

Example

A field count indicates that about 40% of the available worktime on a section of construction work is spent on unproductive work. How many observations are required to be sure that the proportion is within 2% accuracy? Given that 95% confidence is required.

If the field count is repeated on many occasions and the proportion of unproductive workers plotted graphically, it is quite likely that the data

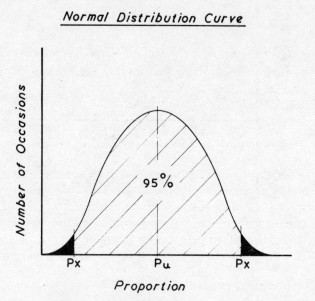

Fig. 4.3 Normal distribution curve.

will fit a normal distribution as illustrated in Fig. 4.3. Such data can then be interpreted statistically in the following way.

Pu = mean proportion of unproductive workers
Px = proportions within 95% of the area under the curve

Now $\qquad\qquad Px \pm Pu = 2\%$
and $\qquad\qquad Px \pm Pu = \sigma \times Z$
where σ = standard deviation for the distribution, and $Z = 2$ for 95% confidence. Hence

$$0 \cdot 02 = \sigma \times 2 \qquad\qquad (1)$$

But the data are also well represented by the binomial distribution, thus

$$\sigma = \sqrt{\frac{P(1 - P)}{n}} \qquad\qquad (2)$$

where P = observed proportion, and n = number of observations.

By substituting for σ in equations (1) and (2)

$$0 \cdot 02 = 2 \times \left[\frac{P(1-P)}{n} \right]^{\frac{1}{2}}$$

$$n = \frac{4 \times 0 \cdot 4(1 - 0 \cdot 4)}{0 \cdot 02^2}$$

$$n = 2400 \text{ observations}$$

Therefore, by taking 2400 observations the proportion of unproductive work is determined to within 2% accuracy.

More generally the formula is written as

$$N = \frac{Z^2 \times P \times (1 - P)}{L^2}$$

where N = number of observations required, P = percentage of activity observed (usually assessed from a pilot study), L = limit (%) of accuracy required, and Z = value obtained from statistical tables depending upon the level of confidence required for the estimate (usually taken as 2, which corresponds to 95% confidence).

Activity Sampling Procedure

1. First, carry out a preliminary survey to get a feeling for the problem. The information collected will help in deciding on the size of the section of work to be studied and the number of workers involved.

2. Identify the workers by name, and list the operations and tasks to be studied. Sometimes this need only be 'Working' or 'Not working', but for a much fuller investigation greater detail will be required, such as 'Fixing formwork', 'Cleaning shutter panels', 'Receiving instructions' etc.

3. Prepare a suitable observation sheet (Fig. 4.4) for recording the information.

4. Consult the supervisor of the work and ensure that everyone is fully informed. Failure to do so may cause unrest, which can quickly escalate and feed smouldering grievances.

5. The number of observations required is normally quite large; therefore, a planned timetable of observation times should now be assembled. In mass production work these times are normally chosen randomly since the work patterns tend to be regular. However, in construction work, activities by their very nature take a random time to complete and thus the observations can be taken at regular intervals. Even so, caution is required with some types of building work, e.g. bricklaying.

Observer				Place				Date				

Observation round	Time		Worker					Operation					
	hour	min	A	B	C	D	E	FS	CL	RF	RI	I	A
1.	8	00	✓					✓					
				✓				✓					
					✓					✓			
						✓							✓
							✓			✓			
2.	8	10	✓					✓					
				✓					✓				
					✓					✓			
						✓					✓		
							✓				✓		
3.	8	20	✓								✓		
				✓						✓			
					✓					✓			
							✓						✓

Fig. 4.4 Activity sampling observation sheet. *Key*: Worker A = F. Smith, B = J. Jones, C = R. Roberts, D = K. Baker, E = M. Kay; operation FS = fixing formwork, CL = cleaning formwork, RF = removing formwork, RI = resting, I = idle, A = absent.

6. Choose a suitable position for taking the observations.

7. Record each activity that is in operation at the instant it is observed, together with the worker involved.

8. From the percentages of the activities observed select the activity or activities which show a disproportionate amount of time being spent on them. Corrective action can then be considered.

Example (using Fig. 4.4)

A preliminary study of 25 separate observations on a gang of five carpenters revealed that the time spent on fixing formwork was 40% of working time. The other activities gave lower results, but indicated a disturbing amount of ineffective time.

Calculate the total number of observations required to determine the proportion of ineffective time within ± 5% with 95% confidence.

Solution

(a) Using the formula $N = Z^2P(1 - P)/L^2$ and taking as usual 95% confidence and hence $Z = 2$ then

$$N = \frac{4 \times 0.4 \times 0.6}{0.05^2}$$

$= 384$ observations

Twenty-five observations have already been recorded, therefore a further 359 are required.

(b) Establish the observation times:

The number of observations in each observation round = 5

Therefore the number of observation rounds $= \dfrac{384}{5} = 77$

Already 25 observations have been taken, so six observation rounds each hour over the next two days will complete the study. A sample of these observations is shown in Fig. 4.4 and summarised in Table 4.1. Clearly, in Table 4.1 all the operations are within the $= 5\%$ limits desired. This is because 400 observations were taken and not the 384 calculated. Had the total number been 384 observations exactly and the FS operation percentage was say 45% then

$$N = \frac{4 \times 0.45 \times 0.55}{0.05^2} = 396 \text{ observations}$$

That is, a further 12 observations would be required. Thus the formula can be applied at any time during the study to check the number of further observations required. Furthermore, as the percentage accuracy desired is reduced, the number of observations needed falls off rapidly.

Table 4.1 Observation summary sheet

Operation	Observations Number	% of total (P)	$L = \sqrt{\dfrac{Z^2P(1-P)}{N}}$	Min.	Max.
FS	148	37.0	±4.8	32.2	41.8
CL	40	10.0	±3.0	7.0	13.0
RF	80	20.0	±4.0	16.0	24.0
RI	32	8.0	±2.76	5.24	10.76
I	60	15.0	±3.58	11.42	18.58
A	40	10.0	±3.00	7.00	13.00
Total	400 (N)	100.0			

Percentages of total time Accuracy (L)

Output Rates

The Activity Sampling technique can, if carefully applied, be used to determine production output data for use in estimating and planning the duration of activities.

When recording the number of observations for each operation, the performance level of the operative, or machine etc. is assessed at each observation on the standard rating scale described in the previous chapter under Time Study and the mean rating for the operation together with time spent as a proportion of the whole activity are calculated. If the total elapsed time of the activity is also recorded, then the basic times of the individual operations in the task can be calculated.

Example

Referring to the FS operation in the previous example, 37% of the time is spent in fixing formwork. If the mean rating is 85 and 50 m² of formwork is fixed in position over an elapsed 40 hours of working time by a gang of 5 carpenters, then:

Basic time for the FS operation is $0.37 \times 40 \times 0.85 = 12.6$ hours or $12.6 \times 5 = 63$ man hours.

Basic Output $= \dfrac{50}{63} = 0.8$ m² per man hour.

The standard time should provide for allowances and therefore:

Standard Output $= \dfrac{50}{(63 + \text{allowances})}$ m² per man hour.

However, caution is required when extracting the man hours involved as due account must be taken of absenteeism, the changes in the gang size, extensive delays, etc.

EXERCISES
Exercise 1
An activity sampling study is taken to determine the performance of a crawler crane on a construction site. The recorded observations are as follows:

No. of observations

160 shows the crane either lifting or lowering a load
80 show the crane travelling to its place of work
60 show the crane waiting while either unloading or having its slings adjusted prior to lifting
100 show the crane was idle

(a) From the above observations determine the proportion of the time the crane was idle and the degree of accuracy of the result. 95% confidence is required in the results.

(b) If the accuracy required is to be 2%, how many more observations are needed?

Exercise 2

Figure 4.5 shows the pattern of work over a 5-day period for a concreting gang on a large civil engineering contract. Time study reveals 77·5% placing concrete, 15% necessary delays and 7·5% unnecessary delays. To obtain these data with normal time study techniques requires much skill and effort. The objective therefore is to use activity sampling to arrive at similar results.

Procedure

As a trial take four observations each hour, selected randomly from the random number table. Mark these in pencil above each daily strip, on Fig. 4.5, e.g. a random number say 50 means that the observation took place on the half hour.

Note what is happening at each pencil mark.

Calculate the percentages for each operation and the resulting accuracy of each, for the total number of observations undertaken.

Compare the sampled results with the time study results for a range of desired accuracies.

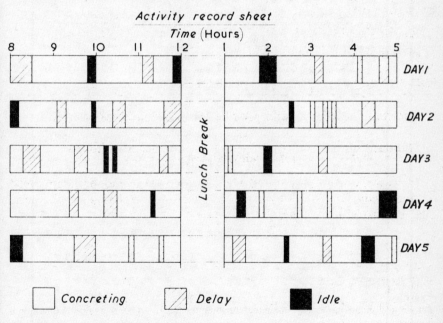

Fig. 4.5 Activity record sheet.

RANDOM NUMBERS

References and Bibliography

1. Hamburg, M. *Statistical Analysis for Decision Making.* Harcourt, Brace and World, 1970.
2. Currie, R. M. *Work Study.* Pitman, 1968.
3. Barnes, R. M. *Work Sampling.* Wiley, 1957.
4. Carney, J. *Activity Sampling.* Unpublished paper presented to a construction plant and method short course. Construction Industry Training Board, in conjunction with Loughborough University of Technology, January 1974.
5. Geary, R. *Work Study Applied to Building.* Godwin, 1962.
6. Fleming, M. C. Price in construction: the relationship of constants to productivity. *Building Technology and Management,* December 1978.
7. Ashworth, A. The source, nature and comparison of published cost information. *Building Technology and Management,* March 1980.
8. Stevens, A. J. *Activity sampling studies aided by the use of an optical reader.* Building Research Station, January 1967.
9. Forbes, W. S. and Mayer, J. F. *The output of bricklayers.* Building Research Station, March 1968.
10. Forbes, W. S. *Modular bricks and productivity.* Building Research Establishment, April 1977.
11. Forbes, W. S. *The rationalisation of house-building.* Building Research Establishment, September 1977.

CHAPTER 5

INCENTIVES

Summary

The work of Maslow and Herzberg on human motivation to work is described and an attempt is made to relate financial incentives to motivation theory. The main incentive schemes used by the construction industry are explained and examples demonstrating their use are provided. The difficulties and shortcomings of depending too heavily on financial forms of motivation are also highlighted.

Introduction

Incentive schemes are widely used throughout British industry, almost to the extent that, in many cases, workers cannot be recruited unless a bonus scheme is operated. The history of incentive payments, however, is not a happy one, having been responsible for a large proportion of the conflicts between management and the workforce. It is widely believed by construction unions that incentive schemes have tended to keep the basic rate of payment low for the construction worker, the bonus having been used to lift the average wage to those levels enjoyed by workers in other industries.

The construction industry is involved in project-type work. As a result, data collection is unreliable because of the one-off nature of such projects restricting the advantages to be had from steady-state conditions. The output targets set by management, upon which the bonus earnings depend, are therefore often inaccurate. Consequently workers suffer wildly fluctuating incomes, which leads some unions to demand the replacement of incentive schemes with a high basic rate. Management, on the other hand, has to deal with a fairly unskilled, poorly educated and transient workforce. It is therefore reluctant to give up its bonus schemes and pay high basic rates for fear of simply 'jacking up' the cost of the job. The situation which now prevails is one whereby incentives are, in the main, paid to induce the man to work at his normal pace.

Motivation Theories

Maslow (ref. 1)

Maslow suggests that man seeks to satisfy his needs sequentially as shown in Fig. 5.1.

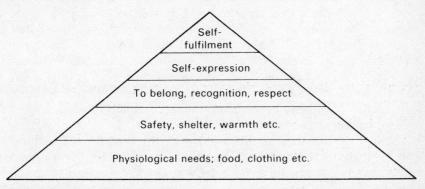

Fig. 5.1 Maslow's hierarchy of needs.

He argues that as each one of these needs is gratified then a new set of needs emerges. The implications are that man is self-motivating, and research by many others has not been in violent disagreement with this view, although McGregor (ref. 2) puts forward a persuasive argument to the contrary.

Basic needs

The society in which we live has developed from an agricultural base into a highly developed technological and socially interdependent organism. Each development along this path of progress has tended to improve the standard of living for the worker. This is a continuing process which now involves the State itself, e.g. social security, pensions, government spending, budget deficits, state ownership of industry. It appears that society is tending to reflect the desire of the individual to satisfy his hierarchy of needs. Firstly by securing a job the worker is able to purchase food, clothing, housing and so on; these basic needs once satisfied, in due course lead to the desire for better working conditions such as shorter hours, holidays with pay, adequate heating and lighting, security of tenure etc.

Higher needs

Maslow postulated that people like to feel necessary in their jobs; they wish to gain respect, both from their employer and fellow workers, and in many instances positively wish to identify with a particular skill.

Construction companies, in general, fair badly with regard to this need to belong. The turnover of staff and workmen in many companies is high, although it is true to say that many workers remain in the industry and more particularly take some pride in being associated with one particular skill.

Many workers are dissatisfied with their jobs simply because there is no opportunity for self-expression. Unfortunately, with the present emphasis on output as opposed to craftsmanship, it is possible that a breakdown in Maslow's hierarchy might occur unless the fault can be corrected. The problem is not so severe in the construction industry fortunately, largely because the construction worker does at least create a one-off type of product. But the unrelenting march of standardisation, particularly in building construction, may eventually lead to problems both for workers and engineering staff.

Finally, Maslow tops his hierarchy with the need for self-fulfilment. It is difficult to see any hope for satisfaction of this desire, outside purely creative work, and on this basis it would be limited to the self-employed, the very senior posts in an organisation and purely independent workers.

Herzberg (ref. 3)

Maslow's higher needs can be grouped under the heading 'Motivating needs'. Frederick Herzberg discovered some interesting pointers to motivation and identified the following contributory factors:

1. *Job satisfaction*
   (i) achievement
   (ii) recognition
   (iii) the work itself
   (iv) taking responsibility
   (v) the chance to advance

2. *Job dissatisfaction*
   (i) working conditions
   (ii) salary
   (iii) relations with superiors
   (iv) company policy

He called the first 'motivating' factors and the second 'hygiene' factors. Herzberg concluded that the 'hygiene' factors had little positive effect on job attitudes but served primarily to prevent job dissatisfaction. Thus if a company fails to provide adequate 'hygiene' factors the worker is dis-satisfied – no matter how adequate are salaries, working conditions, etc., the worker will not be satisfied until all the other motivators are also satisfied.

The construction industry, particularly with regard to production workers, appears to have concentrated on only one of Herzberg's 'hygiene' factors, namely pay, to the exclusion of much of the rest of the motivating needs. As a result the industry has provided only a partial answer to improved productivity as far as labour is concerned.

Payment Systems, Remuneration and Performance

There is no simple formula that will control human behaviour. Bearing in mind, however, the work described earlier on human motivation, there are certain ways in which men can be induced to give better performance. It is management's responsibility to find the best solution. In the United Kingdom the methods are generally to offer financial incentives to manual workers and non- or semifinancial incentives to managerial and clerical

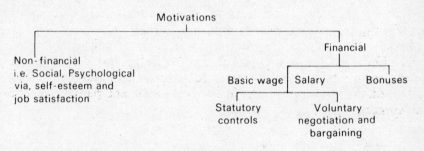

Fig. 5.2 Methods of encouraging motivation to work.

workers (Fig. 5.2). However, some overlapping between the two approaches has occurred. More attention is slowly being given to the working conditions etc. for manual workers, unfortunately less as a result of positive thinking by employers than from pressures exerted by the construction unions.

Non-Financial Incentives

The incentives involved are fairly intangible, and are the ones related to Maslow's higher needs and involve in particular the fulfilment of those needs defined by Herzberg as the 'motivating' needs. Thus the incentives offered acknowledge the importance of the individual and recognise his need for group participation to provide social satisfaction. Certain types of occupation require little to be provided by the employer as an incentive, much of the work is itself self-motivating: workers in famine relief, ministers of religion, nurses, for example, can be said to get satisfaction almost entirely from the job. Few areas of employment can create adequate responses from the individual as described. It is therefore necessary in most cases to offer additional incentives of a more tangible nature and associated with the 'hygiene' needs, often expressed in the form of semifinancial incentives.

Semifinancial Incentives

Such incentives do not rely on the cash motive, but concentrate on fringe benefits such as holidays with pay, canteens, luncheon vouchers, sports facilities, pension schemes, company cars, paid telephone bills, expense accounts. These sorts of benefits are generally offered to salaried staff, whose jobs are difficult to measure in crude productive terms.

Financial Incentive Schemes

It is a widely held belief that people are motivated to work harder if there is a direct financial reward, particularly if the work is based on a measured quantity of output. Many schemes have been developed to suit different tasks in the various industries, those most applicable to the construction industry are demonstrated and a summary of the main types of scheme are given in Table 5.3 at the end of the chapter.

The objectives of financial incentive schemes
1. To improve productivity
2. To encourage better methods of working
3. To provide opportunity for increased earnings, but without increasing unit costs

Profit sharing
The company pays out either yearly or half-yearly a lump sum to its employees, based on the profit earned by the company. This system has been used by many British contractors in the past, but is only suitable in fairly small firms where a more co-operative spirit and sense of purpose is likely to be found in the workers. As companies have grown, this payment system has tended to become unsuitable although it seems to work well in the Japanese culture.

Daywork
An hourly rate is paid related to the skill required by the task, the worker is then simply paid for attendance at work. The system is most

suitable for highly skilled operations where either there is great complexity involved or craftsmanship is desired. High rates of pay are often necessary coupled with semifinancial incentives to attract and keep the worker, although the work itself can act as a motivator. Few areas of modern construction work provide such rewarding employment.

Workers involved in maintenance, inspection, canteens and cleaning, transport and stores, however, although not of the above category, can often only be paid in such a way – sometimes supplemented with some form of merit-rated bonus.

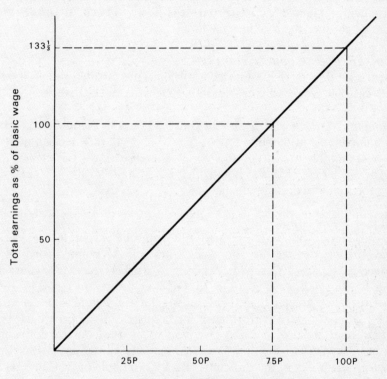

Fig. 5.3 Piecework system expressed graphically. The target is set so that at any performance above 75P the worker gains (100P is standard performance).

Piecework

Straight piecework is the payment of a uniform price per unit of production. The principle is expressed graphically in Fig. 5.3 whereby, as a worker improves his output, his earnings increase proportionately.

Example If a man is paid 10p for each item or unit completed and he completes 10 units, payment $= 0 \cdot 1 \times 10 = £1$.

Such a system is best installed on repetitive-type activities where the standard time for doing the work can be accurately fixed. Hence it is most popular in manufacturing industries. It has not gained much favour in the construction industry, with the possible exception of materials manufacturing. The system is less reliable in terms of controlling costs from the employer's point of view, because of the introduction of a minimum wage, enabling some workers to achieve wages above their productive performance. In practice, if targets are set out of line, morale will quickly fade and industrial unrest is likely to occur until the targets are re-established at an achievable level.

Standard time, or hour, system

Essentially this is the same as a straight piecework system, but the targets for the worker are expressed in time units rather than money.

Example A worker is given a target of 8 hours to complete an activity. He completes it in 6 hours. Payment $= 8 \times$ hourly rate. He can now start the next unit 2 hours earlier and thereby increase his overall earnings.

The advantage of this system is that if new hourly rates are negotiated, the time standards remain unchanged.

Hours-saved system

If a production bonus is operated at all on a construction project, then a favoured system is the hours-saved system. A common form of this system is the 75–100 scheme whereby a worker receives a guaranteed wage for any performance up to 75% of standard performance (100P). If a performance greater than this level is achieved then a bonus is earned, such that at standard performance the bonus is $33\frac{1}{3}\%$ of the basic wage. This system at least tends to be favoured by the construction unions, but has drawbacks which have resulted in many abuses and disputes. The main problem lies in the difficulty of setting reliable output targets, thus causing ambiguities in the efforts required to earn bonus. For example, a misjudged but generous target set for a concrete gang may cause unrest in a formwork gang struggling to earn bonus on a difficult shuttering operation requiring much skill.

Example It is considered by a site manager that a bricklayer engaged on building drainage manholes, each containing 720 bricks, should be able to lay 60 bricks per hour at standard performance. If the bricklayer can achieve this target then he will be entitled to a bonus of $33\frac{1}{3}\%$ added to his basic rate of payment.

Calculate the bricklayer's earnings when his performance is 50P, 75P,

100P and 120P. (100P is standard performance.) The basic rate of payment is £1·00 per hour.

Solution   Actual time required to build the manhole when working at standard performance = 720/60 = 12 manhours.

Bonus is paid at $33\frac{1}{3}$% of basic wage for working at standard performance. Figure 5.3 shows that when using a 75–100 scheme the hours saved are directly proportional, since the gradient of the graph is 1.

Let time allowed for doing the job = a, and actual time required at standard performance = b. Then

$$a = b + \tfrac{1}{3} \times b \times \frac{1}{\text{gradient}}$$

Therefore

$$a = 12 + \tfrac{1}{3} \times 12 \times 1 = 16 \text{ hours}$$

Thus, 16 hours is the target allowance of time for building the manhole.

Some workers tend to work faster than others, and more efficiently. The reasons for this are many and ill-defined, but certainly basic intelligence, education and training are important influences. Table 5.1 shows the effect of worker performance both on the worker's own earnings and on the cost of the job to the contractor. Clearly, if the performance of the worker is below 75P the cost of the job increases quite rapidly. This situation can easily arise if the output targets are set too tight; the worker in this situation will quickly lose morale and thereby perform badly. It is recommended, therefore, that this system should only be used with experienced workers who are familiar with the type of work involved.

Table 5.1 Directly proportional incentive scheme calculation

Level of performance	Actual time taken (hours)	Time allowed = 16 h at £1 per hour			
		Hours saved	Bonus	Hourly earnings	Cost of job
120P	10	6	£6·00	£1·60	£16·00
100P	12	4	£4·00	£1·33	£16·00
75P	16	0	£0·00	£1·00	£16·00
50P	24	0	£0·00	£1·00	£24·00

Geared Schemes

The direct incentive scheme described above enables only the fast and skilful worker to earn bonus. This is not always to the employer's

Table 5.2 Geared incentives schemes calculations

Level of performance	Actual time taken (hours)	Hours saved	Target = 17⅓ h 75% payment			Target = 20 h 50% payment				Target = 28 h 25% payment			
			Bonus	Hourly earnings	Cost of job	Hours saved	Bonus	Hourly earnings	Cost of job	Hours saved	Bonus	Hourly earnings	Cost of job
120P	10	7⅓	£5·50	£1·55	£15·5	10	£5·00	£1·50	£15·00	18	£4·50	£1·45	£14·50
100P	12	5⅓	£4·00	£1·35	£16·00	8	£4·00	£1·33	£16·00	16	£4·00	£1·33	£16·00
75P	16	1⅓	£1·00	£1·07	£17·00	4	£2·00	£1·13	£18·00	12	£3·00	£1·19	£19·00
50P	24	0	0	£1·00	£24·00	0	0	£1·00	£24·00	4	£1·00	£1·04	£25·00

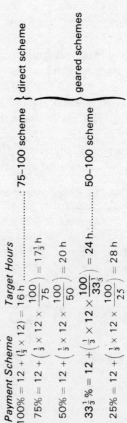

Payment Scheme   *Target Hours*

$100\% = 12 + (\tfrac{1}{3} \times 12) = 16\ \text{h}$ .... 75–100 scheme $\Big\}$ direct scheme

$75\% = 12 + \left(\tfrac{1}{3} \times 12 \times \dfrac{100}{75}\right) = 17\tfrac{1}{3}\ \text{h}$

$50\% = 12 + \left(\tfrac{1}{3} \times 12 \times \dfrac{100}{50}\right) = 20\ \text{h}$

$33\tfrac{1}{3}\% = 12 + \left(\tfrac{1}{3} \times 12 \times \dfrac{100}{33\tfrac{1}{3}}\right) = 24\ \text{h}$ .... 50–100 scheme

$25\% = 12 + \left(\tfrac{1}{3} \times 12 \times \dfrac{100}{25}\right) = 28\ \text{h}$

geared schemes

advantage, particularly when beginning a new contract, as the work will be unfamiliar to the labour force. Furthermore, when the work is in country districts the men may also be unskilled and thereby unable to earn bonus. In order to alleviate this problem and maintain morale, some bonus payment for the slower worker is often necessary. To try to achieve this, more generous targets are set but the payment is based only on a proportion of the savings made. To illustrate the method, Table 5.2 shows the bonus earnings when payments are given for 75%, 50% and 25% respectively of the hours saved. A similar method, with an example of use in the building industry, is described by Geary (ref. 4).

Table 5.2 is shown graphically in Fig. 5.4. It is clear that, for example, by using a geared scheme of 25% payment, a worker can earn bonus

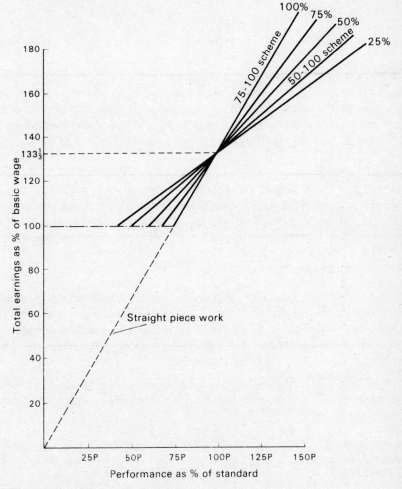

Fig. 5.4 Geared incentive schemes.

when working below 50P performance, although of course the cost of the job is high. If the contractor takes account of this fact, it may well be in his interest to start off the contract with the low based scheme, building up gradually over the first few weeks to the full proportional scheme when the workforce has become familiar with its duties.

It will be noticed that in all the schemes the bonus earned at standard performance is the same.

A popular scheme used to deal with the above situation is the 50–100 scheme (Fig. 5.4). At a performance of 50P the worker begins to earn bonus.

Plus rate, or Spot bonus

A minimum bonus, sometimes called a fallback bonus, is paid whatever the output. Such an incentive is often used to attract labour from other work in the area. It can also be used to pay a competitive rate when the basic rate is low.

Job and finish

The worker is offered a lump sum of money to complete an operation. This sort of bonus is useful on large concrete pours, or similar work, when the gang will complete the work as quickly as possible and then go home, but be paid for the full day's work and any bonus earned.

Group schemes

Much of the work carried out on construction sites is in gangs, making it almost impossible to apply individual bonus schemes. But, at the same time, the different classes of skilled worker in the gang need to be acknowledged in the scheme. This can be done by apportioning the bonus on a shares basis, usually with the gang foreman being paid slightly more than other members.

Example The site manager responsible for the construction of a large concrete pumphouse set the workers a target of 50 manhours to erect the formwork for the concrete in the base pour. The gang comprises five men. Calculate the bonus earned by each man, given that the gang completed the work in the times shown below:

Worker description	Shares entitlement per hour worked	Actual time (hours) worked on activity	Total Shares
Gang foreman	$1\frac{1}{2}$	8	12
Carpenter No. 1	$1\frac{1}{4}$	8	10
Carpenter No. 2	$1\frac{1}{4}$	8	10
Labourer No. 1	1	8	8
Labourer No. 2	1	4	4
		36	44

Basic rate of payment is £1·00 per hour
Hours saved $= 50 - 36 = 14$ h
Bonus $\quad = 14 \times £1·00 = £14·00$

Bonus per share $= \frac{14}{44} = £0·318$ per share

Gang foreman $\quad = 0·318 \times 8 \times 1\frac{1}{2} = £3·83$
Carpenter No. 1 $= 0·318 \times 8 \times 1\frac{1}{4} = £3·18$
Carpenter No. 2 $= 0·318 \times 8 \times 1\frac{1}{2} = £3·18$
Labourer No. 1 $\;= 0·318 \times 8 \times 1 \;\;= £2·54$
Labourer No. 2 $\;= 0·318 \times 4 \times 1 \;\;= £1·27$

$$\overline{£14·00}$$

Indirect Incentive Schemes

Certain categories of work are difficult to include in normal productive
bonus schemes because they cannot be measured in physical terms. These
include site fitters, hoist operators, stockyard gang, and workers generally
providing a service. The most common way of dealing with these workers
is to pay a bonus related to the workers they serve, e.g. fitters might be
paid a bonus equal to the average bonus for the site as a whole. Care
must be taken when establishing this type of incentive, since if the
number of workers being serviced is increased, the workers actually
providing the service will be doing more work and at the same time
getting no more bonus, thus the gang ratios must be carefully balanced.
The alternative method is to offer an enhanced rate based on merit. This
method, however, is best suited to workers isolated from productive
bonus schemes, otherwise they will invariably wish to become associated
with them.

Principles of a Good Incentive Scheme

The merits of the various incentive schemes are shown in Table 5.3. To
get the best out of them is not easy, the following rules offer a guide:

1. Bonus should be paid to workers in direct proportion to the effort
   applied.
2. The earnings of the worker should not be limited in any way.
3. The set targets should be attainable and thereafter remain unaltered.
   In the construction industry this is not always possible due to the
   lack of reliable data on which to base the targets.
4. Unavoidable hold-ups should be excluded from bonus paid hours and
   paid at basic rate.
5. The scheme must be easily understandable to the worker so that he

can calculate his bonus, otherwise considerable confusion is likely to occur requiring much time and effort on the part of management to allay any fears of malpractice. It is for this reason that geared and other more complex systems have not found much favour with workmen or unions.

6. Bonus schemes can lead to substandard work and therefore penalties should be included and enforced. Much opposition will often be offered, requiring a tough-minded attitude from management.

7. The scheme should comply with local union arrangements.

8. Good planning to ensure that drawings are updated, materials arrive on time etc.

Table 5.3 Summary of incentive schemes

Incentive scheme	Advantages	Disadvantages
A. Daywork Employee paid a basic wage for attendance	1. Simple and easy to understand 2. Simple to calculate wages 3. Low clerical requirements 4. Facilitates labour flexibility	1. No reward for efficiency 2. Slack workers gain at the expense of fast workers 3. Strict supervision required 4. Accurate budget forecasts are difficult
B. Piecework A uniform price is paid for each job or unit completed	1. Direct incentive to increase output 2. Simple to understand 3. Wage cost per unit of production is constant (only when applied without min. wage)	1. Changes in wage rate necessitate altering targets 2. Can lead to poor quality
C. Straight proportional Hours-saved scheme All time saved on the target set is given to the worker	1. Incentive is related to effort 2. There is a guaranteed wage 3. Provides cost control data 4. Better quality control than with piecework	1. Expensive to operate 2. Tends to favour fast workers 3. Requires sound data to establish target rates 4. Causes problem initially when labour is inexperienced
D. Geared schemes Similar to C above but only a proportion of time saved is given to worker	1. Useful to start off new work 2. Provides an incentive for slow and inexperienced workers	1. Encourages loose rate fixing 2. Fast workers are not fully rewarded
E. Group schemes Similar to C and D, but individuals paid on a shares basis	1. Assists elimination of slackers 2. Suitable when gangs of workers are necessary, thus particularly suited to construction industry 3. Encourages co-operation	1. Increases clerical work 2. Faster workers suffer at expense of slower workers
Taylor 2 Piece scheme *Rowan* *Halsey (or Weir) Scheme* *Graded and measured daywork* *Other piecework schemes*	These schemes are not widely used in the construction industry and are covered adequately in other texts	

Setting Target Rates

The construction industry, unlike that of manufacturing, has few sources of accurate output data nor can it rely on work study to any great extent. Some of the sources of information available to the site manager for use in setting target outputs for incentive schemes are as follows.

Personal experience   Given a wide and varied experience of planning, estimating and site engineering over a period of years, the manager should have gained a reasonable knowledge of gang sizes and expected outputs of plant and men involved in the major construction operations.

The advantages of using self-knowledge are that it is immediate, inexpensive and readily accepted. It has the disadvantages of being of limited range, not documented, and above all is open to bias. Much of the estimating in the industry is done on this basis and the estimator's build-up sheets generally provide the basis upon which to fix the bonus targets.

Feedback   Often within an organisation there exists records of costs, bonuses, job records for contracts which have been completed. Some of the information may be useful, but frequently cost control and data collection is given low priority on construction contracts, because it is expensive to collect and is historical anyway. Such data offers rough guidelines only, since it normally applies to one-off type projects.

Work study data   Work study has not yet found much acceptance in the construction industry; as a result there is not much information available. To obtain such data requires a skilled practitioner and is expensive and time-consuming. Caution should also be exercised when using the data, as output on construction work can fluctuate wildly from so-called standard.

Manufacturers' ratings   These provide only a rough guide since they are likely to be optimistic. Many estimators halve the manufacturer's rating.

Site demonstration of equipment offers a guide, but care must be taken to view the exercise in overall terms.

Standard information   Average outputs are provided in several published works (ref. 12, 13 and 14). Naturally these schedules are only approximate and will not accurately reflect the possible outputs in individual firms.

EXERCISES

Exercise 1
Discuss the relevance of the theories proposed by Maslow and Herzberg to the construction industry.

Exercise 2
Describe the principles on which a sound financial incentive scheme should be based.

Exercise 3
Differentiate between direct and indirect incentive schemes and give examples of when and how each scheme can be used.

Exercise 4
The manager responsible for the painting subcontract on a housing site reasonably considers that a painter should take 16 working hours to paint all the doors in a house. If he does so, he will be entitled to a 25% bonus. Compute a direct scheme and a 60% geared scheme for this work. The basic rate of payment is £1 per hour.

Exercise 5
The shuttering gang on a civil engineering contract has been set a target of 100 manhours to erect the formwork for the walls of a pumphouse. The manager decides to pay bonus using a direct scheme. The gang consists of a chargehand paid $1\frac{1}{2}$ shares, two carpenters paid $1\frac{1}{4}$ shares each and two labourers paid 1 share each. On completion of the work the bonus clerk analyses the time allocation sheets submitted by the charge-hand. The records are:

Chargehand	2 days at 10 hours per day
Carpenter No. 1	2 days at 10 hours per day
Carpenter No. 2	2 days at 8 hours per day
Labourer No. 1	2 days at 10 hours per day
Labourer No. 2	1 day at 10 hours

Work was held up for 4 hours due to inclement weather. If the basic rate of pay is £1 per hour for an 8 hour day and overtime is paid at time and a quarter, calculate the bonus earned by each man in the gang and his total earnings.

References and Bibliography

1. Maslow, A. H. *Toward a Psychology of Being*. Van Nostrand, 1968.
2. McGregor, D. *Leadership and Marketing*. MIT Press, 1966.
3. Herzberg, F. *Work and the Nature of Man*. Staples, 1968.
4. Geary, R. *Work Study Applied to Building*. Godwin, 1962.
5. Department of the Environment. *Incentive Schemes for Small Builders*. HMSO, 1974.
6. Imrie, R. S. *Building Site Organisation*. Crosby Lockwood, 1972.
7. Wilson, A. Incentive-bonusing: various types of incentive schemes. *Construction* (pp. 9–11), January 1972.
8. Smith, G. F. Productivity in building—a union viewpoint. *Illustrated Carpenter and Builder* Vol. 160, pp. 22–23, 1970.
9. Tredwell, J. E. B. Incentives and the smaller firm. The principles of an incentive scheme. *Illustrated Carpenter and Builder* Vol. 161, pp. 15–18, 1970.
10. Rougvie, A. Incentives in the construction industry. *Building Technology and Management* Vol. 9, pp. 7–8, 1971.
11. Herzberg, F., *et al. The Motivation to Work*. Wiley, 1969.
12. *Spon's Architects' and Builders' Price Book*. E. & F. Spon (annual).
13. Geddes, S. *Estimating for Building and Civil Engineering Works*, 5th edition, ed. Chrystal-Smith, G. Newnes/Butterworth, 1971.
14. Chrystal-Smith, G. (Ed.) *Hutchins Priced Schedules*. Lake, 1972.
15. Willsmore, A. W. *Managing Modern Man*. Pitman, 1973.
16. Alderfer, C. P. *Existence, relatedness and growth: human needs in organisational settings*. The Free Press, 1972.
17. Neale, R. H. *Motivation of construction workers: theory and practice*. Institute of Building, Site Management Information Paper No. 78, 1979.

CHAPTER 6

COST CONTROL

Summary

The main features of the several cost control methods used by management on construction projects are summarised. An illustration is given of a cost control system which is fairly typical of current practice. Finally the problems of controlling material costs are enumerated and guidelines for their control described.

A Cost Control Procedure for Construction Works

Introduction

The construction industry unlike many manufacturing situations is concerned mostly with one-off projects. This naturally creates difficulties for effective management control, because each new contract often has a fresh management team; labour is transient and recruited on an *ad hoc* basis; sites are dispersed throughout the country, which tends to cause problems in effective communications with other parts of the company; subcontractors and 'lump' labour are common; added to all this are the everchanging weather conditions. These are some of the problems which have prevented the typical contracting company from installing the Standard Costing System as known by the manufacturing industry.

Fundamentals

To *control* cost is an obvious objective of most managers. It should be recognised that no amount of paperwork achieves this control. Ultimately the decision of the manager that something should be done differently, and the translation of that decision into practice, are the actions which achieve control. The paperwork can provide guidance on what control actions should be taken and, while we shall continue to call it 'the cost control system' it should more properly be called 'the cost information system'.

The elements of any control system are:

Observation
Comparison of observation with some desired standard
Corrective action to take if necessary

The domestic thermostat is a good example of a controller. The instrument measures the temperature, compares it with the desired range and then switches the temperature heating system 'on' or 'off', or leaves it 'on' or 'off' depending on how the current temperature compares with the desired range.

A cost control system should enable a manager to observe current cost levels, compare them with a standard plan or norm, and institute corrective action to keep cost within acceptable bounds. The system should help to identify where corrective action is necessary and to provide pointers as to what that action should be.

Unlike the humble thermostat, most cost control systems have an inordinately long response time. Even the best current system provides information on what was happening last week or last month. As the work is typically part of a one-off project it is quite likely that the information is only partly relevant to the work going on now. So the scope for corrective action is limited. For example the system might indicate on 1 May that the formwork operation in March cost too much. If formwork operations are still continuing the manager will give this work particular attention, but if formwork is complete nothing can be done to correct the situation. A research project (P. F. Miller, ref. 1) undertaken in the early 1970s examined 19 separate systems of cost control; none was found to be entirely satisfactory. The manager should therefore reconcile himself to the fact that his company's system will probably not be ideal and that he will have to augment the information it provides with his own intuitive judgement.

There are two current developments which show promise of improving the situation. They are:

1. Short-term planning and control. This system is being developed at Loughborough University in association with a contractor. It aims to merge the planning and supervision and hence to obtain a more or less zero response time.
2. Project Cost Model. This is a system developed by Dr Martin Barnes

(ref. 2) for simulating alternative future actions and thus guiding the manager in his choice between them.

These systems will not be described in detail as the experience of their use is still somewhat limited.

In the more conventional systems which are described below two fundamental points are important. First, all costs must be allocated even if this is on a very 'coarse-grained' coding arrangement. If only the major items are monitored you can be sure that the wasted time will be booked against the items which are not being monitored. Thus the manager will be deluded by the reports on the 'important items' into thinking the whole site is satisfactory; in fact it might be incurring disastrous hidden losses. Secondly, there must always be a standard against which to compare recorded costs. In simple projects this might be the bill of quantities; generally, however, a properly prepared and appropriately updated contract budget forms a better basis.

Systems in Current Use

The following systems and variants of them are in use in the construction industry. The selection of a system depends in part on the size and complexity of the contract, but more on the attitudes and level of sophistication of top management.

By Overall Profit or Loss

The contractor waits until the contract is complete and then compares the sums of money that he has been paid with the monies incurred in purchasing materials, payments for labour, subcontractors, plant and overheads. The figures are normally extracted from the financial accounts compulsorily kept by all companies. Such a system is useful only on very small contracts of short duration involving few men and little construction equipment. It scarcely qualifies as a control system as the information it produces can only be used to avoid the recurrence of gross errors in later contracts.

Profit or Loss on each Contract at Valuation Dates

The total costs to date are compared with valuations gross of retentions. Care has to be taken to include the cost of materials delivered but not yet invoiced and to exclude materials on site not yet built into the permanent work. If the certificate is not a time reflection of the value of work done, a further adjustment is necessary. This system suffers from the disadvantage that there is no breakdown of the profit figure between types of work; it therefore provides guidance only on which contract requires management attention. It is not suitable for contracts which involve significant set-up costs which are distributed over the unit rates.

Unit Costing

In this system costs of various types of work, such as mixing and placing concrete, are recorded separately. The costs, both cumulatively and on a period basis, are divided by the quantity of work of each type that has been done. This provides unit costs which can be compared with those in the tender. Considerable care must be taken to ensure that all costs are accounted for, as indicated above under 'Fundamentals'. Any miscellaneous costs must be recorded and allowed for in some way, e.g. by proportional distribution over the defined work-types. It is usually best to record site costs only and to compare with bill rates net of contribution for profit and head office overheads.

Systems Based on the Principles of Standard Costing

Standard costing has been used successfully in manufacturing industries particularly in companies producing a limited range of products or at least a limited range of basic components. Standard minute values are associated with the production of each component and assembly and converted to money values by reference to the hourly rates of the appropriate grades of operatives. Variances are calculated basically by comparing the value of the output with the cost of producing it. A variance is the amount by which the achieved profit differs from the budgeted profit. With appropriate records it is possible to analyse the total variance into subvariances, e.g.

(a) Material price
(b) Material usage
(c) Labour rate
(d) Labour efficiency
(e) Fixed and variable overhead expenditure
(f) Volume of production
(g) Sales

A detailed description of these variances is given by Sizer (ref. 3). The system is seldom directly applicable in construction owing to the variety of the product. This makes the use of standard minute values difficult if not impossible. However, as an alternative, the value of work done can be assessed in relation to the contract budget which in turn must reflect the amount that the contractor can expect to be paid.

One of the important features is the calculation of a sales variance. This encourages the company to define sales (marketing, public relations, negotiations, estimating and bid strategy) as the responsibility of one department. An adverse variance indicates immediately that the level of acquiring new contracts is inadequate.

Altogether, quite substantial departures from the manufacturing system are necessary and this accounts for the fact that standard costing is not in common use in construction. However, the system is basically very sound and provides comprehensive control of the company from boardroom down to workface.

PERT/Cost

This system requires each contract to be networked (PERT = Performance Evaluation and Review Technique). The values of work packages, which in essence are groups of activities, are assessed in advance. The time update of the network provides the value of work done as a 'byproduct' of the calculation. The value can be divided by cost code, provided that the work package information is similarly divided. Thus, when incurred costs are recorded against the same codes, variances can be calculated for management information.

The system cannot be applied directly where the work is valued by a bill of quantities which relates to the completed work rather than the operations. For this reason the system is seldom applied unless the work is the subject of an activity bill or operational bill. In practice, this confines its application to design/construct project. In such situations the contractor can readily provide a valuation document in a form which reflects the operations he intends to perform.

Example of a Cost Control System

The following example of a cost control system for a multistorey office building reflects several of the principles discussed above. Strictly it is a hybrid system as one method is used for labour and plant costs and another for materials. It is illustrative rather than truly representative as a comprehensive set of figures would occupy a disproportionate part of this book.

Labour, Plant and Site Overheads

In order to reduce booking errors, the contractor sensibly decides to adopt a limited number of cost codes against which to generate variances. These are:

Cost code 10	All concrete mixing, transporting and placing (labour and plant)
Cost code 20	All formwork fixing and dismantling (labour and plant)
Cost code 30	All fixing of reinforcement (labour and plant)
Cost code 40	All bricklaying (labour and plant)
Cost code 50	Towercrane
Cost code 60	All earthworks (labour and plant)
Cost code 70	Roads and paving (labour and plant)
Cost code 80	Site overheads and preliminaries

The construction of the works is carefully planned and the budgeted expenditure, excluding head office overheads, profit, materials for each of the cost codes, is allocated to each activity in the programme. (In order that realistic comparisons of budgeted and actual costs can be made, the budgeted allocations must be derived from accurate quantities, carefully taken from working drawings, and any variations must be included.)

Table 6.1 shows the breakdown of the budget expenditure and Fig. 6.1 shows the first 76 weeks of the programme.

Progress is recorded in the usual way against the programme and this is used as a guide for expediting the work. Costs are recorded against the cost codes. At week 52, for example, the percentage completion of each activity can be extracted from the progress reports which are represented in the revised programme shown in Fig. 6.2; the figures are also shown in the last column of Table 6.2. The other columns of Table 6.2 show the budget figures multiplied by the percentage completions. Hence, by adding the columns, the total values of work done in each cost code can be derived. The separately recorded cost figures are also entered in order to calculate the variances. It will be noted that the work to date has cost £2340 more than it should have done and that the reasons for this excess cost are apportioned to the various cost codes. For example, cost code 30, that is steelfixing, shows a variance of −£1100 and clearly this calls for management attention in regard to this trade.

Allocation of Costs

The foregoing cost control system in general allocates costs against a gang of workers, e.g. concrete gang. It is therefore the responsibility of the chargehand of the gang to fill in the daily allocation sheet (Fig. 6.3), on which he records a brief description of the operation upon which the gang was employed and the names and hours worked by each member of the gang. Often this recording is not necessary, particularly if the type of work being done by the gang is fairly static; the cost control engineer then simply extracts the manhours for the gang from the wages

Table 6.1 Budgeted costs

Activity description	Cost code 10	20	30	40	50	60	70	80	Total
Earthworks						900		100	1 000
Foundations	5 000	6 000	7 000					2 000	20 000
Ground floor slab	1 000	1 000	2 500					500	5 000
Columns	200	300	300					200	1 000
Floor slabs	15 000	17 000	18 000		10 000			20 000	80 000
Lift shaft	2 000	3 000	4 000					1 000	10 000
Brickwork and blockwork				13 000				3 000	16 000
Windows and glazing				2 000	1 000			1 000	4 000
Roofing	100	100	100		100			50	450
Internal finishes				1 000	500			3 000	4 500
Plumbing, H and V				500	1 000			5 000	6 500
Electrics								4 000	4 000
External works							1 800	200	2 000
Clear Site							900	100	1 000
Budget totals	£23 300	£27 400	£31 900	£16 500	£12 600	£900	£2 700	£40 150	£155 450

Total value of contract £800 000
Cost of labour, plant and site overheads £155 450
Cost of materials, head office overheads, subcontractors £644 550

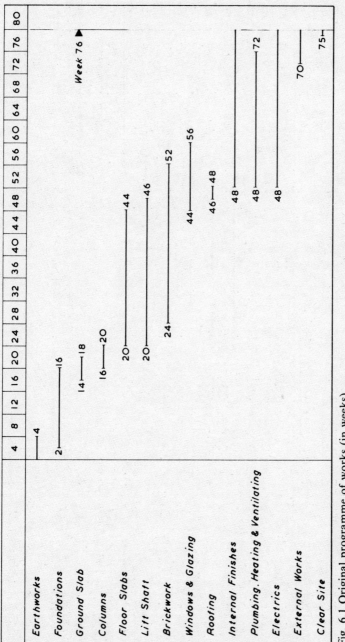

Fig. 6.1 Original programme of works (in weeks).

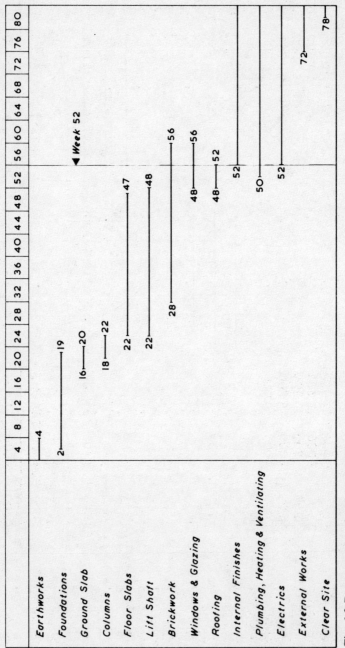

Fig. 6.2 Programme updated at week 52.

Table 8.2 Updated costs at week 52

Activity description	Cost code								Total	Percentage complete
	10	20	30	40	50	60	70	80		
Earthworks						900		100	1 000	100%
Foundations	5 000	6 000	7 000					2 000	20 000	100%
Ground floor slab	1 000	1 000	2 500					500	5 000	100%
Columns	200	300	300					200	1 000	100%
Floor slabs	15 000	17 000	18 000		10 000			20 000	80 000	100%
Lift shaft	2 000	3 000	4 000					1 000	10 000	100%
Brickwork and blockwork				11 200				2 580	13 780	86%
Windows and glazing				1 000	500			500	2 000	50%
Roofing	100	100	100		100			50	450	100%
Internal finishes									—	Nil
Plumbing, H and V				33	67			330	430	$6\frac{2}{3}$%
Electrics									—	Nil
External works									—	Nil
Clear site									—	Nil
Value to end week 52	£23 300	£27 400	£31 900	£12 233	£10 667	£900	—	£27 260	£133 660	
Actual cost to week 52	£23 000	£28 000	£33 000	£12 500	£11 000	£500	—	£28 000	£136 000	
Variances	+£300	−£600	−£1 100	−£267	−£333	+£400	—	−£740	−£2 340	

Note: In practice the proportions of each code completed for an activity will vary, e.g. 'Construct founds' may involve the concrete, formwork and reinforcement being at different stages of completion.

Company Ltd _____		Form No _____							
Daily time allocation sheet									

	Name	Smith	Jones	Roberts	McKay	Baker	Neale	Shaw	Total Hours
Cost Code	Clock Number	041	042	030	061	172	141	124	
20	Formwork to Bases	8	8	8					24
20	Formwork to Columns				8	8			16
20	Formwork to Stairs						8	8	16
		8	8	8	8	8	8	8	56

Contract _____ Date _____

Chargehand _____ General Foreman _____

Fig. 6.3 Daily time allocation sheet.

sheet. Whenever a bonus system is operated on the project, the gang bonus must be added to the basic costs derived from the wages sheet in order to arrive at the actual cost of doing the work. The careful book-keeping that is usual with the bonus system provides figures that can be used to assess the value of work done, since the measurement engineer has had to take a weekly measurement of progress to enable the bonus to be calculated.

Note that *all* costs of labour and plant should be allocated against the cost codes. If this proves difficult, the device of introducing a code for miscellaneous work is sometimes adopted. This can encourage the inappropriate booking of wasted manhours and is not recommended. If, despite this advice, a miscellaneous code is used, the costs in this code should be retrospectively allocated to the other codes.

Materials Control

So far materials have not been considered in the cost control system, this is because if anything it is more difficult to control material variances than anything else. Once again this is largely due to the nature of construction sites.

The factors which add to the difficulty of keeping precise control of material costs can be divided into price and quantity variances.

Price variances
(*a*) Inflation
(*b*) Changes in the buying situation since the estimate was prepared, e.g. bulk buying, discounts, shortages, and changes in quality demanded by the client or available at the time

Quantity variances
(*a*) Wastage and breakages
(*b*) Theft and loss
(*c*) Short deliveries
(*d*) Remedial work
(*e*) Delays in the recording system
(*f*) Inaccurate site measurement of work done

Very careful, comprehensive records would enable all these variances to be calculated for various material cost codes but the expense of undertaking this work would probably far exceed the potential savings (see end of chapter for points to consider in choosing a cost control system). In practice it is probably sufficient to generate an overall materials variance thus:

		£
Materials represented in measured work to end of last period		a
Materials in measured work in this period		b
∴ Materials value to date		$c = a+b$
Cost of materials used to end of last period		d
Cost of materials delivered in this period		e
∴ Total cost of materials purchased to date		$f = d+e$
Materials currently on site		g
∴ Materials used to date		$h = f-g$
Materials variance		$j = c-h$

The values of materials (a, b and c) should be net of contribution.

Costs should be based on a careful combination of the information from invoices and delivery notes. (Some relatively sophisticated computer systems have been devised to improve the reliability of this summation.)

When adverse materials variances reach unacceptable levels the manager will institute *ad hoc* investigations and will take action to prevent recurrences. There is a tendency for cost control in construction to be directed more towards the control of labour and plant than to the control of materials. There is growing evidence, however, that losses due to materials are often significantly higher than those due to other causes. Thus greater attention to materials control may pay significant dividends in the form of increased profit. Some of the methods available, in addition to the keeping of reliable records are:

1. Keep a neat and well laid-out site with adequate storage space and room for movement. Use mechanical handling equipment whenever possible.
2. Employ a reliable storekeeper, possessing clerical experience and well trained in stores control.
3. Maintain a well-kept bookkeeping system. This often means employing a materials engineer, to plan the flow of the right quantity of material at the right time. It will also be his duty to see that all

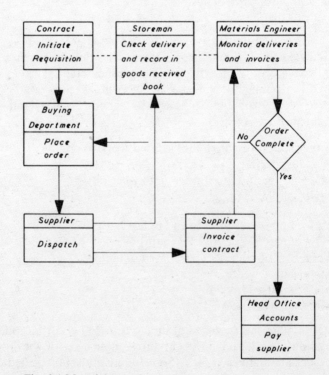

Fig. 6.4 Materials supply.

invoices fulfil the original order and to enact reordering when requirements are not met. This duty is in addition to that of keeping a 'goods
received' book from which the invoices are checked. A flow diagram
representing a workable procedure is shown in Fig. 6.4.

4. Double signing of delivery notes, particularly ready mixed concrete.
5. Weighbridge spot checks for aggregate deliveries.
6. Spot checks on moisture content for sand deliveries.
7. Insist on palletised delivery of bricks etc.
8. Check thoroughly all deliveries against the delivery notes as the goods
   are being unloaded.

Points to Consider When Choosing a Cost Control System

1. Any cost control system involves an addition to overheads; usually
the tighter the control the more expensive will be the system, thus there
is a breakeven point which is clearly demonstrated in Fig. 6.5. As
expenditure on cost control increases, the direct cost of the project can

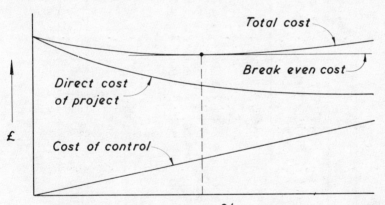

Fig. 6.5 Cost control expenditure graph.

be expected to decrease. However, there will come a point at which extra
effort will secure no further reduction. Thus the curve is concave upwards
as shown in Fig. 6.5. The addition of the cost of control gives the total
project cost and this will in most cases come to a minimum and then start
rising. This provides some indication of the optimum level of effort.

It is unlikely that firm data will ever be available to draw a reliable
graph of direct cost against expenditure on the control system, as suggested in Fig. 6.5. However, graphs based on the judgement of the
managers of individual projects often provide useful guidance on the form
of the curve and thus on the optimal level of expenditure on control.

Table 6.3

Item	Labour category	Labour (£)	Plant (£)	Materials (£)	Subcon- tractors (£)	Site O/H (£)	Head office O/H (£)	Profit (£)	Total (£)
A Excavation	1	3 500	5 000	—	—	400	300	1 800	11 000
B Concrete foundations	2	2 300	3 000	1 500	—	800	400	1 400	9 400
C Ground slab	2	1 800	2 500	1 200	—	800	400	1 200	7 900
D Columns	2	800	1 000	800	—	700	300	900	4 500
E Roof structure	3	1 200	1 000	2 600	—	600	300	500	6 200
F Brick infill panels	4	1 800	600	1 500	—	300	200	400	4 800
G Roof cladding	5	900	600	1 800	—	300	200	100	3 900
H Glazing	—	—	—	—	2 500	300	200	—	3 000
I H and V and Electrical services	—	—	—	—	11 000	800	500	—	12 300
		£12 300	£13 700	£9 400	£13 500	£5 000	£2 800	£6 300	£63 000

Cost headings

2. It is suggested that a coarse-grained system, such as that described involving no more than 15 cost codes, be used. Such a system, however, can serve only as a rough check to avoid gross errors.

Work by B. Fine (unpublished) suggests that recording cost data become highly erroneous when large numbers of codes are used and for this reason alone a coarse-grain system is the only suitable one for construction-type work. The figures suggested by Fine are:

30 cost headings	About 2% of items are misallocated
200 cost headings	About 50% of items are misallocated
2000 cost headings	About 2% of items are correctly allocated

3. The system described, together with almost all others found in the construction industry, are backward-looking. By this is meant that the information provided relates to some past occasion and it is frequently too late to take proper corrective action. It is to be hoped that the two forward-looking systems referred to under 'Fundamentals' will help to improve the position.

4. Cost control systems are complex, quite expensive to operate and far from perfect. The crucial link in the system is the manager's response to the information provided. For these reasons, any cost information system, if it is to be effective, must be operated by properly motivated, cost-conscious staff. Thus top management will be well advised to institute training courses and seminars which alert those attending to the factors which minimise cost and maximise profit.

EXERCISES

Exercise 1

Table 6.3 shows the contract budget for a small factory building. All items of work are being carried out by the main contractor except items H and I, which have been placed as fixed price contracts with sub-contractors.

At the end of month 3 the progress report showed the following percentage completions: A, 80%; B, 40%; C, 15%; and items D to I not yet started. The analysis of the recorded site costs at this time revealed the variances shown in Table 6.4.

Table 6.4

Labour categories									
1	2	3	4	5	Plant	Materials	Subcon-tractors	Site O/H	Total
−£140	−£220	—	—	—	−£100	−£20	—	+£40	−£440

Total variance = 3·9% of contract value to date (negative sign indicates an adverse variance)

The decision of the site management at this time was to increase the amount of supervision on site by employing another engineer with the specific tasks of looking after progress and materials reconciliation.

At the end of month 6 the progress report showed the following percentage completions: A, 100%; B, 100%; C, 90%; D, 75%; E, 20%; F, 10%; and G, H and I not yet started.

The recorded costs at the end of month 6 are shown in Table 6.5.

Table 6.5

| | Labour categories | | | | | | | | |
1	2	3	4	5	Plant	Materials	Subcon-tractors	Site O/H	Total
£3 600	£4 700	£250	200	—	£11 200	£3 680	—	£3 105	£26 795

Draw up a table of variances for the site costs and calculate the total variances as a percentage of the value completed.

Comment on the effect of the management's decision at month 3 and suggest what future policy should now be adopted.

Comment on the distribution of profit throughout the items indicating why the contractor may have distributed his profit in this manner, and suggest a reason why no profit is allocated to items H and I.

Exercise 2

A contractor has a £47 700 contract for which the contract budget is shown in Table 6.7. Against each item of work is shown the value of that work subdivided among the various cost headings such as labour, plant etc.

Included in the cost heading 'Site overheads' are salaries of supervisors. At the end of month 7 a progress check shows the following percentage completion: A, B, C, D, E, F, G, all 100%; H, 80%; I, 50%; J, 30%; K, 30%; L, 10%.

The cost allocations at the end of month 7 are shown in Table 6.6.

Table 6.6

| | Labour category | | | | | | | | Total site costs |
1	2	3	4	5	Plant	Materials	Subcon-tractors	Site O/H	
£4 800	£370	£200	£100	£600	£5 000	£4 200	£3 300	£2 300	£20 870

Draw up a table of variances, calculate the percentage variance of the value completed and forecast the profit for the complete project, if present trends continue.

If you were the contracts manager, what advice would you give the site agent?

Table 6.7

Code	Item	Labour category	Cost headings							Total value (£)
			Labour (£)	Plant (£)	Materials (£)	Subcontractors (£)	Site O/H (£)	Head office O/H (£)	Profit (£)	
A	Strip soil	1	200	600	—	—	200	200	400	1 600
B	Excavate	1	600	1 000	—	—	400	400	500	2 900
C	Conc. founds	1	600	400	600	—	200	200	500	2 500
D	G. F. slabs	1	1 000	600	600	—	300	300	400	3 200
E	Cols. G to 1st	1	400	400	400	—	200	200	300	1 900
F	1st Slab	1	1 200	800	800	—	300	300	400	3 800
G	Cols. 1st to roof	1	500	600	400	—	300	300	300	2 400
H	Roof structure	2	400	300	900	—	200	200	300	2 300
I	Roof cladding	3	300	300	500	—	200	200	300	1 800
J	Glazing and cladding	4	200	600	1 000	1 000	400	400	400	4 000
K	Services	1	200	—	—	10 000	1 000	1 000	100	12 300
L	Internal finishes	5	3 000	200	4 000	—	800	800	200	9 000
			£8 600	£5 800	£9 200	£11 000	£4 500	£4 500	£4 100	£47 700

References and Bibliography

1. Miller, P. F. *Control of Building and Civil Engineering, Projects During Construction*. Thesis presented to Loughborough University as partial fulfilment for the Master's Degree, 1973.

2. Barnes, N. M. L. & Revay, S. G. *The Project Cost Model*. Paper presented to the Fifth International Seminar Symposium of the Project Management Institute, Toronto, October 1973.

3. Sizer, J. *An Insight into Management Accounting*. Penguin Books, 1969.

4. Pilcher, R. *Appraisal and Control of Project Costs*. McGraw-Hill, 1973.

5. Nedved, J. C. *Builders Accounting*. Newnes-Butterworths, 1973.

6. Gobourne, J. *Cost Control in the Construction Industry*. Newnes-Butterworths, 1973.

7. Nisbet, J. *Estimating and Cost Control*. Batsford, 1961.

8. Turner, W. Financial control of contracts. *Building* (Vol. 216), No. 7, pp. 136–138, 1969.

9. Harris, F. C. Controlling Costs on Site. *Building Technology and Management*, November, 1976.

10. Harris, F. C. and McCaffer, R. Evaluating the Costs of Adverse Weather. *Building Technology and Management*, October 1975.

11. Cooke, B. and Jepson, W. B. *Cost and Financial Control of Construction Firms*. Macmillan, 1979.

CHAPTER 7

PLANT MANAGEMENT

Summary

Plant acquisition options are briefly considered, including hire, purchase, lease and hire-purchase. A systematic approach in deciding the best buy for an item of construction equipment is demonstrated. The analysis is then extended to describe the factors involved in setting a realistic hire rate for the machine. Finally some of the important aspects in the maintenance of plant are highlighted.

Plant Acquisition

Generally a construction company has two options in acquiring plant: it may either own its machinery and equipment or hire it. In recent years, the growth of the independent plant hire sector of the construction industry has greatly facilitated this latter option and approximately 50–60% of plant presently used on projects is hired. Many firms, however, prefer to hire only those items of plant which are required to meet peak demand or specialised duties. The alternative decision to purchase will have important financial consequences for the firm, since considerable capital sums will be locked up in the plant, which must then be operated at an economic utilisation level to produce a profitable rate of return on the investment. When examining the need to own plant the following points must be considered:

(a) Will the item of plant generate sufficient turnover to provide an adequate rate of return on the capital employed?
(b) Is ownership of the plant, rather than obtaining it by some other method absolutely necessary for the business?
(c) Is outright purchase the only way of acquiring the plant?

If the answer to these questions is not a confident and positive reply then there should be some other sound commercial reason for making the purchase.

The Financing of Plant

The firm, having made the decision to purchase rather than hire a piece of plant, has the following methods of arranging the finance.

Cash or Outright Purchase

The plant may be paid for immediately at the time of purchase, thereby providing a tangible asset shown on the Balance Sheet. Clearly this option is only possible if cash is available, and therefore presupposes that profits have been built up from previous trading or that funds are available from investors such as shareholders, bank loans, etc. Also, large or technically unusual contracts sometimes include monies to permit the contractor to purchase the necessary plant at the start of a project.

Tax legislation with respect to purchase allows capital allowances at a percentage of the purchase price to be set against the firm's profit during the year of acquisition. This facility is a government-inspired policy acting as an investment inducement: therefore, before the purchase decision is taken, consideration should be given to the level of return expected from the investment to ensure that using the capital in this way is the most profitable method of investing.

Hire Purchase

Purchase of plant by this method involves a contract between the purchaser and supplier of finance, in which the purchaser pays specified rentals during the contract period. At the end of this period the title of the asset may be transferred to the purchaser for a previously agreed sum, which is often nominal in amount. The hire purchase option is particularly useful in that treatment for capital allowances is the same as outright purchase. Furthermore, the need for large capital sums is avoided, and the repayments on the borrowed funds can be staged progressively. Hire purchase, however, often involves high levels of interest and is frequently subject to government regulation, but not usually retrospectively.

Leasing

A leasing arrangement is fundamentally different from either outright or hire purchase in that the title theoretically never passes to the lessee (user). A lease may be defined as a contract whereby, in return for payment of specified rentals, the lessee obtains the use of a capital asset owned by another party (the lessor). Within this definition, however, there are several varieties of lease to suit the parties concerned, of which the *finance lease* and *operating lease* are two forms appropriate to plant acquisition.

Finance Lease

This type of lease is generally arranged by a financial institution such as a Finance House. The rental charges will cover the asset's capital cost, except for its expected residual value at the end of the lease, together with a service charge designed to meet the lessor's overheads, interest charges, servicing costs and an element for profit. The lease usually will be divided into two parts: in the *primary period*, which normally lasts three to five years, rentals are set at a level sufficient to recover all the above-mentioned costs. The *secondary (or continuation) period*, which could be of a fixed time interval, is extended to suit the lessee's needs and may require only a nominal rental.

At the end of the lease the asset is sold by the lessor, but not directly to the lessee, this being specifically written into the contract to comply with the terms of the current taxation legislation.

Because the lessor often has no direct interest in the leased asset, it is usual that the contract cannot be cancelled until the lessor has realised his investment at the end of the primary period. Meantime the lessee has full use of the asset as though it were owned. Unlike outright purchase, however, leasing does not afford the lessee company to take advantage of the capital allowances on the asset. But this sometimes may be beneficial to a firm which has little or no corporation tax liability or is even in a tax deferred situation.

Operating Lease

Whereas a finance lease is generally offered by a financial institution, the lessors in the case of an operating lease are likely to be the manufacturers or suppliers of the asset, whose purpose is to assist in the marketing of the item. The primary period lease would be uncancellable and charges are frequently lower than those required by a finance lease, because the type of asset involved would either have a good second-hand value, or be tied to a lucrative service agreement or supply of spare parts. Indeed the profit expected by the lessor might well come from these latter services, which would continue into the Secondary period of the lease. Clearly this type of arrangement is most appropriate for large and/or technically sophisticated plant items where the manufacturers have skilled personnel and are capable of carrying the required servicing and maintenance. Some haulage truck manufacturers have offered this method of trading when a healthy second hand market existed.

A further advantage to the lessee is that the title remains with the lessor but unlike Finance Leases no entry is required on the lessee's Balance Sheet. Consequently the capital gearing would remain unchanged and this could therefore be particularly convenient to a highly geared company, which might otherwise find difficulty in raising loan capital for direct purchase or even hire purchase of the plant item. The lease charges are considered as a business expense and so are included as costs in the Profit and Loss Account.

Summary of Plant Acquisition Options

1. It may be cheaper to lease than to buy where profits are too low to make full use of capital allowances. The tax allowances are recouped by the lessor and reflected in the lease charges.
2. For rapidly expanding companies and others with capital raising difficulties or high gearing, the lease allows assets to be acquired and potential turnover increased without altering the firm's existing capital structure.
3. Both leasing and hire purchase are long-term commitments, and therefore the revenue (turnover) budget and operating costs budget must be able to accommodate the rental charges over the agreed period of the financial contract.
4. All of the above options imply direct or indirect ownership of the plant, and special facilities will be needed for servicing and maintenance, together with experienced management and skilled staff. Thus, the alternative of hiring in plant should not be overlooked.

Systematic Plant Selection

The decision to purchase an item of plant should be based on economic considerations because, unless it can be demonstrated that the investment will yield a satisfactory rate of return, there should be no purchase at all. However, in practice several more factors need to be considered before a decision to buy is possible. Many makes of machine are available; sometimes the broad technical details between the products of the different manufacturers can be closely compared, but often this is not possible. Intangible areas exist, such as after-sales service, maintenance, delivery and payment arrangements. They are often not quantifiable and frequently take on a disproportionate influence during the decision-making process. Hence all the important and complex factors involved when deciding on the purchase of an item of plant or equipment should be taken into account. Only after careful consideration of all the facts, involving many separate judgements, can a decision then be reached. Obviously the final choice is bound to be a compromise between what the manager wants ideally, and what can actually be obtained.

The problem is best tackled in a systematic and disciplined way. Kepner and Tregoe (ref. 1) in the 1960s developed a decision-making procedure for use in the design process which has been adopted by many manufacturing companies. The method was further developed for application in the construction industry by M. D. Willetts at Loughborough University (ref. 8).

The Essential Characteristics of a Decision Situation

Dixon (ref. 2) describes decision as follows:

> Decision making is compromise. The decision maker must weigh value judgements that involve economic factors, technical practicabilities, scientific necessities, human and social considerations, etc. To make a 'correct' decision is to choose the one alternative from among those that are available which best balances or optimises the total value, considering all the various factors.

Arising from the above, Kepner and Tregoe, among others, established seven essential factors to be considered in a decision situation:

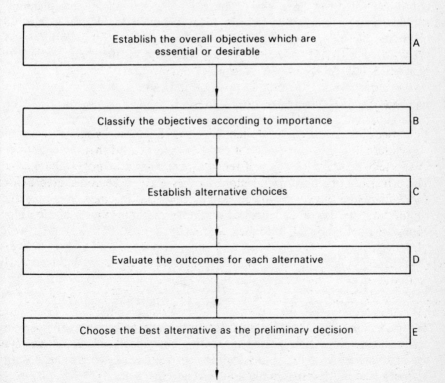

| Establish the overall objectives which are essential or desirable | A |

| Classify the objectives according to importance | B |

| Establish alternative choices | C |

| Evaluate the outcomes for each alternative | D |

| Choose the best alternative as the preliminary decision | E |

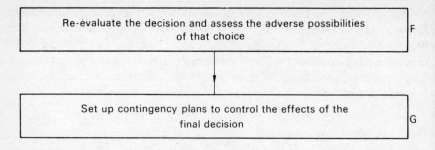

To illustrate the advantages to be gained by making decisions in such a logical and disciplined way, the following example is described.

Example: Crane Selection

Problem

A construction company has just been awarded a contract for the construction of a sewage works. Its policy is to purchase most of its plant requirements, as the managing director believes there is always enough continuity of work involving concrete. The site agent and planning engineer responsible for the project, after careful thought, decide that the most suitable method for placing the concrete is with a crawler-mounted crane fitted with a 1 m^3 capacity concrete skip. At this stage, the plant manager's advice is sought. A simple, but accurate sketch of the site layout incorporating the crane's position indicates that maximum lift will be 3000 kg at 14 metres radius. No such cranes are available in the plant yard, and a decision to purchase one is therefore required.

Investment Analysis

The crane is to be used on the contract for two years only. Calculations show that, if a 10-year working life is possible, the rate of return on capital using a discounted cash flow (DCF) method is satisfactory. The appraisal is based on the following figures:

Purchase price	£45 000
Working life	10 yrs.
Resale value	£2000
Running cost	Based on similar machines

The plant manager feels that sufficient work can be obtained for such a crane during a 10-year period, providing that it is possible to convert the machine for dragline and backhoe use. He decides to go ahead with a purchase on that basis having rejected the possibility of hiring a machine. There are many cranes of this type on offer, by British and by foreign manufacturers. The problem is to decide which is the best buy to suit both the short-term needs of the contract and the possible other uses for the crane during its 10-year working life.

Procedure

A. *Choose the overall objectives which are essential and desirable*
The individuals involved in selecting the crane, the agent, engineer and plant manager, have so far only loosely established the specification of the machine requirements. When choosing small items of plant such information and some experience with a few of the popular manufacturers might be enough evidence on which to base the purchase decision. But too often important purchases are also dealt with in this way, and this has led to some very poor investments. To reduce this possibility, the plant manager decides to adopt a more systematic procedure. This demands that a precise list of requirements be written down, including advice from the foreman or crane driver. These are shown as objectives A–G, 1–23 on the decision analysis sheets (Tables 7.1, 7.2, 7.3). It is recommended that the objectives be classified into two groups, economic (E) and technical (T), so that in the final analysis the importance of each is demonstrated.

B. *Classify the objectives according to importance*
A careful examination of the listed objectives will reveal that some are essential, some are important but not critical to the machine's function, while others are desirable and would be useful if available.

The essential objectives are taken aside and labelled MUSTS. They set the limits which cannot be violated. The impossible alternatives are then easily recognised and quickly eliminated. The remaining objectives are described as WANTS, and some wants will always be more important than others. The next step therefore is to rank the importance of the want objectives. This is done by attaching a ranking expressed on a suitable scale. In practice, a 1–5 or 1–10 system has been found to be a good compromise, with the importance of the objective increasing with numerical value. The ranking is done on a subjective assessment based on experience.

C. *Establish alternative choices*
At this juncture the plant manager selects those machines on the market which appear to satisfy the MUST objectives. In this case three models only are found:

ARB-38
Koppelstein 4B
Vickerman Lion

Table 7.1 Evaluation of cranage selection – Crane No. 1

Ref.	Objectives — MUSTS	Alternative — ARB-38	GO/NO GO
A	Track-mounted crane	Yes	✓
B	At least 25 m boom as lift crane	36·6 m max.	✓
C	Capable of conversion to dragline	Yes	✓
D	Capable of conversion to backhoe	Yes	✓
E	Capable of lifting 3 tonnes at 14 m radius	3·6 tonnes	✓
F	Max. purchase price £45 000	Yes	✓
G	Conform to BS statutory regulations	Yes	✓

No.	WANTS	E/T	Ranking		Information	Rating	Weighted score	
1	Delivery less than 10 weeks	E	10		6 weeks	8	80	
2	High lifting capacity	T		10	30 480 kg max.	8		80
3	Easy dragline conversion	T		9	1 day	5		45
4	Easy backhoe conversion	T		9	1 day	5		45
5	Good service facilities	E		8		7		56
6	Low maintenance costs	E/T	7	7		9	63	63
7	Low running costs	E	9			8	72	
8	Simple to set up on site	T		6	$\frac{1}{2}$ h	9		54
9	Low ground-bearing pressure	T		4	0·55 kg/cm²	7		28
10	Good safety features	T		8		6		48
11	Simple driver controls/view	T		5		4		20
12	Independent third drum	T		2	500 × 75 mm	10		20
13	Air clutch control	T		4		10		40
14	Fast slewing speed	T		7	3·55 r.p.m.	7		49
15	Fast hoist speed	T		7	45·5 m/min	7		49
16	Good manoeuvrability around site	T		4	1·52 km/h	6		24
17	Good range of spares	T		8		2		16
18	Long working life/good trade-in price	E	7		10 years – £2 050	8	56	
19	Air control on all movements	T		3		9		27
20	Audible and visible safe load indicator	T		10		2		20
21	Automatic power boom lowering	T		2		10		20
22	Safety crawler brakes	T		6		10		60
23	Low purchase price	E	10		£44 050	7	70	
E	Economic element	27%	43					
T	Technical element	73%		119			341	764
	Totals	100%	162				1105	

Remarks: All MUSTS O.K.

Table 7.2 Evaluation of cranage selection – Crane No. 2

	Objectives		Alternative	
Ref.	MUSTS		Koppelstein 4B	GO/NO GO
A	Track-mounted crane		Yes	.
B	At least 25 m boom as lift crane		27·4 m max.	✓
C	Capable of conversion to dragline		Yes	✓
D	Capable of conversion to backhoe		Yes	.
E	Capable of lifting 3 tonnes at 14 m radius		3·4 tonnes	.
F	Max. purchase price £45 000		Yes	✓
G	Conform to BS statutory regulations		Yes	.

No.	WANTS	E/T	Ranking		Information	Rating	Weighted score	
1	Delivery less than 10 weeks	E	10		9 weeks	7	70	
2	High lifting capacity	T		10	34 860 kg max.	7		70
3	Easy dragline conversion	T		9	4 h	8		72
4	Easy backhoe conversion	T		9	4 h	8		72
5	Good service facilities	E		8		2		16
6	Low maintenance costs	E/T	7	7		2	14	14
7	Low running costs	E	9			4	36	
8	Simple to set up on site	T		6	½ h	8		48
9	Low ground-bearing pressure	T		4	0·5 kg/cm²	8		32
10	Good safety features	T		8		3		24
11	Simple driver controls/view	T		5		4		20
12	Independent third drum	T		2	Not available	0		0
13	Air clutch control	T		4	Mechanical	1		4
14	Fast slewing speed	T		7	4 r.p.m.	8		56
15	Fast hoist speed	T		7	35 m/min	5		35
16	Good manoeuvrability around site	T		4	2 km/h	7		28
17	Good range of spares	T		8		2		16
18	Long working life/good trade-in price	E	7		8 years – £4000	8	56	
19	Air control on all movements	T		3	Mechanical	1		3
20	Audible and visible safe load indicator	T		10		7		70
					Not available	0		0
21	Automatic power boom lowering	T		2		10		60
22	Safety crawler brakes	T		6		9	90	
23	Low purchase price	E	10		£40 125			
E	Economic element		27%	43				
T	Technical element		73%	119			266	640
	Totals		100%	162				906

Remarks: All MUSTS O.K.

Table 7.3 Evaluation of cranage selection – Crane No. 3

Ref.	MUSTS	Vickerman Lion	GO/NO GO
	Objectives	**Alternative**	
A	Track-mounted crane	Yes	✓
B	At least 25 m boom as lift crane	35·4 m max.	✓
C	Capable of conversion to dragline	Yes	✓
D	Capable of conversion to backhoe	No	×
E	Capable of lifting 3 tonnes at 14 m radius	4·1 tonnes	✓
F	Max. purchase price £45 000	Yes	✓
G	Conform to BS statutory regulations	Yes	✓

Remarks: Does not meet MUST requirement D and is therefore eliminated.

This stage should be thorough, but since only the MUSTS are considered the search should not prove to be too tedious. (Much information is available in publications such as *Cranes Annual* published by Morgan Grampian Limited, but a good plant department ought to have an up-to-date library of manufacturers' literature.)

D. *Evaluate the outcome for each alternative*

Those cranes which do not comply with all the MUST objectives are eliminated. Thus unsuitable machines are eliminated early on, without the plant manager and his staff devoting too much effort to a detailed analysis. Next, the WANT objectives for each alternative left in the analysis are rated. Again there arises the problem of choosing the best rating system. The 0–5 or 0–10 method has been widely used. A value of 0 indicates that the alternative does not meet the objective in any way. Both the ranking and rating systems should be used boldly or there will be insufficient 'spread' of the total values in the final result. However, before any analysis of this sort is attempted some of the potential difficulties must be considered.

Economic and financial considerations   In the example, cost is a critical factor, but the advertised prices for the alternatives are not always easy to compare. Table 7.4 demonstrates this problem. The information assembled for each crane varies in its detail and any decision on price can only be a compromise. But a meaningful comparison is often possible within the slight differences in each manufacturer's equipment, given that the plant manager has sufficient experience with the type of plant in question. It must also be remembered that discounts and payment arrangements are an important cost consideration.

Furthermore, the question of a spares holding policy needs to be considered. The importance of the future availability and costs of spares from different suppliers can of course be reflected in the ranking and rating of the desired objective. However, if the company is already geared up to equipment from a manufacturer and in consequence is carrying stocks of spares, then this situation may override all other considerations. This question of spares must be carefully studied when comparing British and foreign makes, as the cost of foreign-made spares may be affected by the value of the British pound. This aspect should be taken into account in the ranking and rating assessments, when considered necessary.

Technical and performance standards   The plant manager's decision is influenced by factors relating to the technical and performance standards of the equipment. Some may form MUST objectives, while others appear in varying degrees of importance as WANT objectives. Many details can

Table 7.4 Cost comparison of alternative crane purchases

Description	Cost (£)		
	ARB-38	Koppelstein 4B	Vickerman Lion
Base machine with			
700 mm wide shoes	31 000	27 000	34 000
800 mm wide shoes	31 200	27 150	N/A
Basic boom (10·67 m)	inc.	inc.	inc.
Boom inserts			
(1·52 m) Varies	(175 ea.)	(225 ea.)	(250 ea.)
(3·05 m) slightly with	(200 ea.)	(305 ea.)	(325 ea.)
(4·57 m) each make	(300 ea.)	(450 ea.)	(375 ea.)
Max boom length (27·4 m)	1 800*	2 700	2 250*
Fly jibs (4·75 m)	300	310	350
(6·1 m)	375	400	450
(7·62 m)	400	475	505
(9·14 m)	500	550	600
(strut)	440	400	375
Counterweight	400	375	500
Hook blocks 20 tonne	200	180	150
10 tonne	175	100	105
5 tonne	80	60	75
Telescope boom stops	⎫	inc.	inc.
Pendant suspension ropes	⎬ 1 500	inc.	inc.
Fairlead	⎮	inc.	inc.
Mast	⎭	inc.	inc.
Safe load indicator	1 800	1 000	900
Cab accessories	inc.	100	110
Parts to convert to 1 m³ dragline	3 000	2 900	4 000
Parts to convert to 1 m³ backhoe	4 500	5 000	N/A
1 m³ bottom opening concrete skip	150	170	160
Max. total cost	£44 050	£40 125	£42 560

* Boom length can be extended beyond 27·4 m.

be easily obtained from the manufacturer's literature, such as, lifting capacity, machine weight etc. For other factors the answers are more intangible, and more subtle sources of information must be found, for example:

Site demonstrations
Further discussion with manufacturers
Company records for similar equipment
Personal contacts in the plant industry
Discussions with machine operators

With the details assembled for all the objectives, the task of evaluating each alternative can now go ahead. The MUSTS are assessed on the GO/NO GO basis and those alternatives violating any objective are eliminated. A comparison of the three cranes proposed reveals that the Vickerman Lion does not have the facility for a backhoe conversion. Hence although this machine passed the preliminary screening it must now be marked NO GO against objective D and eliminated from further consideration.

The WANTS have previously been considered carefully and ranked on the 1–10 scale so now each alternative is rated on the 0–10 scale against each objective. By multiplying each individual ranking by its corresponding rating, the weighted score for each objective is determined. This weighted score represents the performance of the alternative against its objective. By adding each of the individual weightings, the total for each alternative gives the relative position in regard to the specified objectives. In this example the total weighted score for the two remaining alternatives is as follows:

	Percentage of	Weighted score	
Element	total	ARB-38	Koppelstein 4B
Cost and service element (E)	27%	341(31%)	266(29%)
Technical element (T)	73%	764(69%)	640(71%)
Total	100%	1105	906

Note: It must be remembered that the numbers are derived largely by subjective judgement based on careful thought and analysis of the available facts, and do not make the decision in themselves. But this systematic approach does assist in coping with many independent facts which otherwise could not be easily related.

E. *Choose the best alternative as the preliminary decision*

The alternative that receives the highest weighted score is presumably the best course of action to take, in this case the ARB-38. It is, of course, not a perfect choice – for instance, one would probably prefer a machine with a Rolls-Royce engine. But the choice is at least one which draws a reasonable balance between the good and bad features of the machine. Fortunately both the technical and cost element totals are greater for the ARB-38. The decision would be far more difficult if one of the elements were larger for Koppelstein 4B crane. Some further balance would then be needed between economic resources and the technical benefits coming to the company.

The preliminary choice is the one which best satisfies the objectives overall. It is thus a compromise, as undoubtedly the alternatives have some superior features. But the method used shows the manager how he arrived at this decision and therefore where the possible pitfalls may lie.

F. Re-evaluate the decision and assess the adverse possibilities of that choice

When many alternatives are available, the weighted scores of one or two are sometimes quite close, so, before the manager makes the final decision, any adverse consequences must be considered. He must look for snags, potential shortcomings or anything else that could go wrong. The probability (P) of the adverse consequences should be assessed and a seriousness weighting (S) given to its possible effect. An expression of the total degree of threat may be obtained by multiplying the seriousness weighting by the probability estimate.

In this example the plant and site managers arrange a meeting to discuss the implications of the proposals.

(i) *Possible adverse consequences of the ARB-38*

A strike threat is rumoured at the factory, which may delay delivery. A closer investigation reveals that this type of situation has arisen before with a strike only occurring twice in the past 10 years, but strikes have not increased in the past four or five years. The probability of a strike is therefore assessed at a 20% chance of occurring. The duration of the first strike was only one week but the last strike, two years ago, lasted five weeks. However, in view of the existing climate between management and unions, a prolonged strike this time is not envisaged. Should a hire crane be necessary for, say, 3 weeks, the extra cost to the contract is £250 per week plus transport cost of £50. The degree of threat is therefore $(3 \times 250 + 50) \times 0.2 = £160$.

(ii) *Possible adverse consequences of the Koppelstein 4B*

A serious accident has just revealed a major design fault in the clutch mechanism of the winch. A temporary modification will be made to all existing models and stocks held. But a completely new part is not available for six months and will require taking the crane out of service for one week at that time. The probability that this service is required is 90% and the cost of hire for another crane is £250 per week plus £50 transport cost, thereby directly increasing the contract cost at this rate. The degree of threat is $(1 \times 250 + 50) \times 0.9 = £270$.

The choice, therefore, is still the ARB-38. Had the consequences been reversed, then a much closer examination of the advantages and disadvantages would be necessary, making the decision much more difficult.

G. *Set up contingency plans to control the effects of the final decisions*
The adverse consequences represent potential problems. They must be prevented from causing too much inconvenience. This is done either by taking preventative action to remove the cause or deciding upon a contingency action if the potential problem occurs. In our case, the simple remedy is to ensure that alternative machines are available for hire at suitable times or arrange work on site so that interruption is minimal.

Comments
The decision reached is to buy the ARB-38 and this is the best choice based on the judgement of the plant manager concerned. For someone else with different experience the assessment of the objectives might be quite different and would possibly produce a different result. But even accepting this obvious weakness, the method at least forces the manager to consider most of the facts. It provides a record of his thought processes and will help him to sort out points of confusion. For it is almost impossible for him to store all the facts and relationships in his head, except for the very simple choices. In such cases the decision process can be adequately carried out mentally without the need for the elaborate method described. Finally, the decision process is written down on paper and is available for all to see.

Setting Hire Rates

Setting a realistic hire rate is not an easy task, particularly in times of rapid inflation. Factors largely outside the control of the company make it almost impossible to forecast the scrap value, the utilisation factor, running costs over a period of perhaps as long as 10 years. Most companies periodically review the hire rates to keep them in line with the movements of prices and costs, a policy which will not necessarily generate the replacement cost. To take care of this problem an inflation allowance should ideally be built into the calculations from the outset. This is not easily done when inflation fluctuates over short periods.

Conventional Method of Tabulating the Hire Rate

It is usual for companies who own plant to set the hire rate per hour for use in estimating purposes when tendering for new work or for charging an item of plant against a contract. The factors involved are:

(a) The capital cost of the plant
(b) Depreciation   } Ownership cost
(c) Running and repair costs
(d) Licence and insurance cost   } Operating cost
(e) Overheads

Capital
Quite often the capital needed to purchase an item of plant is raised through a loan. The interest payments are a charge and therefore should be incorporated into the hire rate. Even when the plant is bought using reserve capital, an equivalent charge should again be allowed since the money, if not used to buy plant, could be earning interest.

Running costs
The cost of maintenance and repairs varies considerably for different types of plant, conditions of work and also with the hours worked. Experience with similar equipment and the keeping of detailed records are the only ways of estimating such costs. The allowance is normally expressed as a percentage of the initial cost, but this is far from an ideal method, since most plant requires more maintenance as it becomes older.

The cost of fuel and lubricants varies with the size, type and age of the equipment. Again, experience is the best guide, but the manufacturer's data does provide figures which, with reasonable judgement, can be used to estimate the machine's consumption of such materials.

Licences and insurances
The amount and type of insurance required depends upon whether the plant is to use public roads or not. For plant which will not be used on public roads, the premium is quite small and may only cover fire and theft. Plant using the public highway will naturally have to be covered by the minimum legal requirements, as do any other road users. Again, licences are a small charge when the plant is not used on public roads but become a considerable expense otherwise.

Lifting appliances such as cranes have to be inspected by an insurance company, which adds an additional cost.

Establishment charges
It is usual these days for a contracting company to group its plant either into a separate profit-making division or at least into some sort of self-contained unit to provide a service function. Therefore an allowance for all the normal administration and other overheads needs to be included.

Depreciation
Depreciation is the loss of value resulting from usage or age. A contractor normally recovers this loss by including a sum of money equivalent to the depreciation cost in his rates for doing the work or hiring out the plant. In normal practice, the revenue is used for many other purposes and not allowed to accumulate idly. When the asset is finally replaced, the capital is either borrowed or withdrawn from the company cash balances. However, several factors can interfere with such arrangements: inflation may mean that the revenue was not enough to replace the old asset, or perhaps the depreciation allowance was misjudged. The only recourse thereafter is extra borrowing.

Methods of Depreciation

In the following paragraphs some fairly common methods of calculating depreciation are described. The reader should note that the choice of method is arbitrary and not of crucial importance. However, with current tax legislation the company's profit level is affected by its depreciation policy, as the amount of depreciation which may be offset against profits in the form of capital allowances is subject to the approval of the Inspector of Taxes.

1. Straight line depreciation
Example   It is decided to purchase a mechanical excavator costing £42 000 to work an average 2000 hours per year. The life of the machine is expected to be 10 years, after which time the salvage value will be £2000.

Purchase price	£42 000
Residual value	£2 000
Total depreciation	£40 000
Annual depreciation	£4 000
Hourly depreciation	£2

2. Declining balance depreciation

Using the above example, this time the depreciation is made on a fixed percentage basis rather than the fixed sum.

Table 7.5 Declining balance depreciation example (at 26.2%)

End of year	Depreciation (%)	Dep. for year (£)	Book value (£)
0	26·2	0	42 000
1	,,	11 004	30 996
2	,,	8 121	22 875
3	,,	5 994	16 881
4	,,	4 423	12 458
5	,,	3 264	9 194
6	,,	2 409	6 785
7	,,	1 778	5 007
8	,,	1 312	3 695
9	,,	968	2 727
10	,,	727	2 000
	Total	£40 000	

Table 7.5 is more easily calculated from the formula

$$d = \left(1 - \sqrt[n]{\frac{L}{P}}\right) \times 100$$

where L = salvage value, P = purchase price, n = life of asset and d = percentage depreciation.

3. Sinking fund method of depreciation

A fixed sum is put aside from revenue each year and invested with compound interest throughout the life of the asset. After successive instalments the sum accumulates to produce the original purchase price less the scrap value.

Taking the given example and assuming 6% interest is earned on savings, the annual amount required is £3034, i.e.:

Sinking fund deposit factor over 10 years = 0·075 86
Therefore annual payment = 0·075 86 × (42 000 − 2000) = £3034

Table 6.6 gives a detailed breakdown of the analysis.

Table 7.6 Sinking fund example (6% interest on savings)

Year	Payment (£)	Interest (£)	Depreciation (£)	Book value (£)
1	3 034	0	3 034	38 966
2	3 034	182	3 216	35 750
3	3 034	375	3 409	32 341
4	3 034	581	3 615	28 726
5	3 034	798	3 832	24 894
6	3 034	1 028	4 062	20 832
7	3 034	1 271	4 305	16 527
8	3 034	1 529	4 563	11 964
9	3 034	1 803	4 837	7 127
10	3 034	2 093	5 127	2 000
		Total	£40 000	

4. *Sum of digits method*

$$\text{Life} = 10 \text{ years}$$
$$\text{Digits} = 1 + 2 + 3 + 4 + 5 + 6 + 7 + 8 + 9 + 10 = 55$$

Table 7.7 Sum of digits depreciation example

Year	Factor	Depreciation (£)	Book value (£)
1	10/55	7 273	34 727
2	9/55	6 545	28 182
3	8/55	5 818	22 364
4	7/55	5 091	17 273
5	6/55	4 364	12 909
6	5/55	3 636	9 273
7	4/55	2 909	6 364
8	3/55	2 182	4 182
9	2/55	1 454	2 728
10	1/55	728	2 000
	Total	£40 000	

5. *Free depreciation*
The asset is totally depreciated initially.

Graphical comparison of the Depreciation Methods

Figure 7.1 demonstrates the main features of the declining balance method and the sum of digits method. In the early years the asset is

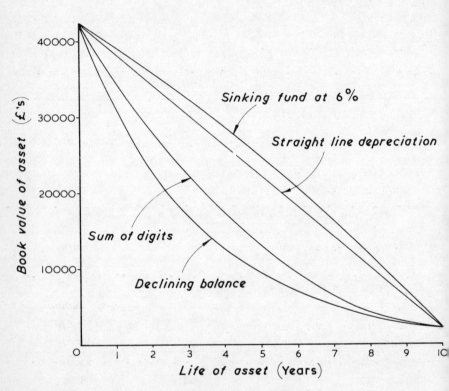

Fig. 7.1 Graphical comparison of depreciation methods.

heavily written down, which is particularly helpful in the case of construction plant as the repair and maintenance costs are likely to be low when new, but increase with age and usage.

Example using the crane selection study

Calculate the hourly hire rate for the ARB-38 given the following information:

Initial cost	£44 050
Resale value	£2 050
Average working hours per year	2 000
Years of life of machine	10
Insurance premiums per year	£200
Licences and tax per year	£100
Fuel at 20 litres per hour	£0·10 per litre
Oil and grease	10% of fuel cost
Repairs and maintenance	15% of initial cost per year
Required rate of return on capital	15%

Note: Overheads not included for simplicity.

Item	*£ per annum*
Depreciation—straight line	

$$= \frac{£42\,000}{10} \qquad\qquad 4\,200$$

Interest on finance, expressed in terms of an annual mortgage type payment

$$\frac{44\,050 \times 0·199 \times 10 - 44\,050}{10} \qquad 4\,361$$

Insurance and tax	300
Ownership cost	£8 861

Item	*£ per annum*
Fuel (litres)—20 × 0·10 × 2000	4 000
Oil and grease	400
Repairs—15% × 44 050	6 608
Operating cost	£11 008
Total cost	£19 869

$$\text{Marginal hire charge} = \frac{19\,869}{2\,000} = £9·93 \text{ per hour}$$

(*Note*: When considering other types of equipment, e.g. rubber-tyred excavators, the cost of the tyres should be subtracted from the purchase price and then analysed separately because the rate of depreciation is likely to be much higher on the tyres. This may also apply to tracked machines working in some ground conditions.)

The above calculations allow for the generation of sufficient income to replace the asset, to cover operating costs and to provide a return on the initial capital invested. An additional sum must be added to cover company overheads and profit.

Alternative analysis using DCF   Refer to Chapter 13
The method described above is widely used and has stood the test of time, but no account is taken of the timing of the cash flows. A more logical way of doing the analysis is to express the problem in the way that it actually occurs, i.e. as a series of cash flows. Then an effort is made to balance the outgoings with adequate income to yield a satisfactory return. The problem is thus restructured as shown in Table 7.8.

Table 7.8 Calculating a crane hire rate using DCF method

Year	Capital (£)	Scrap value (£)	Operating costs (£)	Tax and insurance (£)	Total cash out (£)	Cash in (£)	Total (£)
0	−44 050		0	−300	−44 350	0	− 44 350
1			−11 008	−300	−11 308	x	x − 11 308
2			−11 008	−300	−11 308	x	x − 11 308
3			−11 008	−300	−11 308	x	x − 11 308
4			−11 008	−300	−11 308	x	x − 11 308
5			−11 008	−300	−11 308	x	x − 11 308
6			−11 008	−300	−11 308	x	x − 11 308
7			−11 008	−300	−11 308	x	x − 11 308
8			−11 008	−300	−11 308	x	x − 11 308
9			−11 008	−300	−11 308	x	x − 11 308
10		+2 050	−11 008	0	−8 958	x	x − 8 958

Clearly, to return 15% on the investment, x must be sufficiently large so that, when cash out and cash in are reduced to net present value, the last column (total) is in balance. Expressed mathematically, the equation is:

$$44\,350 = (x - 11\,308) \times 4{\cdot}7715 + (x - 8958) \times 0{\cdot}24\,718$$
$$44\,350 = 4{\cdot}7715x - 53\,956 + 0{\cdot}2472 - 2214$$
$$100\,520 = 5{\cdot}02x$$
$$x = £20\,024$$

The annual receipts must be £20 024 or £10·01 per hour hire charge.

Information: (1) 4.7715 is the present worth factor of a uniform series for 9 years at 15% interest; (2) 0.2472 is the present worth factor of a single sum at year 10 for a 15% interest rate.

The Effect of Inflation

During the past few years inflation has been running at more than 10% per annum. The traditional method of allowing for this in the hire rate is simply to increase periodically the hire rate in line with the movement of prices, but usually only to compensate for the *previous* year's inflation. The effect of this policy is shown in Table 7.9, where all figures are adjusted to take account of a 10% annual rate of inflation including the extra cost of replacing the asset. The results of Table 7.9 indicate that the normal policy of compensating for inflation is totally inadequate, if sufficient capital is to be generated to allow for the increase in the price of a new asset (up from £44 050 to £113 811) and still provide the desired rate of return of 15%. The hire rate should be calculated in the context of the whole series of cash flows, which can then be adjusted for any rate of inflation.

Plant Maintenance

A contractor that owns plant must be prepared to provide maintenance and servicing of the equipment if economic levels of utilisation are to be obtained. Effective maintenance is expensive and requires depot facilities, workshops, experienced staff, etc. Many firms have tried to avoid these costs by providing the minimum of maintenance, and the result has often been unexpected breakdowns, lost production and inefficient machinery. Alternatively, the contractor can implement a system of planned maintenance, which can be broadly divided into either preventive or corrective options. (See refs. 10, 11.)

Planned Preventive Maintenance

This system requires the implementation of planned regular procedures aimed at reducing wear, maintaining the plant in good working condition and preventing unforeseen stoppages. The maintenance actions are as follows:

(i) Daily servicing and superficial inspection performed roughly half an hour before and after working hours.
(ii) Regular full maintenance and inspection, including periodic overhaul.
(iii) Replacement or repair of component parts within a working period based on the expected duties and conditions.

This is a very comprehensive system and can be instituted only by firms with adequate workshops, experienced staff and the ability to substitute other plant whilst the full overhaul is undertaken. The method thus requires both shut-down and running maintenance facilities.

Planned Corrective Maintenance

This means providing the minimum of maintenance to enable the plant to operate while on site. Work is then undertaken to restore it to an acceptable level after completing its duties on site or through sudden failure.

This method is usually favoured by construction plant operators as the necessary workshop facilities to perform major overhauls are more likely to be available only at the central depot and not on the individual construction sites.

This system requires running, shut-down and breakdown maintenance facilities. The latter usually is best carried out by an auxiliary emergency breakdown service, consisting of a well-equipped mobile vehicle, such as a Land Rover, and fitters.

Monitoring of Maintenance

In order that the maintenance policy may be executed efficiently, it is necessary to install a recording and costing system, which shall include:

(i) An Asset Register comprising an inventory of each plant item in the fleet, with information on the date of purchase, registration or code number, purchase price, current value, location, hours operated, etc.

(ii) A Maintenance Schedule indicating the type of maintenance and servicing required on each plant item together with the time intervals between each plant maintenance operation.

(iii) Job Cards to be filled out by the fitter each time maintenance work is performed, and which should include a description of the work done, materials used, time taken, recurring defects, etc.

(iv) History Record Cards. The information on the job card is transferred for each individual machine to its history card, together with the hours operated and fuel used. The monthly records are then abstracted to prepare costs for comparison with budgeted values. The variances are subsequently used in controlling maintenance, adjusting the hire rate and ultimately in making decisions with respect to replacement or sale of the item of plant.

Exercises
Exercise 1. Example of Kepner and Tregoe Analysis

A large building contractor has been awarded three large contracts for houses of traditional construction, all of which are due to start in about 3 months time. The results of comprehensive research into materials handling have indicated that the use of ten forklift trucks would be economic if they could be obtained for £7000 each (or less), complete with reasonable accessories.

The plant manager arranges a meeting with the three site agents, who agree that, since

Table 7.9 The effect of inflation on the rate calculation

Year	Capital (£)	Scrap value (£)	Operating cost (£)	Tax and insurance (£)	Total cash out (£)	Cash in (£)	Total cash flow (£)	Adjusted cash flow (£)	Net P.W. at 10% (£)
0	−44 050		0	−300	−44 350	0	−44 350	−44 350	−44 350
1			−12 108	−330	−12 438	20 024	+7 586	+7 586	+6 890
2			−13 318	−362	−13 680	22 026	+8 346	+8 346	+6 890
3			−14 650	−399	−15 049	24 227	+9 178	+9 178	+6 890
4			−16 115	−439	−16 554	26 664	+10 095	+10 095	+6 890
5			−17 728	−483	−18 211	29 315	+11 104	+11 104	+6 890
6			−19 500	−531	−20 031	32 248	+12 217	+12 217	+6 890
7			−21 451	−584	−22 035	35 472	+13 437	+5 936	+3 040
8			−23 595	−643	−24 238	39 020	+14 782	—	—
9			−25 955	−707	−26 662	42 921	+16 259	—	—
10	−69 761*	+5 317	−28 551	0	−23 234	47 214	−45 754	—	—
									approx. NIL

* Extra cost of replacing the asset at year 10.

Return on capital is 10%. Compare this rate with i_r, the real rate of return given in Chapter 13.

Table 7.10 Details of forklift trucks

Description	Superfork	RON 361	Unitruck	Trimloader
Price (£)	6450	6870	8320	3250
Engine (Diesel)	4 stroke	4 stroke	2 stroke	4 stroke
Engine noise (dB)	75	80	86	68
Max. lift length (m)	3·300	3·300	4·200	3·100
Hydraulics	Low pressure	High pressure	High pressure	High pressure
Gross weight (kg)	2100	1800	2800	1300
Delivery period (weeks)	6	10	6	Ex. stock
Safety	To BS	To BS	Exceeds BS	To BS
Outreach (m)	1·800	1·600	Not available	1·500
Turning circle (m)	6·100	4·300	8·750	4·200
Max. load (kg)	1100	1300	2400	750
Accessories	Reasonable	Good	Poor	Good

Supplied by the kind permission of R. H. Neale, Department of Civil Engingeering, Loughborough University of Technology.

bricks and blocks are delivered in 1000 kg unit loads, the truck must be capable of placing this weight on to a scaffold at first floor level (2·800 m high). It is also essential that the truck has an 'outreach' facility. The site agents also valued manoeuvrability, low weight and an efficient repairs and maintenance service.

The plant manager obtained details of many forklift trucks and quickly eliminated those which were obviously unsuitable, leaving four: the Neale's Superfork; the Unitruck by Harris Manufacturing; the RON 361 by Clydebank Crane and Hoist; the Conman Engineerings' Trimloader. Details of these trucks are given in Table 7.10.

The plant manager favoured the Superfork because he had many machines made by Neale in his plant fleet, and some spares would be interchangeable. Neale's service was also better than Clydebank Crane and Hoists, and the service of the others was poor. However, he knew that there were rumours of problems with Neale's hydraulic valves, which would require a design change and a delay of 3 months. He estimates that the cost of the delay would be £10 per week per truck, and that the probability of a redesign being necessary was 0·3.

The RON 361 sometimes suffered mast failure due to metal fatigue. The nature of low cycle metal fatigue is not understood, but it appeared that the masts either failed very early in their lives or after about 12 months normal usage. The probability of an early failure was 0·1, and the cost would be £10 per week per truck, as before. The probability of a failure after 12 months was 0·05, but because the contracts would be working at peak production, the costs would be £100 per mast failure plus £50 per week. It usually took Clydebank three weeks to replace a mast.

Exercise brief

1. Advise the plant manager which truck to purchase. Use the Kepner and Tregoe method of analysis, and other suitable techniques. Choose your own scores and weightings appropriate to the information given, and do not distinguish between technical and service factors.

Exercise 2

Determine the direct cost per hour of owning and operating a $\frac{1}{4}$ cu. yd capacity, hydraulic backhoe excavator from the following data:

Initial cost	£15 000
Resale value	Negligible
Useful life	10 years
Interest on capital	15% p.a.
Fuel consumption	2 gallons per hour
Cost of fuel	30p per gallon
Oil and grease	10% of fuel cost
Repairs to machine	10% of initial price p.a.
Operator	'all-in' cost of £1·50 per hour
Insurance and tax	$1\frac{1}{2}$% of initial price p.a.
Average working hours per year	2000

Exercise 3
Calculate the hire per hour required if the annual rate of inflation is 8%, and 15% return on capital is still required for example No. 2.

Exercise 4
Calculate the hire rate for example No. 2 if machine were rubber-tyred. Take the cost of tyres to be £1000 per set with a life of 6 months.

References and Bibliography

1. Kepner, C. H. & Tregoe, B. B. *The Rational Manager*. McGraw-Hill, 1965.

2. Dixon, J. R. *Design Engineering—Inventiveness Analysis and Decision Making*. McGraw-Hill, 1966.

3. Merrett, A. J. & Sykes, A. *The Finance and Analysis of Capital Projects*. Longman, 1965.

4. *An Introduction to Engineering Economics*. The Institution of Civil Engineers, 1969.

5. Kerr, D. *The Factors which Affect Cash Flow and Net Profit Margins in Construction Projects*. Internal project report, Department of Civil Engineering, Loughborough University, 1972.

6. Mackay, I. B. *A Computer Program for Cash Flow Forecasting*. Internal project report, Department of Civil Engineering, Loughborough University, 1971.

7. Sivey, G. P. *The Effects of Inflation on Contractors' Operations and Profitability, With Particular Reference to Plant and Equipment*. Internal project report, Department of Civil Engineering, Loughborough University, 1975.

8. Willets, M. D. *A Systematic Approach to Problem Solving and Decision Making*. Unpublished paper, Loughborough University of Technology, 1973.

9. Mead, H. T. and Mitchell, G. L. *Plant Hire for Building and Construction*. Newnes-Butterworths, 1972.

10. Harris, F. C. and McCaffer, R. *Construction Plant: Management and Investment Decisions*. Granada, 1982.

11. Harris, F. C. *Construction Plant: Excavating and Materials Handling Equipment and Methods*. Granada, 1981.

SECTION TWO

CHAPTER 8

COMPANY ORGANISATION

Summary

The role and responsibilities of the manager, the lines of communication in an enterprise and the structural arrangements to be found in the managerial organisation of some contracting companies are discussed and described.

Introduction

Much has been written theorising on the methods to be adopted by management in assisting control of companies for most types of industry, but it must be remembered that many successful companies have relied solely on the dynamism and entrepreneurial skill of one man. As yet there is no set of rules and regulations to guarantee commercial success.

The purpose of this chapter is to highlight the managerial arrangements which prevail in most construction companies and have proved necessary to ensure their continued viability.

The Function of a Manager

Peter Drucker (ref. 1) argues that management is the function which involves getting things done through other people. The practical implications of this definition, however, depend on each individual business.

A business or firm is simply a fairly efficient way of combining the skills and talents of people into an organisation that can produce the goods and services in sufficient quantity to satisfy the material desires of the community in which it exists, and at the same time provide a sufficient return on the capital invested. It may therefore be argued that the primary responsibility of management is to ensure that the resources available to the business are used in the best possible way to produce economic wealth, while placing no rights or restrictions on the interests of the general public. (However, the aftereffects of such activities, now appearing in the form of chronic pollution, have hitherto not been considered by many enterprises.)

It seems therefore that no hard and fast rules can be set for commercial success, but certain clearly definable arrangements are desirable for any business, because in essence it is management's duty to weld the various parts of an enterprise together so that they can operate in unison.

The Company Objectives

First the company, or more correctly its management, must establish clearly:

1. *The best kind of business to operate in* The entrepreneur often bases this decision on instinct and personal experience, but more careful analysis is needed for the established and growing company.

2. *The kind of goods and services to be offered* As far as the construction market is concerned this may mean taking decisions about whether to concentrate on building schools or houses, speculative or contract work, negotiated or tender projects, as well as laying emphasis on quality, delivery on time and developing good and continuing relations with the client.

3. *The desired share of the market*

4. *The possible changes and fluctuations of the market in future years* By setting these major objectives, top management is in a better position to lay down policies which other managers throughout the organisation can strive to follow.

Company Policy

Different firms may set many different objectives and policies but a few are common to most, as follows:

(*a*) To achieve maximum profit without seriously affecting other objectives. For example, it is unlikely that the safety or welfare officer can pay the same single-minded attitude to this objective as the project manager in charge of a construction site.

(*b*) To improve the quality and value of the work carried out by the company and to offer better services to the client whenever possible.

(*c*) To look for growth into other markets where opportunities arise and the company is suitably placed in terms of resources and skills possessed.

(*d*) To strive continually for improved productivity since, in the long term, this is one of the most important factors in sustaining the highest possible standard of living for both management and workforce.

(*e*) To meet the standards and obligations desired by the society in which the company operates.

Objectives, however, are of little value without the strategies to achieve them.

Company Strategy

To assist in achieving the desired objectives, many companies find that the best strategy is to subdivide the organisation and group-like functions into single departments. Naturally this is a compromise as many of the objectives set for each of the sections will conflict. But, by and large, most construction companies subdivide into the following functions:

Production—project construction
Selling*—estimating, tendering and negotiation
Services—central planning, temporary works design, cost and budgetary control, payment and claims, work study, plant
Financial control—capital procurement, cash flow, bookkeeping, accounts, statutory returns
Administration—health and welfare, wages and salaries, training and education, public relations, records, maintenance and legal matters.

* The word 'selling' is not often used in this way in the construction industry. However, the industry would do well to recognise more fully the importance of this function.

Each department should be given clear and, if possible, measurable objectives which can be either short or long term, so that it can work within the company's overall policies and objectives.

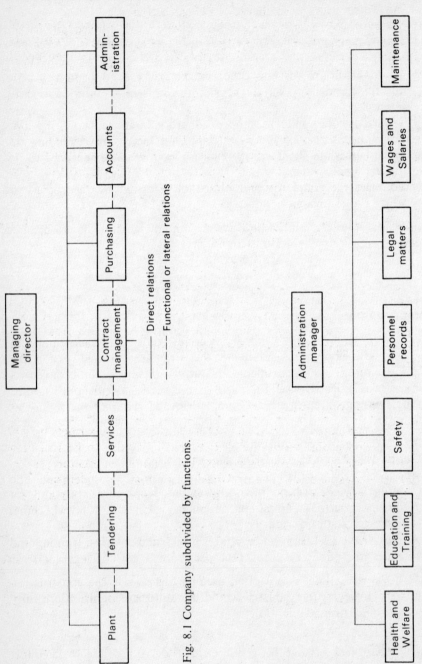

Fig. 8.1 Company subdivided by functions.

Fig. 8.2 Administration subdivided into elements.

Company Organisation Structures

The choices of managerial structure best suited for the company are many and depend upon several factors such as the size of the company, its geographical location, the type of work being done, and the managerial and technical skills available.

Small Companies

The most simple form of organisational structure is that shown in Fig. 8.1 where the company is divided by functions. This type of structure is used by the smaller company with construction interests limited to a few specialities only, e.g. one or more of the following:

> Concrete structures
> Steel erection
> House building
> Earthmoving
> Pipelaying, etc

It is also well suited to the small and medium size local construction company, where technical specialities are few and departments are controlled by a single manager, and all the contracts handled from head office, with perhaps only general foreman or unsophisticated management on site.

Medium-size Companies

As a company increases the volume of its turnover, the contracts undertaken tend to become more complex. Extra skills need to be recruited to service these more involved projects. The head office structure, therefore, not only expands but is also forced to subdivide into elements. The structure begins to take on the form shown in Figs. 8.2, 8.3 and 8.4

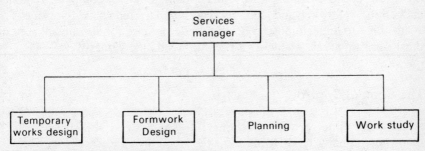

Fig. 8.3 Services subdivided into elements.

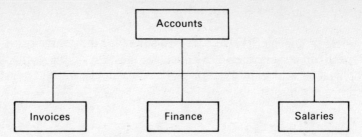

Fig. 8.4 Accounts department subdivided into elements.

with additional service departments often as subdivisions of the major functions.

Large Companies

The large company generally undertakes contracts of many types and sizes with a considerable variation in resource requirements, demanding skills over a wide spectrum. The underlying principle of the simple form of structure is often retained, but with a fundamental decision regarding decentralisation allowing the company to subdivide into product groups. For example, (*a*) civil engineering, building, housing, and/or (*b*) by geographical area as in Fig. 8.5. Structure type (*a*) is particularly common with the medium-size contractor with a national coverage of contract work. The separate groups are usually largely autonomous with only major policies controlled from a central source. Structure type (*b*) is adopted by the very large national contractor with enough turnover to set up almost autonomous units in strategic geographical locations throughout the country. These area divisions also have much of the simple type of structure, again with only major policy decisions taken at head office. Functions such as personnel, legal matters, marketing, design and technical services, and finance are based at head office to provide a group service. The decentralised approach may be under increasing pressure in the future because of the improvements being made in computerised data collection, recording and communications. The tendency is always for head office to superimpose centrally made policies for its subsidiaries in most decision areas, whenever it becomes technically possible.

The Span of Control

A company either grows or declines; it cannot stand still. If it expands, then the company tends to develop the structures shown above, necessitating differing levels of management. The task of co-ordinating the

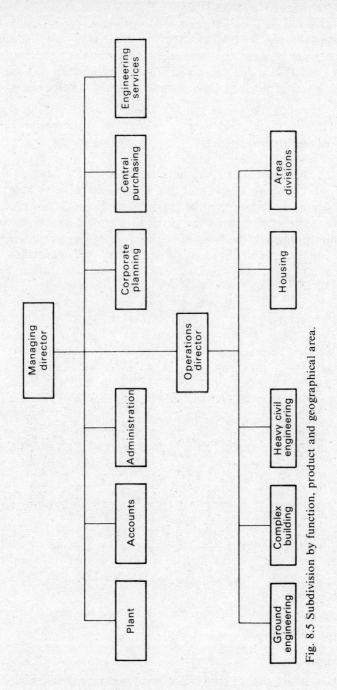

Fig. 8.5 Subdivision by function, product and geographical area.

various activities is soon beyond the capacity of one man; it is therefore essential that management be prepared to delegate responsibility, coupled with some authority, to subordinates. Practice has shown that a manager can cope with between five and eight subordinates reporting to him. Lemarie (ref. 2) in a survey of construction companies showed that, on average, one contracts manager can reasonably control about five site managers.

Pattern of Communications

The pattern of command in the industry is much the same as that used by the military, with *direct lines* of command between manager and assistants in each department. In nearly all companies, however, service functions are necessary. The usual procedure is for the service manager to communicate through the head of the department which is receiving the service. For example, formwork designs may be undertaken at head office for implementation on site. Officially the head office man only provides a service and will have no authority on site, but in practice considerable authority is vested in him by virtue of his superior specialist skills. Such relationships are called *functional* ones, and their success depends very much upon co-operation between individuals. Managers at similar levels of responsibility in the organisation who report to the same superior, or to a different superior at a common level, need to co-operate with one another since no direct line of authority exists between them. Much of the communication in a company is at this level. Workable relationships are thus of the utmost importance if the company is to operate successfully. Typically the important relationships are at the levels of contracts manager, chief estimator, chief planner, chief quantity surveyor, chief buyer, temporary works designer and plant manager levels, and are called *lateral* relations.

Many companies try to lay down a formal management structure in the form of a 'family tree', but in practice many informal relations are demanded by the organisation. The newly appointed manager is well advised to settle in slowly and understand these lines of communication before making many decisions. A family tree illustrating the formal lines of communication of a typical construction project is given in Fig. 8.6.

Manager Attitude

Opportunity

A good company should have a policy of manager development to assist promotion from within the organisation. Most employees favour the

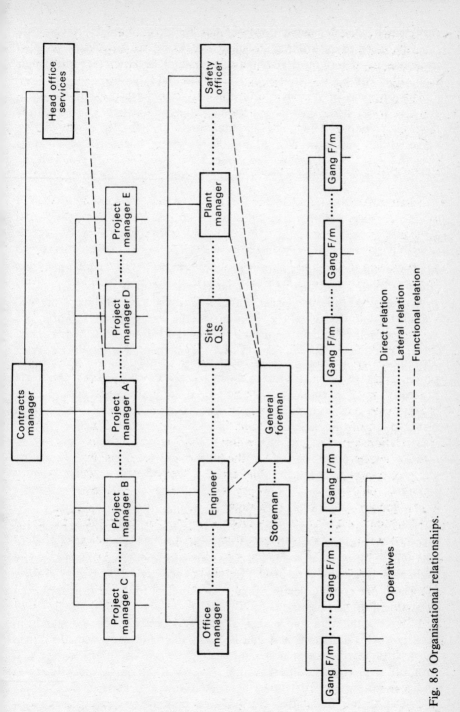

Fig. 8.6 Organisational relationships.

firm which provides good opportunities for promotion. However, care must be taken to ensure that sufficient 'outsiders' are introduced to resist the tendency to loss of drive when relationships become stagnant. People from other companies often bring fresh ideas and attitudes.

The problem of manager selection can become critical if the company is in a rapid growth situation. Extensive outside recruitment is then unavoidable. The possible outcome is a shambles of conflicting personalities and attitudes. Many of the more successful companies over the past 15 years have experienced this problem. The result in the public eye is a poor image of a 'flying by the seat of the pants' type of industry.

Training

Manager development implies training. This means recruiting well educated people and then giving them experience in as many parts of the organisation as possible. The young engineer permanently on site will gain little knowledge of the working of the company as a whole. To become a well-rounded manager, it is essential to spend one or two years in a head office-based department, well supplemented with short courses providing information on modern management techniques. A continual process of training enables a man to be tested long before he gets a top job. If he then fails, it is always possible to try and locate him in a specialist function where perhaps his technical skills and up-to-date knowledge can be of value.

Motivation

It is the duty of every manager to coach his assistants. This will go a long way in encouraging their motivation, essential if the members of the team are to pull their weight effectively and wholeheartedly. Morale must be high; nothing is more inspiring than a feeling of confidence. Many managers unwittingly destroy this confidence by being over-secretive, aloof and not communicating small but significant information about the department to their assistants.

It is of vital importance that a manager knows where he stands in relation to his assistants and that he gains their fullest respect. In return the assistant will expect some interest to be shown in his career and promotion prospects, otherwise able men will be quickly disillusioned and look elsewhere for employment. A negative attitude in this respect can lead to an unhealthy cluster of people at the top, leaving few experienced men to take over when the time arrives.

Leadership

It is a manager's job to lead a team, to combine human resources and obtain the best from them. To do this, orders are necessary. These orders can only be really effective if the assistant is willing to carry them out efficiently. He will not do this without respect for his superior. The manager, by implication, should be a man of experience, understanding and vision, and should have enough confidence to delegate responsibility and stand by his decisions. But at the same time he must be able to instil discipline. *Good management rests on building a confident team through mutual respect reinforced by discipline.*

Head Office Departments

Estimating

The construction industry is such that virtually all companies tender for the bulk of their turnover. As a rule of thumb, roughly one contract is won for about ten tenders. The usual procedure is for a single estimator to be responsible for pricing the work to which a mark-up is finally added, this latter amount being decided by the managing director.

The usual practice is for the estimator to be given one to two months, depending upon the size of the project, to prepare the estimate. Assistance is required from the planning department in preparing the tender programme and from the buying department for obtaining quotations for materials supplies and subcontractors' work.

Head Office Planning

The functions of central planning are usually twofold:

(a) To support the estimating department in providing tender programmes, method statements and generally co-ordinating the whole tendering exercise
(b) To provide planning and co-ordinating services to site for those tenders which turn into contracts

Such arrangements have created problems for virtually all planners at head office, irrespective of the company. The problems essentially arise due to lack of authority. In situation (a) the estimator alone feels responsible for the final tender, and in case (b) the site manager often prefers to plan the work his way, which is compounded by the difficulties of distance and communications between himself and head office planning. Furthermore, site personnel have a natural mistrust of head office interference. The result is that few people wish to make head office planning a career.

The tendency is for management to locate spare engineers in a planning department for a few months until new contracts materialise. Such a policy has led to poor planning and a lack of confidence in the planning function by those who carry greater responsibilities, such as the estimator and site managers.

Purchasing

The buying department is responsible for obtaining all materials quotations and subcontractor procurement for both the tender and contract stages. At the tender stage the usual procedure is for a buyer to be given responsibility for a project and to liaise with the estimator and planner responsible, so that the necessary quotations are at hand when required. Once a tender turns into a contract, the buying responsibility is then handed over to a more experienced buyer who can hopefully negotiate the most favourable terms for the contract before placing the final orders. For a detailed analysis of the procedures for initiating an order, see Fig. 6.4, Chapter 6.

The advantages of centralising purchases are:

(a) One man can be responsible for several contracts.
(b) Standard procedures can be adopted.
(c) Bulk purchasing is possible.
(d) Experience is developed.
(e) Head office administration facilities are readily available.

Quantity Surveying

Quantity surveying in a construction company is that function responsible for the measurement and the subsequent correct payment for work done on site. In practice this extends into the responsibility for the negotiation of new work, variation orders, subcontractor payments and claim situations for each contract. Usually the quantity surveyor is site based. A small department at head office is required to co-ordinate unfinished business on completed contracts and to co-ordinate site staff.

Engineering Services

Unless the project is very large, functions such as formwork design, temporary works design, and work study are located at head office, together with the cost control function, unless this is controlled by staff under a contracts manager in the production department.

Administration and Personnel

The administration function is often too large to control as a single duty and is to be found in separate elements in most companies. The list includes, health and welfare, safety, training, social facilities, postal services, legal and insurance facilities, wages and salaries, records, maintenance. The function is headed by a personnel/administration manager with subordinate managers, responsible for groups of the above elements, reporting directly to him. Very few of the duties are site based, with the possible exception of responsibility for safety, workmen's wages and canteen arrangements.

Production

The production department thinks of itself as the main function above all others. Once a contract is secured, to a large extent the manager on site is independent of the rest of the company, relying on service departments only when necessary. The wealth of the company is generated by the skill of the site staff, and as a result the career structure for the construction manager is centred largely in the production department (starting at site engineer through to site manager and then contracts manager). This is borne out by the power of contracts managers (head office based), who can usually make specific demands on service managers, although the official relationship is only a lateral one. Company directors usually have a production department background, but increasingly the top people are coming from those with financial experience.

Accounts

The company accountant is responsible for the bookkeeping function and the payment of all invoices, together with providing information in keeping with companies Acts, in the form of trading, profit and loss accounts and balance sheet and any other financial information that is required. The accountant has an important function and often works closely with the managing director in controlling the overall financial affairs of the company. Although each individual contracts manager is informed about the financial position of his project and must endeavour to keep within tender figures, it is the accountant's concern to monitor the overall financial position of the company.

Plant

The location of the plant department in the company organisational structure depends upon many factors. Some companies prefer the plant department to operate as a profit-making division, hiring out plant both internally and in the open market-place. In this situation, only fundamental policies are controlled from the company centre, and it is then usual for the plant manager to be responsible directly to the managing director. Other companies prefer to use the plant department as a service department, providing only those common items of equipment necessary on most contracts. In this case the plant responsibility is often attributable to the services director. Whatever the choice of structure, plant ownership represents relatively large capital investments which pose different types of problems compared to the management of construction work and therefore should be an option which is taken up only after considering all the consequences for the enterprise, as described in Chapter 7. The alternative arrangements for operating plant and some of their management features are shown in Figure 8.7.

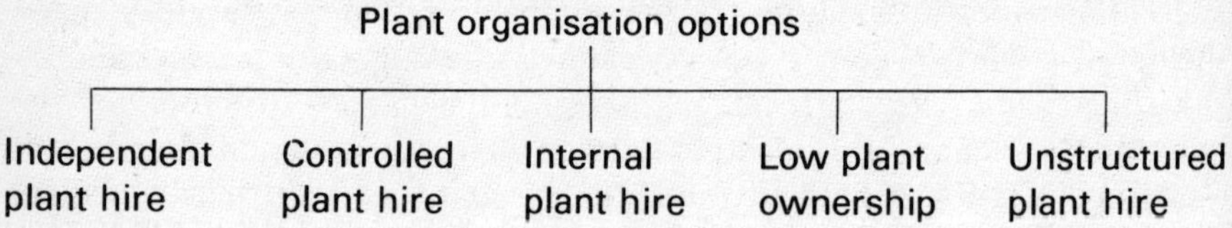

Plant organisation options

| Independent plant hire | Controlled plant hire | Internal plant hire | Low plant ownership | Unstructured plant hire |

Fig. 8.7 Plant organisation options.

Plant Organisation Options

Independent plant hire

Such a firm operates in effect as a plant hire concern, in which plant is owned either by an independently formed company or a separate division of a construction company, or similar, and hired out to clients with the main objective of making a profit. Should the needs of the parent construction company arise, then this would be met on a similar basis to any other client.

Such plant hire companies, would usually hold a range of the popular items in demand, although there is an increasing tendency towards specialised plant. The independent plant hire sector accounts for about 50% of the turnover value of plant used by the construction industry.

Controlled plant hire

Few construction companies can build up sufficient and diverse plant holdings to provide an independent plant hire service. However, some of the large concerns possess considerable plant assets and, to encourage profitability, external hire is sometimes undertaken to raise utilisation levels. But, because outside hire must meet the demands of the market, there exists the danger that such matters as servicing and maintenance of the externally hired plant may receive priority over the internal needs of its own construction sites. As a 'rule of thumb' the ratio of 'hired internally' to 'hired externally' should not fall below two to one, to reduce this tendency.

Internal plant hire

Some contracting companies prefer to restrict their plant holdings to a purely service function by supplying only the internal needs of the company. A suitable rate of return on capital is required and the plant department is operated as a cost centre in order to encourage profitability. But since there is little external competition, frequently items of plant are acquired to suit the needs of the construction contracts; thereby economic utilisation levels cannot always be achieved and consequently hire rates get distorted. Unfortunately for many companies where plant plays a relatively small role in relation to the overall operations of the company, this option is often the only viable arrangement.

Low plant ownership

Plant ownership requires workshop facilities, experienced and mobile maintenance crews and administrative facilities etc. Many companies prefer to avoid this problem by operating only a very few plant items, such as concrete mixers, small excavators, etc. Any major requirements are simply hired in from the vast choice of hire firms available in the independent sector. Where there is a steady demand for hired in plant, the company may sometimes institute a policy of hiring through a central administration to take advantage of competitive hire rates and even facilitate the transfer of plant between sites. The major disadvantage of this system arises when market rates change markedly between the time of tender for work and the actual hiring of the item on the construction project.

No plant structure

The final option is to have an unstructured organisation, whereby individual contracts purchase their plant requirements and are credited with resale values when the plant leaves the site. In this case care has to be exercised in assessing equitable sums when purchases and resales are internal transactions. This alternative method is usually confined to special items, e.g. grouting pumps, which are unlikely to be used subsequently by other general contracts.

References and Bibliography

1. Drucker, P. T. *The Practice of Management*. Pan, 1968.
2. Lemarie, M. Insight on management. *Building Technology and Management*, Vol. 13, No. 6, pp. 5–8, 1975.
3. Koontz, H. and O'Donnell, C. *Principles of Management*, 5th edition. McGraw-Hill, 1972.
4. Hardwick, C. T. & Landuyt, B. F. *Administrative Strategy and Decision Making*. Southwestern, 1966.
5. Barnes, M. C., *et al. Company Organisation, Theory and Practice*. Allen & Unwin, 1970.
6. Brech, E. F. L. (Ed.) *The Principles and Practice of Management*, 3rd edition. Longman, 1975.
7. Calvert, R. E. *Introduction to Building Management*. Newnes/ Butterworths, 1970.
8. Dressel, G. *Organisation and Management of a Construction Company*. McLaren, 1968.
9. Institute of Cost and Management Accountants. Management by objectives, *Management Accounting*, July 1969.
10. Pugh, D. S. (Ed.) *Organisation Theory*. Penguin Books, 1971.
11. Brech, E. F. L. *Construction Management in Principle and Practice*. Longman, 1971.
12. Harris, F. C. and McCaffer, R. *Construction Plant: Management and Investment Decisions*. Granada, 1982.

CHAPTER 9

MARKET PLANNING

Summary

All companies need to seek new markets in order to survive in an increasingly competitive situation. The principles involved in formulating the marketing strategy are described and provide the framework upon which a detailed market analysis and corporate plan can then be constructed.

Introduction

The Institute of Marketing states:

Marketing is the management function which organises and directs all those business activities involved in assessing and converting customer purchasing power into effective demand for a specific product or service, and in moving the project or service to the final customer or user so as to achieve the profit target or other objectives set by the company.

In the past, little interest has been shown by construction companies in marketing matters. Much of this disinterest is probably due to the way work is obtained by the tendering process, wherein the concept and the design of the project is largely under the control of an architect or consulting engineer and the contractor's area for commercial influence is therefore limited. The large contractor, however, and to some extent those companies operating in the speculative house building market, should benefit considerably by carrying out marketing studies since some of their turnover comes from negotiated contracts often involving design and construction. It is in this field that contractors can offer attractive packages to the client and thereby have more control over revenue.

The above introduction may give the impression that, unless the company is large and able to offer a wide range of services, there is no place, for marketing, but it should be remembered that no firm is immune from the damaging effects of unpredicted changes in the market.

In practice, most contracting companies carry out market analysis in some form. The details of the approach will vary from company to company, but in essence three stages are clearly definable: *identifying*, *promoting* and *satisfying* the customer's needs at a profit (ref. 1).

In simple terms, marketing involves seeking out the customer's material wants and desires, so that the company can organise itself in the best possible way to satisfy those wants. Selling, often falsely identified with marketing, is a separate function which seeks methods of persuading the customer to buy the goods the production department produces.

Identifying the Customer's Needs

Drucker (ref. 2) says that the primary objective of a company is to survive, but in practice many other objectives are necessary to satisfy the desires of the shareholder, management and workforce. Quite naturally, in a capitalist market, the need to return a profit for shareholders is very important, but other objectives include the desires of top management to see the company grow and continually increase turnover, to become a well known and respected company in its field, to operate in more stable markets, to keep up with competitors: these are but a few aims. The ability of the company to achieve such objectives is continually being influenced by changes in the market as indicated by pressure on profits, by supply outpacing demand or vice versa, by competitors being more successful, and through changes in customer tastes and requirements. Marketing should therefore be the management function which enables the company to keep in touch with the customer needs and thus help to ensure that the business remains a profitable one.

The Marketing Strategy

Most construction projects take one or more years to complete; they are often unique and require specialist equipment. The alternatives open to a construction company, once embarked upon a particular type of work, are likely to be those which can only be introduced slowly and in the long term, e.g. expanding into civil engineering works from a building background. To be fully confident in setting the new objectives, the

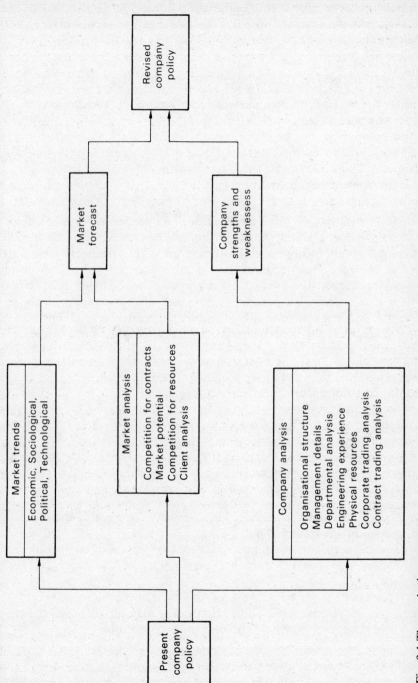

Fig. 9.1 The marketing process.

company must be prepared to undertake the most thorough investigation of itself and the market. Broadly, the investigation should involve two separate stages.

1. Formulating a market forecast
2. Assessing the strengths and weaknesses of the company

The matching of these two exercises enables senior management to set the new policies (see Fig. 9.1).

1. The Market Forecast

All companies buy or hire factors of production, in the form of labour, materials and equipment. Initially capital is borrowed or saved to purchase the goods, which are then turned into other products which are sold at a profit. The lender of the capital is thus rewarded for putting his money at risk. The company that knows its market well is in a good position to improve its competitiveness and also improve profitability. The market forecast is made possible only after considering many separate factors; the main areas for a typical construction company are identified as follows:

The Market Analysis

Analysing the competition for contracts
A brief survey of the past performance of other companies may bring to light those areas of contracting which have been successful, and are therefore favourable for development, or conversely areas to avoid because of fierce competition. The main points to determine are:

(a) The present market share of the company for each of the different classes of work carried out
(b) The market share and turnover for each of the major competitors
(c) The recent growth record and profitability of the major competitors.
(d) The record of obtaining work of each type in competition, related to the past mark-up levels. This information may indicate the improvement necessary in order to become more competitive

Analysing the potential of the market
Although a thorough knowledge of the competitor's position is essential before entering new markets or expanding old ones, the market itself

must be thoroughly researched in the hope of finding out patterns and trends for the future. The information required should include:

(a) The type and volume of work available for tender and negotiation during the past years.

(b) The number of competitors tendering for the different contracts put on the market (this information is often difficult to obtain), the location of the work and the clients involved.

(c) A forecast of the likely growth of the market sector by sector. The Government is now heavily involved by way of the large amounts spent in the public sector. Thus government projections for development areas indicate potential work both directly in the form of cash injections to the area and indirectly through the additional services demanded by a modern growing community once established.

Government forecasts of expenditure in the nationalised industries, the effects of EEC (Common Market) membership on development of South-east England, the size of the budget deficit, the rate of growth of the gross domestic product and the trade balance all need to be taken into account. These latter points are also particularly important for assessing the future requirements in the private sector, as the rate of investment is often governed by the confidence that industry has in the prospects for the country as a whole.

The above findings will help to establish which are the buoyant sectors and the types of company operating in them. Furthermore, the information will indicate which sectors are investing and therefore likely to require new facilities.

Analysing the competition for resources

There is very little point in making elaborate plans for a new market venture if the resources in the form of capital, materials and labour are not there to supply it.

Capital   Any new venture first of all needs money before the equipment and materials to make the finished goods can be purchased. But the availability of capital will depend upon how successful the company has been in the past in making profits and building up a reserve of funds. The lending institutions are also more likely to risk their capital in a firm with a sound record of achievement, with substantial resources to match those to be invested or loaned. However, the question of capital availability is so inextricably bound up with the condition of the national economy, and the policy of the Government in its reaction to it, that any long-term company plans will inevitably be upset. A cursory glance at the national statistics will reveal constant economic cycles of boom followed by slump, and the policy of governments to use the construction industry as an economic regulator – directly by controlling the amount of work put out to tender in the public sector and indirectly in the overall control of the money supplied to lubricate the economy. This latter policy tends to cause fluctuations in interest rates and inflation, which compounds the difficulties of making forward projections for capital requirements.

Materials To base new market strategy on an assumption of a steady supply of plant, equipment and, in particular, materials is very risky indeed. Records show that both raw materials and manufactured goods have suffered severe and unpredictable bottlenecks in their supply. Nevertheless some supply projection must be attempted and a useful method is to separate the supplies by location of the sources:

  (i) Supplied from domestic sources
 (ii) Supplied from overseas markets with similar economies
(iii) Supplied from unstable and unreliable overseas markets

   Situations (i) and (ii) usually relate to the supplies of manufactured goods. These sources are generally reliable, both in price and delivery. Competition is severe and substitutes are therefore often available to the purchaser. The availability of such goods generally reflects the growth patterns of the western economies and is affected by short-term deficiencies only, as dictated by demand in the individual countries. However, several major western economies are becoming so closely aligned that a major upswing in demand is experienced by all at the same time, causing quite severe shortages and the inevitable escalation of prices.
   Case (iii) is very different since these are mainly the raw materials supplied from unstable and politically volatile countries. Only very broad guesses at what might happen are possible. The whole materials supply situation is susceptible to erratic changes in the foreign policies of such nations, e.g. oil in the Middle East, copper in Central Africa and rubber in the Far East.

Labour The big problems are to recruit skilled labour and experienced, well-trained management. They are not short-term problems and any company not able or willing to devote the necessary resources to training is best advised to leave alone the sectors where skill predominates.

Analysing the client
Any records kept on clients should be very revealing and may have considerable bearing on the final decision to enter a market. For example, profitability may have varied with different clients, depending upon the

attitude to claim situations or interpretation of the contract documents. Some clients prefer to select on the basis of tenders, others by negotiation; if the company has been dropped from a client's tendering list, the reasons why may be important. Also, until recently it was the contractor's financial position that was questioned: today even the client has money problems; there is little point in obtaining contracts if payment by the client is open to doubt.

2. Company Strengths and Weaknesses

A change in company policy regarding new markets will be unsuccessful if the new objectives are frustrated by fundamental weaknesses in the company structure. Therefore any search for new markets should be coupled with an equally thorough examination of the company itself.

The Company Analysis

Organisation structure
Most companies have a 'family tree' which represents the official structure of the management organisation. In practice, the actual lines of command and communication are likely to be more subtle than those formally recognised. However, this 'family tree' is a good starting point in high-lighting potentially weak structural arrangements.

Management details
The quality of the present managers will be tested upon entering new markets. Much information is often held by the personnel department on such matters as salary, qualifications, education, training and experience. These data help to identify potentially strong management areas and those which have failed to develop a healthy ladder of achievement for the younger men to gain experience upon. If the process is repeated for each department, gaps and stagnant areas become apparent.

Financial and operational control departments
This review should be extensive and probably should not be undertaken until policies have been tentatively made. The likely candidates for investigation are the accounts, buying and estimating departments, since they tend to be labour-intensive and reluctant to accept rapid changes. Such departments contribute largely to the overheads, which may rapidly increase when the company expands into new markets. Overheads should also be borne in mind when moving from a fairly low technical market, say housing, to a specialised market requiring high technical competence and support from service departments such as temporary

works design, formwork design, cost control, work study, central planning, etc.

Engineering experience

The management and operational control surveys may yield much information about the nature of the company and its employees. But the construction business requires good managers to be good engineers also. Any change in policy should spring from a sound base of experience; it is far too risky to rely entirely on imported skills when undergoing change. Hence a careful analysis is required of the existing skills within the company to see if they will provide an adequate basis.

Physical resources

To put new objectives into practice may necessitate new office space and stores facilities. This is a very important consideration if bottlenecks are to be prevented. But the acquisition of land and the construction of new facilities takes time, is expensive, and requires careful planning of the location.

Corporate trading analysis

To assess the financial strength of the company and to compare its performance with that of major competitors, the following financial ratios yield important information:

> Return on capital employed
> Profit on turnover
> Turnover of capital
> Growth in capital employed and in net profits
> Current assets to current liabilities
> Stock value to sales ⎫
> Debtors to sales ⎬ converted to time periods
> Profit per employee

By comparing figures over the past five years with other companies in similar fields, some judgement is possible on the viability of the firm and its ability to take on new ventures successfully.

Contract trading analysis

The contract trading analysis means looking at individual contracts in a fair degree of detail. The sorts of questions to be asked are:

> What was the effect on profits of contract type, size, location, duration and client?
> What trends in profitability, say during the past five years, can be seen in different sectors of the market?

How did actual profit compare with the bid mark-up for individual contracts? (Once again, trends might be spotted, indicating perhaps building to be more reliable than civil engineering work.)

What effect would the changing of mark-up on each tender have had on the turnover and profit expectations for the various types of work?

The results, however, need to be considered with care, since those contracts where profit is high tend to be those which have high risk or require special technical skills.

Trends which may upset forecasts

Once the forecast patterns of demand and competition are assessed and the analysis made of opportunities and risk in the new market together with the assessment of the company strengths and weaknesses, the revised corporate policy is formulated.

We have now arrived at the last box in Fig. 9.1. No specific guidelines can be offered for the means by which the new policies will be generated, but once the relevant facts are known, experienced managers will usually see what changes need to be made. The important point is that policies should be specifically formulated and recorded.

However, no matter how good is the information on which the new policies are formulated, new facts will soon emerge and errors will appear in some of the estimates. Some of these may be due to normal fluctuations but other influences may be more far-reaching, e.g. political changes; sociological changes, such as shifts in consumer outlook on such fundamental issues as pollution; technological developments that disrupt past trends; economic influences caused by movements in the economies of other countries. Most of these factors are difficult to quantify but they should be kept under continuous review and the policies adjusted when necessary. Care should be taken, however, not to over-react to new evidence as this can cause loss of confidence at middle management level.

Promotion of the Product or Service

The Institute of Marketing states that: 'Promotion is the activity which takes one from the identification stage to the moment of sale and covers all the aspects of persuading the customer to buy.'

The techniques for persuading the customer to buy are many. The construction industry is conservative in its approach to clients, regarding many of the normal selling techniques to be unsuitable. The following methods of communication with the customer are simple and inexpensive.

They do not constitute high-powered selling methods and are more suitable for the construction industry.

Advertising
Advertising should take many forms, such as:

 (i) Eye-catching yet pleasing advertisements in the press for new management appointments and other employees
 (ii) A standard and attractive colour scheme for all company plant and goods vehicles embellished with clearly identifiable trade markings
(iii) Good quality notepaper and attractive letter headings
(iv) Advertising in the trade journals, giving emphasis to successful contracts carried out
 (v) Sales brochures outlining the activities of the company, which can be sent to prospective clients and other interested parties
(vi) Hoardings installed at football grounds etc. in the hope of catching the television cameras
(vii) Topping-out ceremonies photographed in the local press

Public relations
Good public relations are fostered by:

 (i) Exhibitions, particularly by encouraging students at the institutions, universities and colleges to visit the company's construction works.
 (ii) Lecturing to interested parties on any subject for which the company is qualified to do so. Such activities help to enhance the stature of the company in the industry generally.
(iii) Writing articles for learned journals and magazines by company specialists.
(iv) Spreading the news by all available methods about the company's training schemes, health and welfare facilities, safety record etc.
 (v) Producing films illustrating the best features about the company and its technical abilities. By keeping the advertising low key, the films, if well made, will be suitable material for teaching and lecturing purposes at universities and colleges.
(vi) Developing a reputation for good quality, early completions, few labour problems and low emphasis on contract claims.
(vii) Keeping neat well-established sites with clear directional and other signs.
(viii) Projecting the image of the company as being technically advanced, employing well qualified experienced managers. Many prospective clients are also impressed by support facilities from head office, e.g. planning, temporary works design, cost control etc.

Selling
In general, only those companies involved in speculative housing or package deals have any real opportunity to engage in the selling techniques developed by the consumer industries.

Customer relations
Above all others, *well satisfied customers are excellent salesmen.*

Satisfying the Customers' Needs at a Profit

The marketing process does not end as soon as the market opportunities are established and contracts obtained. It is particularly important in construction work that everyone actually concerned with construction supports the overall market strategy and at the same time directs his efforts towards making a profit for the company. The opportunities for doing this vary from company to company and from contract to contract, but several fairly obvious opportunities exist:

1. The materials used on most construction projects are specified by the client in detail. But a careful search of the market alternatives may yield better goods at competitive prices delivered at the right time. Any improvement in relations with the client may help to provide continuity of work, which will go a long way in enabling advantage to be taken of discounts for bulk purchasing. Furthermore, an increase of efficiency in materials control will satisfy not only the client, but at the same time also improve the whole construction process.

2. It is essential, if one wishes to continue to be offered work by a client, to develop good relationships and a fair attitude in all business dealings. This includes adhering to the specified construction programme, so that all the parties involved can align their activities in advance. Completion on time is especially important for the client with deadlines to meet. For example, the supermarket company wishing to take advantage of a particular part of the selling season might well be willing to pay more for early completion. On the other hand, the public client with perhaps less interest in completion time, but who is much more concerned with the cost overrun (the implications being the use of taxpayers' money), is likely to remember excessive profit maximisation by the contractor. Several large companies in the past have lost their place on tender lists by a too-aggressive stance to claim situations.

3. Many clients are impressed by 'added values'. Clearly the contractor with back-up services of experienced and well qualified staff in central planning, temporary works design, law and insurance, industrial relations, research and development, will tend to be a more credible

company than one without such facilities, always, of course, assuming a sound financial situation exists in that company.

4. The company should, whenever possible, provide a good after-sales service during and after the maintenance period. This can be so extensive as to include co-operation with client in improving designs and contract procedures in the light of the experience gained on the completed project. Such co-operation can only lead to a better tendering situation and the use of more serial and two-stage tendering arrangements.

References and Bibliography

1. Dove, J. E. How to sell builders' services. *National Builder.* May, 1972.

2. Drucker, P. F. *The Practice of Management.* Pan Books, 1968.

3. 'Is Quality Enough?' Series of marketing papers presented to the Institute of Building, 1974.

4. *Marketing in the Construction Industry.* Second report of the Working Party, Institute of Marketing, 1974.

5. Smallbone, W. D. *An Introduction to Marketing.* Staples Press, 1968.

6. Ansoff, H. I. *Corporate Strategy.* McGraw-Hill, 1965; Penguin Books, 1968.

7. Argenti, J. *Corporate Planning.* Allen and Unwin, 1968.

8. Barnes, M. C., *et al. Company Organisation, Theory and Practice.* Allen and Unwin, 1969.

9. Ghrinyer, P. H. Systematic and Strategic Planning for Construction Firms, *Building Technology and Management*, 1972.

Sources of Information

There is a vast amount of published information which can help contractors to evaluate aspects of their market, e.g. market size, trends in new orders, breakdowns of output by regions and type of work. These publications can also provide lists of potential customers for negotiated/ package work and help evaluate the cost of reaching these customers.

When considering the need for information, contractors must not forget that they have a wealth of data in their files which, if extracted and evaluated, can form a valuable addition to the published information.

A list of some of the more relevant sources of information is given in the following pages together with a brief summary of content, the publisher and the price. Every effort has been made to ensure accuracy at the time of compiling this list but details are frequently changing.

The Economist

This periodical publishes good articles on the economic situation with occasional general reports on the construction industry.

National Institute Economic Review

This consists of excellent but sophisticated articles on the current and future path of the main sectors of the economy, balance of payments etc. Useful for a company economist, for instance. It is obtainable from the National Institute of Economic and Social Research, 2 Dean Trench Street, Smith Square, London SW1. Quarterly.

Monthly Bulletin of Construction Statistics

Gives:

1. Value and volume of output and new orders for construction, broken down by five sectors; new orders, broken down by 19 sectors; and new orders by the ten economic planning regions, by five sectors of work.
2. Production and deliveries of 21 building materials and components.
3. Number of direct labour operatives by number of authorities, regions and value and type of work.
4. Other information on housing and industrial building derived from other publications.

Obtainable from the Department of the Environment (Tel. 01-735 7611. ext. 1826). Monthly: no charge.

NEDO – The National Economic Development Office

The new joint forecasting committee for building and civil engineering is not favoured at present by some sectors of the industry, probably because forecasts have proved inaccurate. However, they do serve a useful purpose, since they are assessments by industrialists, trade unionists and academics, working together, with access to governmental information. They are intended to *aid* the industry in the *prediction of patterns and trends*. The new style forecasts will be issued twice per year: one following the Budget, and the other following the Public Expenditure White Paper in the autumn. They offer the forecaster a platform from which to start his own individual and knowledgeable assessment. Obtainable from NEDO, 21 Millbank, London SW1.

Housing Statistics (Department of the Environment)

A compilation of most of the available information on the housing sector is available from this major government department. It gives statistics or other information for:

1. Dwellings started, under construction and completed by private and public sectors, by economic planning region.
2. Estimates of completion times.
3. Dwellings, by public and private sectors, by numbers of bedrooms and storey heights.
4. Percentage of local authority dwellings which are industrialised plus a list of the numbers of completions by system.
5. Analysis of areas and costs, housing densities and contract size and type for local authority dwellings.
6. Information on improvement grants and slum clearance.
7. Information on the main sources of finance for private housing, e.g. building societies' shares and deposits, mortgages by type of property, purchase price, age of dwellings, income of borrower and guarantees by local authorities.
8. Miscellaneous information on, for instance, the stock of dwellings by region, garage and parking space in housing schemes, average weekly rental of local authority dwellings.

Obtainable from HMSO. Monthly.

Local Housing Statistics England and Wales

This is a breakdown of public and private housing to the Urban District Council and Rural District Council level. It gives figures for tenders approved but not started, starts, projects under construction and completed by County Boroughs, Boroughs, Urban and Rural Districts. Obtainable from HMSO. Quarterly.

Sample Census 1966 – Summary Tables

These tables give, for 19 regions of Great Britain, the population, numbers of private households and dwellings, total numbers of dwellings and household spaces, dwellings and household spaces by numbers of rooms, private households by size, rooms occupied and sharing of dwellings, private households by density of occupation and size of household, dwellings by tenure and rooms, private households by numbers of cars. Obtainable from HMSO.

Housing Statistics (Institute of Municipal Treasurers and Accountants)

Covering 960 County Boroughs, Boroughs, Urban [and] Rural Districts, this gives 65 items of information concerning the housing account, e.g. number of dwellings in housing revenue account by number of bed-rooms; an analysis of the income and expenditure under the housing revenue account; an analysis of the housing revenue repairs account; a breakdown of the rents charged and a breakdown of the cost of dwellings recently constructed. Obtainable from Institute of Municipal Treasurers and Accountants, 1 Buckingham Place, London SW1.

Regional Economic Reports

Reports have been published by the Regional Economic Planning Councils for the ten economic planning regions (not Scotland or Wales). Some are a few years old and have had supplementary reports.

These reports tend to cover (for the region) the population, employ-ment and industry, agriculture, mining and fishing, manpower, housing, communications, construction, education and health and welfare. They do not relate too closely to the immediate needs of the contractor but provide an excellent background to the economics of a region.

Hospital Building England and Wales
Hospital Building in Scotland

These give progress under each Regional Hospital Board and list future large projects. Obtainable from HMSO annually.

The Times 500

List of the top 500 companies as well as leading property, finance, American companies etc. Available from *The Times* newspaper.

Extel and Moodies Cards

Both Extel Statistical Services Ltd, Extel House, East Harding Street, London EC4, and Moodies Services Ltd, King William Street House, London EC4 will provide cards at a small fee, giving any company's main activities, subsidiaries, directors, details of the capital structure, recent balance sheets, and profit and loss statements over 10 to 15 years.

The Education Authorities Directory and Annual

Published by The School Government Publishing Company Limited, Darby House, Bletchingly Road, Merstham, Surrey.

UK Kompass Register

Two volumes giving details of products and company information on 29 000 British firms. Published annually at £15·75 by Kompass Publishers Ltd, RAC House, Lansdowne Road, Croydon, CR9 9EH.

Who Owns Whom

A directory of parent, associate and subsidiary companies. Published by O. W. Roskill & Co. Ltd, 14 Great College Street, London SW1. Annually.

Abstract of Regional Statistics

A compilation of many regional statistical series. Especially useful for the construction tables which give public investment in new construction by several categories. Published annually by HMSO.

Published Company Accounts

These yield some information about the competition's progress, aims and aspirations.

BMP Weekly Information

A very useful summary of current construction information from national and trade press, government reports, Hansard etc. Obtainable from The National Council of Building Material Producers, Suite 18, Chantrey House, Eccleston St, London SW1. Weekly.

Directory of Construction Statistics

A master list of almost all the published statistics related to construction. Obtainable from HMSO.

Directory of Directories

Published by CBD Research Limited, 154 High Street, Beckenham, Kent. Published annually.

Wales

For Wales there is available: *Cymru: Wales 1967* and *Wales: The Way Ahead*, the former being an annual report. Scotland also has an annual report.

Local Planning Reports

There have been several reports published by the Ministry of Housing and Local Government (now the Department of the Environment) as the result of consultants' appraisals of an area for development in a new town, e.g. 'Dawley–Wellington–Oakengates', 'Impact on North East Lancashire' and 'A New City' (Newbury, Swindon, Didcot). As well as speculation these reports include considerable statistical data and some clues as to the future constructional load; these clues should be checked with the planning officers, engineers etc. of the region concerned.

Highway Statistics

This publication gives expenditure on roads by value, by type of work and by county. Obtainable from HMSO annually.

Monthly Digest of Statistics

Gives:
1. Area approved and area completed for industrial building for which IDCs have been issued. Care should be taken because these figures relate only to buildings which require an IDC (usually 5000 sq ft and over) and the 'completed' figures refer only to buildings for companies classified as in manufacturing. The same figures appear in the *Board of Trade Journal*.
2. Educational building in £ by projects approved, under construction and completions for England and Wales and Scotland.
3. Other building statistics mentioned previously in the Department of the Environment publication giving monthly statistics.
4. Many other statistical series, e.g. price indices, unemployment, UK trade figures, fuel consumption etc.

Obtainable from HMSO monthly.

Financial Statistics

A publication of the Central Statistical Office giving almost all the financial information available about the economy, e.g. money supply, transactions affecting government and local authority borrowing, interest rates, capital issues and stock exchange transactions, balance of payment figures. Purely tables and mainly for the economist. Obtainable from HMSO monthly.

Directory of Official Architects and Planners

A list of architects for central and local government and architects and planning officers and public corporations, new towns, universities, hospitals, other statutory bodies and private commercial firms. Obtainable from Architecture and Planning Publications Limited, The Builder House, Catherine Street, London WC2. Annually.

Directory of British Associations

Published by CBD Research Ltd, 154 High Street, Beckenham, Kent. Published annually.

Government Publications:

HMSO Monthly Catalogue. On subscription.

Construction Markets

Construction Markets is a bimonthly bulletin providing regular information on:

Construction output forecasts
Analyses of construction in the ten economic regions
Analysis of specific produce areas, e.g. ceilings in schools
Technical studies
Studies of construction sectors

The bulletin is circulated privately by subscription. It is obtainable from Construction Markets, Axtell House, 23–24 Warwick Street, London W1.

Construction Trends

Comprehensive assessments are made of the demands on, and likely to be made on, the construction industries as a whole; on the various sectors – housing, school-building, road construction etc. – together with the likely impact on the industries producing plant, equipment and materials. Particular attention is paid to costs and to the regional variation of the potential workload. Obtainable from Construction Trends, 32a North Road, London NW11 7PT. Published monthly.

Statistical Bulletin

The RIBA's quarterly gives details of the workload of private architectural practices, as well as results of other surveys carried out by the intelligence. It is available for an annual subscription. Enquiries should be addressed to Royal Institute of British Architects, 66 Portland Place, London W1N 4AD.

This information is published by kind permission of the Institute of Marketing and the Construction Industry Marketing Group.

CHAPTER 10

ESTIMATING AND TENDERING

Summary

The parties involved in the estimating process; the decision to tender; collection and calculation of cost information, all-in-rates; project study; preparing the estimate, operational and unit rate estimating; site overheads; estimator's reports. Tender adjustments; submitting the tender. Computers and estimating.

Introduction

Clients or promoters of the construction industry in the public sector such as central government departments, local authorities and public corporations rely almost exclusively on competitive tendering to justify the awarding of contracts. Clients from private industry tend to follow the practices of the public sector clients and also largely employ competitive tendering procedures. Thus, most construction contracts are awarded after several contractors have submitted a tender and most civil engineering and building contractors derive the major portion of their work load in this way. Construction contractors base these tenders on an estimate of the cost, to the contractor, of executing the work described in the contract documents. The estimating department is therefore of central importance to the commercial success of the contracting organisation.

Most contractors have a director who is responsible for the estimating department and this indicates the importance of the function.

The estimating department is the first department within a contractor's organisation to have any contact with a prospective contract and is required to deal with documents prepared by the client or his representatives. The estimators in the course of preparing an estimate and tender liaise with the client or his representatives and internally, in the company, with planning staff, buying staff, plant managers, temporary works designers, site management staff and senior management. Thus the estimators' tasks are not simply ones of calculation but of managing a fairly complex process of assimilation of the contract details, liaising and co-ordinating with all the parties involved, collecting the relevant data, calculating the costs involved and explaining it to senior management. What is important is that the estimators have to achieve all this normally within a restricted time period of four to six weeks. This chapter describes the parties involved in the production of an estimate and tender, the process of estimating and tendering and the calculations involved.

Parties Involved in Estimating and Tendering

The parties involved in estimating and tendering can be divided into three classes:

1. The client's or promoter's staff or their professional representatives.
2. The construction contractor's personnel including senior management, estimators, planners, buyers, plant managers, temporary works designers and site management staff.
3. The external organisations such as material suppliers, plant hire companies, and sub-contractors.

The contribution of each of these is described below.

1. The Client's Staff or Professional Representatives

The person or organisations for whom the building or works is to be constructed is normally referred to as the client when referring to building works or the promoter when referring to civil engineering works.

In civil engineering works the promoter will appoint an Engineer for the project, and this may be from within his own staff or a consulting engineering practice. The function of the Engineer includes the development, design and technical direction of the works as well as the preparation of specifications, bills of quantities, drawings and other contract documents. It is these contract documents which describe the works to the contractor. The drawings, bills of quantities and specifications are the main sources of information to the estimators who prepare the cost estimates and tenders. The method of measurement used in the U.K. for preparing the bill of quantities is mostly the Civil Engineering Standard Method of Measurement or the Method of Measurement for Road and Bridge Works, or variations of these.

In building contracts the client appoints an Architect who is responsible for development, design, specifications and drawings and a Quantity Surveyor who is responsible for preparation of the bills of quantities and other contract documents and all matters relating to the cost of the project. The architect and quantity surveying staff may be from within the client's own staff or may be practices engaged by the client. The method of measurement used in the U.K. for building works is usually SMM6 as published by the Royal Insitute of Chartered Surveyors.

2. The Construction Contractor's Personnel

Senior management is an expression used to imply company directors and those who hold responsibilities similar to directors. Senior management is usually involved in the decision whether or not to tender for a particular contract and in the decision on what tender to submit, having considered the estimate of costs and resources involved, as produced by the estimators. Most companies have a director responsible for the estimating department or an estimating manager who reports to a director. Thus the day to day activities of the estimating department are closely monitored by senior management.

The *estimators* are the personnel employed in the estimating department charged with the responsibility of producing the estimates and managing the process described in this chapter.

In both civil engineering and building contractors the senior estimators are usually professionally qualified staff with extensive experience of the construction industry. These senior estimators are normally supported by junior estimators who may be aspiring to a career in estimating or may be gaining experience in estimating as part of a wider career development. Other support staff include estimating clerks and comptometer or computer operators.

The *planners* are the personnel employed to produce construction plans or programmes. As far as the estimators' requirements are concerned this means the pre-tender programme which may not be as detailed as one produced for site use but will provide the overall duration of the project and the duration and sequence of the key activities and approximate resource totals for labour and plant. In some companies the estimators produce the pre-tender programme themselves: in others the planners produce it, in which case close liaison is required between the estimators and planners. In some companies the planners are part of the estimating department and in others there is a separate planning department.

Buyers are usually responsible for purchasing materials and placing orders with plant hire companies and sub-contractors. The service they give estimators is to provide quotations for materials, plant hire and sub-contractors. In some companies the estimators are given the task of sending out the enquiries and receiving the quotations.

Plant managers are responsible for the company's plant department and supply estimators with current internal hire rates and advice on likely availabilities of company-owned plant.

Temporary works designers are responsible for designs of major temporary works such as bridge supports or falsework. The estimators would take their advice on the nature and likely cost of major temporary works in civil engineering contracts.

Site management are the personnel who are employed to take responsibility for the execution of projects on site. This expression covers agents, works managers, engineers and surveyors. The contribution of site management to estimating is to provide advice to the estimators on methods of construction and to discuss proposed method statements with them.

3. External Organisations

Material suppliers, plant hire companies and sub-contractors all get involved in the estimating process in that they receive and have to respond to enquiries for quotations from contractors. This also includes consultation with buyers and estimators.

The Estimating Process

The process undertaken to produce a cost estimate which can be used as the basis of a tender is described in the following steps:

1. Decision to tender.
2. Programming the estimate.
3. Collection and calculation of cost information.
4. Project study.
5. Preparing the estimate.
6. Site overheads.
7. Estimators' reports.

The steps described here are for contracts with client prepared contract documents with a bill of quantities, which is the most common type of contract in the U.K. The steps vary for other forms of contracts such as schedule of rates contracts, design-construct contracts and all-in contracts.

1. Decision to Tender

The decision to tender for a particular contract is mainly the responsibility of senior management; there are three possible points during the estimating and tendering process where this decision must be made. The first is during the pre-selection stage, if a pre-selection procedure is being used. This decision would be based on pre-selection information provided by the clients' staff or representatives and would include such information as:

- the name of the job;
- the name of the client, architect and quantity surveyor or consulting engineers;
- the names of any consultants with supervisory duties;
- the location of the site;
- a general description of the work involved;
- the approximate cost range of the project;
- details of any nominated sub-contractors for major items;
- the form of contract to be used;
- the procedure to be adopted in examining and correcting priced bill(s);
- whether the contract is to be under seal or under hand;
- the anticipated date for possession of the site;
- the period for completion of the works;
- the approximate date for the despatch of tender documents;
- the duration of the tender period;
- the period for which the tender is to remain open;
- the anticipated value of liquidated damages (if any);
- details of bond requirements (if any);
- any particular conditions relating to the contract.

The contractor may have signified his intention to submit a tender at the pre-selection stage but has a further opportunity after receiving all contract documents to review them and consider, in the light of fuller information, whether he wishes to proceed or not. The third and final point of decision whether to submit a tender is after the estimate has been prepared and the contractor is ready to submit. A decision at this stage not to tender is rare but allows the contractor to review the events of the intervening four to six weeks and the changes in work-load that have occurred in that time.

The decision to tender is based on such factors as:

- the company's current workload, turnover and recovery of overheads;
- the company's financial resources;
- the availability of resources to undertake the work;

- the type of work;
- the location of the contract;
- the identity of the client or promoter and his representatives;
- a detailed examination of the contract documents.

2. Programming the Estimate

After receiving the contract documents and having decided to tender the tasks required to complete the estimate are programmed and a schedule of key dates established to monitor progress. This is essential as the time to submit a tender is limited. The two main tasks that can now take place are the *collection and calculation of the cost information* required to prepare the estimate and *a study of the project* to gain the required appreciation of the work involved in the contract. These two tasks take place in parallel and are inter-related.

3. Collection of Cost Information

The cost information required by the estimator is for

(a) labour,
(b) plant,
(c) materials,
(d) sub-contractors.

(a) Labour

The estimator is required to calculate the 'all-in' rate for each category of labour, which is an hourly rate covering all wages and emoluments paid to the operative, all statutory costs incurred and allowances for holidays and non-productive overtime. An example of this calculation is set out below. As the all-in rates are calculated by the estimator they can be established early and accurately in the estimating process.

The basis of this calculation is to determine the total worked hours in a year and the total cost for the man year and hence the cost per worked hour. The calculation is complicated by the difference between the hours worked and the hours paid which exceeds the hours worked by such items as overtime allowances, public holidays and inclement weather. The rules for payment are set out in the Working Rule Agreements detailed in references 21 and 22.

The calculations set out in this example are based on a real example and contain data that is available in the Working Rule Agreements, assumptions by the estimator and data relating to statutory obligations.

Working times

Site works 5 days per week.
During the 44 week 'summer' period the daily hours are 8.00 a.m. to 5.30 p.m. This gives a working day of 8 hours plus 1 hour overtime and a working week of 40 hours plus 5 hours overtime. During the 8 week 'winter' period the daily hours are 8.00 a.m. to 4.30 p.m. This gives a working day of 8 hours and a working week of 40 hours.

Holidays

Summer holiday is 2 weeks.
Easter holiday, in 'summer' period, is 4 days.
Winter holiday is 7 days.
Public holidays in 'summer' period total 5 days.
Public holidays in 'winter' period total 3 days.
The total holidays are 29 days or 5 weeks 4 days.

Inclement weather and sick leave

Assume 60 hours of inclement weather and 3 days of sick leave in the 'summer' period and 2 days of sick leave in the 'winter' period.

Weeks worked in one year

Total weeks in year = 52 weeks.
Holidays = 5 weeks 4 days.
Sick leave = 1 week.
Weeks worked in year = 45 weeks 1 day.

Calculation of hours worked

Total hours in year:
Summer period – 44 weeks × 45 hours = 1 980 hours
Winter period – 8 weeks × 40 hours = 320 hours
= 2 300 hours

Hours not worked due to holidays:
Total holidays in 'summer' period = summer holiday + Easter holiday + public holidays = 2 weeks + 4 days + 5 days = 19 days
Hours not worked due to summer period holidays =
19 days × 9 hours = 171 hours
Total holidays in 'winter' period = winter holiday + public holiday = 7 days + 3 days = 10 days
Hours not worked due to 'winter' period holiday = 10 days × 8 hours = 80 hours

Total hours not worked due to holidays	=	251 hours
Hours not worked due to inclement weather	=	60 hours
Hours not worked due to sick leave = 3 days × 9 hours + 2 days × 8 hours	=	43 hours
Total hours not worked	=	354 hours

∴ Total hours worked in one year
= 2 300 hours—354 hours   = 1 946 hours

Calculation of overtime

Possible overtime worked in summer period = 44 weeks × 5 hours	=	220 hours
Less 19 days holiday and 3 days sick leave ∴ Overtime not worked = 22 days × 1 hour	=	22 hours
∴ Overtime worked	=	198 hours

Costs of employing labour

Basic rates of pay:
(a) Labourers   £1.58 per hour
(b) Tradesmen   £1.85 per hour
Overtime is paid at $1\frac{1}{2}$ times basic rate.
Assume a 30% bonus including guaranteed minimum.
Tool money is taken as 85p per week.
Plus rates are assumed to average at 2%.
Holiday stamps and death benefit amount to £8.45 per week.
Sick pay is £4.50 per day.
National Insurance is 13.7% on payroll.
C.I.T.B. levy is £10.00 for labourers and £45.00 for tradesmen.
Assume an allowance of $1\frac{1}{2}$% for severance pay.
Assume an allowance of 2% for employers' liability and public liability insurance.

Calculation of annual costs of labour

Basic costs

	Labourer	Tradesman
Basic rate × 1946 hours	£3 074.68	£3 600.10
Inclement weather		
Basic rate × 60 hours	£94.80	£111.00
Basic total	£3 169.48	£3 711.10

Bonus		
30% on basic total	£950.84	£1 113.33
Non-productive overtime		
Basic rate × $\frac{1}{2}$ × 198 hours	£156.42	£183.15

Public holidays		
Basic rate × 8 days × 8 hours	£101.12	£118.40
Sick pay		
£4.50 × 5 days	£22.50	£22.50
Total money		
85p × 45.2 weeks		£38.42
Plus rate of 2% on basic total	£63.39	£74.22
Paid total	£4 463.75	£5 261.12
National Insurance 13.7% on paid total	£611.534	£720.773
C.I.T.B. levy	£10.00	£45.00
Annual holidays and death benefit,		
47 weeks × £8.45	£397.15	£397.15
Paid total + statutory costs and benefits	£5 482.434	£6 424.043
Allowance for severance pay 1½%	£82.236	£96.360
Allowance for employers liability		
and public liability insurance 2%	£109.648	£128.48
Total annual cost	£5 674.32	£6 648.88

Calculation of all-in rate

Total annual cost for labourers	£5 674.32
Total worked hours	1 946 hours
∴ All-in rate = £5 674.32/1 946 hours	
= £2.92 per hour	
Total annual cost for tradesmen	£6 648.88
Total worked hours	1 946 hours
∴ All-in rate = £6 648.88/1 946 hours	
= £3.42 per hour	

(b) Plant

The hourly or weekly cost of plant can either be as a result of internal calculation or as a result of quotations. Methods of calculating hire rates are given in Chapter 7 which concerns plant management, and in reference 23. Quotations for hire can either be internal rates from the plant department or from the contractor's plant subsidiary, or they can be external hire rates from an independent plant hire company. Calculated rates or internal hire rates can be established very early in the estimating process. External hire rates may take a little longer but it is unusual to suffer serious delays in receiving quotations.

(c) Materials

Materials quotations are more problematical in that materials not only form a significant percentage of the works but due to the volatility of materials prices contractors have to send out unique enquiries for almost all materials in every estimate prepared. The materials enquiries include information such as the quantities required, the specification, the approximate delivery dates and the terms and conditions upon which the quotations are being invited.

To enable these enquiries to be sent out the estimator must go through the bill of quantities and specification and extract the relevant information and prepare his list of required materials. Because of the time taken to send out and receive quotations this task of preparing the materials lists is undertaken very early in the estimating process. In some companies a 'buyer' may send out the enquiries, chase the suppliers who fail to respond and check and compare the quotations. In other companies this task may be undertaken by the estimators.

(d) Sub-contractors

Sub-contractor enquiries also have to be sent out early and the estimator will prepare lists of the items and work that will be sub-contracted. As with materials, these enquiries may be dealt with by a 'buyer'.

4. Project Study

To gain an appreciation of the project the estimator and the planner (where this is a separate person) will undertake the following tasks:

(a) A study of the drawings;
(b) A site visit and meeting with the client's or promoter's representatives;
(c) The preparation of a method statement determining how the project will be constructed.

(a) Drawings

In civil engineering contracts the contract drawings are sent to each contractor tendering. In building work it is now also common practice to issue a set of contract drawings. However, in cases where this is not, so estimators and planners may have to visit the architect's offices to inspect a complete set of drawings and to discuss unclear aspects with the architect. Unclear aspects of the drawings are also frequently clarified by telephone consultation.

(b) Site visit

In civil engineering works it is normal practice for the promoter's Engineer to arrange a site visit which gives the estimators and planners an opportunity to study the site with the design personnel on hand to answer queries. In building work the site visit may not be arranged so formally but nevertheless most contractors arrange one for themselves. As a result of these site visits the estimator and planner prepare a report or set of notes which includes:

- a description of the site;
- the positions of existing services;
- a description of ground conditions;
- an assessment of the availability of labour;
- any problems reflected to the security of the site;
- a description of the access to the site;
- topographical details of the site;
- a description of the facilities available for the disposal of spoil;
- a description of any demolition works or temporary works to adjoining buildings.

(c) Method statement

Method statements are descriptions of how the work will be executed with details of the type of labour and plant required and a pre-tender programme. It is in the preparation of these method statements that alternative methods of construction are considered together with alternative sequences of work, differing rates of construction and alternative site layouts. As these evaluations progress the preferred method of construction is chosen and the pre-tender construction programme illustrating this is prepared.

In preparing the method statements the estimators and planners work closely and also consult with site staff, plant managers and temporary works designers. The pre-tender programme prepared will show the sequence of all the main activities and their durations as well as the duration of the overall project. From this pre-tender programme approximations of the labour and plant resources will be calculated. This pre-tender programme is not an exercise carried out once only and left, but is subject to continual refinement and modification as both the estimator and planner become more and more aware of the implications of the project details. Thus, throughout the preparation of the estimate the estimator and planner remain in close consultation. In many contracts the pre-tender programme is prepared in the form of a bar chart; in some of the larger and more complex projects some form of network analysis is used. Networks are also used in smaller contracts by companies who have become skilled in their preparation and use and aware of their advantages. Bar charts and networks are described in Chapter 2.

5. Preparing the Estimate

The estimator's task is to determine the cost to the contractor of executing the work defined in the contract documents. This cost estimate

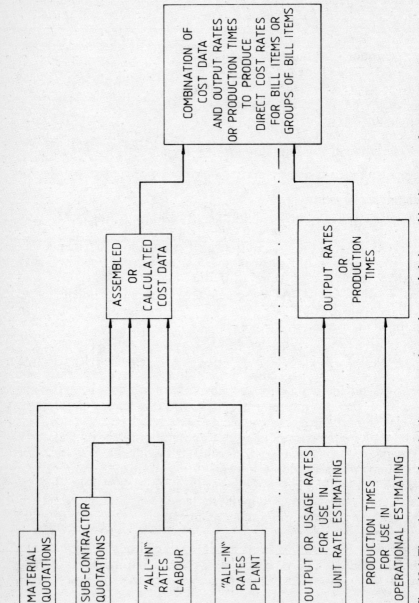

Fig. 10.1 The selection of production rates and cost data and their combination to produce cost rates.

will be modified by senior management in consultation with the estimator to determine the tender or selling price. The estimator is required to establish the direct cost rates for each item in the bill of quantities. A direct cost rate is a rate for the labour, plant, materials and sub-contractors, but exclusive of additions for site overheads, head office overheads and profit. These will be assessed and included later.

Determining a direct cost rate involves selecting the appropriate resources of labour, plant and materials for the item of work (either a single bill item or a group of bill items), selecting the output or usage rates for each resource or determining the elapsed time that each resource (labour and plant) will be employed and combining this with the cost information collected. This combination of the unit cost of resources together with the usage of resources to produce a direct cost for the work described in the bill item or group of bill items is illustrated in Fig. 10.1.

The method of calculation of a direct cost rate based on the output or usage of the selected resources is known as *unit rate estimating* and the method of calculating direct costs based on the elapsed time of employed resources is known as *operational estimating*. These two methods of estimating are the main methods employed in calculating direct costs for bill items or groups of bill items.

Other methods of calculating item rates are *spot* or *gash rate* estimating, whereby the estimator produces estimates of direct cost rates without calculation, that is by experience or use of rates for similar work used in previous contracts. Subcontractor rates with or without attendances, prime cost and provisional sums are the other major entries against bill items.

(a) Operational estimating

In civil engineering work there is an extensive use of *operational estimating*. This is because this method of estimating links well with planning and is effective in allowing for idle time which is common in most plant-dominated work. For example an excavator may be on site from the start of excavation operations to the end of excavation operations but may not be working continuously throughout that time period. Operational estimating would base the costs of the excavator on the time that the excavator was on site, not on an assumed output. The time the excavator was on site would be derived from the construction programme.

The link between operational estimating, planning and the bill of quantities is that the estimator would group together the bill items he would wish to estimate as an operation. This group of bill items would be represented in the construction programme as one or more activities and so the construction programme would provide the duration of the operation. The estimator would select the resources to be used in the operation and use the duration of the activities and unit cost of each resource to produce the total cost of the operation. This total cost has to be assigned back to each bill item. The method of assignment is open to the estimator but the simplest method is to apportion the costs *pro rata* with the item quantity. That is, if a total of 2 550 m³ of concrete placing were contained in 40 different bill items of varying quantity and the total cost of the plant element of the operation was £13 110.00 then the rate would be £5.14/m³ and this would be set against each item together with the labour costs. In general, conventional bills of quantities are not designed to suit operational estimating and operational bills have not come into common use: thus, estimators are faced with undertaking the grouping of items into operations as described. In C.E.S.M.M. bills of quantities there is the opportunity to use 'method-related charges' which suits an operational estimating approach. An example of operational estimating is given in Table 10.1.

Table 10.1 Example of an operational build-up for the plant element for placing concrete.

Assumptions

Total cubic metres of concrete to be placed:	2 550 m³
Duration of concreting operations	38 weeks
Plant required	1 No. Mobile Crane
	2 No. Concrete Skips
	3 No. Dumpers
	3 No. Vibrators

Calculations

Item	No.	Weekly rate		No. of weeks		Cost
Mobile Crane	1	£220.00	×	38	=	£8 360.00
Concrete Skip	2	£10.00	×	38	=	£760.00
Dumper	3	£25.00	×	38	=	£2 850.00
Vibrator	3	£10.00	×	38	=	£1 140.00
				Total cost	=	£13 110.00
				Cost per m³	=	£5.14

This illustrates the operational build-up for the plant element for placing concrete. A similar build-up for labour and for the provision of concrete would be required to satisfy a group of bill items that include providing and placing concrete.

Building contractors use operational estimating to a much lesser extent than the civil engineering contractors. This is because their work is less plant-dominated. However, it is used in estimating the costs of cranage and concrete or mortar mixers. Frequently in building contracts these operationally estimated plant costs are not assigned to the bill items but included in the 'Preliminaries'.

(b) Unit rate estimating

Even civil engineering contractors' estimators do not use operational estimaing exclusively, mainly because of the format of the bill of quantities and they employ *unit rate estimating* for some of the items or groups of items. The use of unit rate estimating is predominate in building work. The basis of unit rate estimating is the selection of the resources required and the selection of the output or usage rates for those resources. Thus for each of the resources (i.e. labour, plant or materials) the arithmetical calculation is the output or usage rate combined with the unit cost. An output rate is expressed as work quantity per hour (e.g. labour for placing concrete m^3/hr) and a usage rate is the time taken to do a fixed quantity of work (e.g. labour for placing concrete, hr/m^3). Thus, by combining these with the cost of the resource (£/hr in the case of labour and plant) the cost per unit (e.g. labour for placing concrete, £/m^3) can be determined. The sum of the cost per unit for all resources is the estimate of the direct cost rate. An example of a unit rate calculation is given in Table 10.2. Supplementary cost calculations for this example are given in Table 10.3. The selection of resources and their associated output or usage rates for each category of work is:

- abstracted from previously recorded company manuals;
- taken from estimator's personal manuals; or
- known to the estimators by experience.

The use of company manuals for recording standard build-ups giving resources and usage rates is common in larger companies. Estimators are, of course, allowed to modify such standard build-ups. The growing use of computers in estimating allows the storage in computer files of these standard build-ups and provides for recall and manipulation before inclusion in the estimate.

(c) Combining operational estimating and unit rate estimating

Fig. 10.2 shows the build-up for an item where the provision of concrete is calculated on a unit rate basis and the placing of concrete is calculated on an operational basis. The operational rates being calculated in two parts – labour for placing concrete and plant for placing concrete.

This illustrates that estimators can use unit rate and operational rates

```
     DESIGN STRUT. CONC. 30 MPA  20 MM. AGGR. OFC
Is this the correct item? Y

Section 1  Page  1  Item 3
Library CESMM code F153.0
DESIGN STRUT. CONC. 30 MPA  20 MM. AGGR. OFC            158.00 M3
Data base resources

Res.  Cat.  Description           Usage rate        Cost           Total

500   PLT.  20/14 MIXER           .160 HR  /M3    1.880 $/HR     $47.53
501   PLT.  2M3 READY-CRETE TRUC  .140 HR  /M3    2.400 $/HR     $53.09
503   DIR.  OFC                   .400 TN  /M3   45.000 $/TN   $2844.00*
505   DIR.  SAND                  .350 M3  /M3   12.500 $/M3    $691.25*
508   DIR.  20 MM AGGR.          1.000 TN  /M3   10.000 $/TN   $1580.00*
511   AUX.  DIESEL               1.050 GA  /M3     .850 $/GA    $141.02
512   PLT.  SILO (50 TONNE)       .160 HR  /M3     .500 $/HR     $12.64
513   LAB.  MIXER DRIVER          .160 HR  /M3    1.405 $/HR     $35.52
514   LAB.  SHOVEL OPERATER       .160 HR  /M3    1.095 $/HR     $27.68

Prices with '*' indicate Quotes are Required
operational rates

Code    Description                          Cost         Total

CONCFL  PLANT FOR PLACING CONCRETE          5.14 $/M3    $812.31
CONCLA  LABOUR FOR PLACING CONCRETE         6.01 $/M3    $949.34

Item rate  45.53 $/M3        Item cost      $7194.37
Do you want a reconciliation of data base resources? Y

Res.  Cat.  Description                       Amount

500   PLT.  20/14 MIXER                       25.28 HR
501   PLT.  2M3 READY-CRETE TRUCK (1 MILE HAUL)  22.12 HR
503   DIR.  OFC                               63.20 TN
505   DIR.  SAND                              55.30 M3
508   DIR.  20 MM AGGR.                      158.00 TN
511   AUX.  DIESEL                           165.90 GA
512   PLT.  SILO (50 TONNE)                   25.28 HR
513   LAB.  MIXER DRIVER                      25.28 HR
514   LAB.  SHOVEL OPERATER                   25.28 HR

Do you want a reconciliation of operational rates? Y
```

Annotations:

- Bill item under consideration
- Quantity
- Provision of concrete — calculated on a unit rate basis.
- to this build up has been added
- Rates for placing concrete — calculated on an operational basis.
- Total item cost and rate/M3
- Reconciliation of the total amount of each resource used in the unit rate calculation.

```
CONCPL  - PLANT FOR PLACING CONCRETE

Res. Cat. Description                        No Week Alloc.
----- ---- -----------                       -- ---- ------
P 989 PLT. MOBILE CRANE                       38.00  100.00
P 991 PLT. CONCRETE SKIP                      76.00  100.00
P 992 PLT. DUMPER                            114.00  100.00
P 993 PLT. VIBRATOR                          114.00  100.00


CONCLA  - LABOUR FOR PLACING CONCRETE

Res. Cat. Description                        No Week Alloc.
----- ---- -----------                       -- ---- ------
  1 LAB. LABOUR                             152.00   50.00


Options are:-
    FILE    - to put item into the contract file
    RATIO   - to change a usage rate by a percentage
    MODIFY  - to add or delete resources or modify usage rates
    OPERATIONAL - to add or delete operational rates
    LUMP    - to apply the calculated rate to other items
    CHANGE  - to change the quantity
    DELETE  - to delete item from the contract file
Option? FI

Item filed
    Commands are:-
             INPUT ITEM
             RETRIEVE ITEM
             EDIT DATA BASE RESOURCES
             BUILD OPERATIONAL RATE
             ADD MARKUPS
             SORT AND EVALUATE
             PRINT REPORTS
             COPY ON
             STOP
```

Reconciliation of the resources used to build up the operational rate.

Fig. 10.2 An example of unit rate and operation rate estimating combined.

Table 10.2 Example of a unit rate build-up

(a) Example of bill item

Item description	Units	Quantity	Rate	Extension
A. One brick wall in common bricks in 1:3 cement mortar	m²	100		

(b) Example of unit rate build-up

Labour	Cost/Hr	Output/Usage		Total cost
Bricklayer-Commons	£4.25	1.8 hrs/m²		£7.65
Labour to unload (at 10 minutes/ 1 000 bricks)	£2.50	1.2 min/m²		£0.05
		Total labour cost		£7.70

Materials	Quant/m²	Net mat. cost	Waste	Total cost
Common bricks	120 NR	£100.00/1 000	10%	£13.20
Mortar (3:1)	0.045 m³	£25.10/m³	5%	£1.19
		Total material cost		£14.39
		Total cost/m²		£22.09

Table 10.3 Supplementary cost calculations in unit rate build-up

(a) Example of calculating the cost of one bricklayer per hour with labourer support

2 bricklayers @ £3.00/hr	=	£6.00
1 labourer @ £2.50/hr	=	£2.50
Total cost of gang	=	£8.50
Cost of one bricklayer per hour (÷ 2)	=	£4.25

(b) Example of calculating cost of mortar per m³

Cement 0.52 tne @ £35.00/tne	=	£18.20
Sand 1.38 m³ @ £5.00/m³	=	£6.90
Total cost per m³	=	£25.10

within the same build-up. The choice of use of operational estimating and unit rate estimating varies widely with different estimators and different companies.

6. Site Overheads

The estimator assesses the site overheads based on requirements such as:

- site staff;
- cleaning site and clearing rubbish;

- site transport facilities;
- mechanical plant not previously included in the item rates;
- scaffolding and gantries;
- site accommodation;
- small plant;
- temporary services;
- welfare, first aid and safety provisions;
- final clearance and handover;
- defects liability;
- transport of men to site;
- abnormal overtime;
- risk.

The costs of these site overheads are frequently allocated to the 'preliminary' section of the bill, but may sometimes be allocated, at least partially to bill item rates.

7. Estimators' Reports

On completion of the estimate the estimators prepare a set of reports for consideration by the senior management. These reports contain:

- a brief description of the project;
- a description of the method of construction;
- notes of any unusual risks which are inherent in the project and which are not adequately covered by the conditions of contract or bills of quantities;
- any unresolved or contractual problems;
- an assessment of the state of the design process and the possible financial consequences thereof;
- notes of any major assumptions made in the preparation of the estimate;
- assessment of the profitability of the project; and
- any pertinent information concerning market and industrial conditions.

The costs of the work included in the estimate are reported to senior management in cost reports that give details of:

- main contractor's labour;
- main contractor's plant allocated to rates and in preliminaries;
- main contractor's materials;
- main contractor's own sub-contractors;
- sums for nominated sub-contractors;
- sums for nominated suppliers;
- provisional sums and dayworks;
- contingencies;

Contract: - A851 ROADBRIDGE   Resource Reconciliation

DATE   28/10/81

SUMMARY OF RESOURCES USED IN UNIT RATE ESTIMATING

Resource Number	Description	Resource Total Quantity	Resource Direct Cost	Resource Contribution
1	LABOUR	42.04 HR	£151.35	£151.35
21	DUMP TRUCK 10.5M3	73.50 HR	£668.85	£668.85
136	JCB 3C EXCAVATOR	36.75 HR	£459.38	£459.38
500	20/14 MIXER	57.12 HR	£107.39	£107.39
501	2M3 READY-CRETE TRUCK (1 MILE HAUL)	49.98 HR	£119.95	£119.95
503	OPC	142.80 TN	£6,426.00	£6,426.00 (Quote)
505	SAND	124.95 M3	£1,561.88	£1,561.88 (Quote)
508	20 MM AGGR.	357.00 TN	£3,570.00	£3,570.00 (Quote)
511	DIESEL	374.85 GA	£318.62	£318.62
512	SILO (50 TONNE)	57.12 HR	£28.56	£28.56
513	MIXER DRIVER	57.12 HR	£80.25	£80.25
514	SHOVEL OPERATER	57.12 HR	£62.55	£62.55
524	STEELFIXER	952.00 HR	£4,284.00	£4,284.00
525	STEELFIXER'S LABOURER	204.00 MH	£744.60	£744.60
530	20 MM DIA MILD STEEL -CUT,BENT & DELIVERED	74.80 TNNE	£17,877.20	£17,877.20
558	FACING BRICKS	9.92 TH	£892.62	£892.62 (Quote)
560	MORTAR	3.76 M3	£85.96	£85.96
561	SCAFFOLDING UP TO THREE METRES	171.00 M2	£410.40	£410.40
562	BRICKLAYER	328.32 HR	£1,477.44	£1,477.44
563	BRICKLAYER'S LABOURER	328.32 HR	£1,198.37	£1,198.37

Fig. 10.3 Resource reconciliation report.

- amounts included for attendance on domestic and nominated sub-contractors; and
- amounts included for materials and sub-contract cash discounts,

and perhaps a bill of quantities marked up with the direct cost rates showing the labour, plant, materials and sub-contractor breakdown for each rate.

As well as reporting the costs estimated for labour, plant and materials the estimators also assemble the total hours for each category of labour and the total hours or weeks for each major item of plant and total quantities for materials. These resource totals are compared with the planners' calculated resource totals and any difference reconciled. Fig. 10.3 shows an example of such a report showing resource totals and costs.

The estimators may also calculate the cash flow for the contract based on a range of assumed mark-ups which will assist senior management's judgement as to what is the appropriate mark-up to select. A description of cash flow calculations is given in Chapter 12.

Tendering Adjustments

Based on the reports prepared by the estimator the staff charged with the responsibility of submitting the tender will assess the estimate and decide on the additions to cater for risk, company overheads and profit. The group of staff concerned, sometimes referred to as the tender adjudicating panel, will comprise representatives of senior management and representatives of the estimating team. It is the resposibility of this panel to satisfy themselves that the estimate is adequate. This is done by studying the reports prepared by the estimator and interrogating the estimator on his assumptions and decisions. It does result on many occasions that the estimate is adjusted usually in the form of lump sum additions or subtractions.

The additions for risk, overheads and profit are frequently referred to as the 'mark-up' and are allowances for:

- 'risk' if the chance or profitability of making a loss is assessed as being greater than that of breaking even;
- 'company overheads' to cover the central head office costs which are involved in administering the contract; and
- the 'profit' considered to be possible in the existing market conditions.

The manner in which contractors assess these additions varies enormously from company to company. These additions are incorporated into the tender in a variety of ways including lump sum additions and subtractions and *pro rata* adjustments.

The 'discounts' taken on materials and sub-contract quotations are sometimes considered as an extra source of profit and it is not unknown for a contractor in very poor markets to submit a tender with a zero or negative profit allowance and rely on such discounts to produce the profit required. Thus, strictly speaking, the 'discounts' should be considered as part of the tender additions.

Submitting the tender

The tender figure arrived at above is entered by the estimators into the contract documents in the manner required by the contract documents, which is either as a priced bill of quantities or submitted on a form of tender with no bill of quantities.

Tendering with a Priced Bill of Quantities

In submitting a tender with a priced bill of quantities the direct cost rates calculated for each item need to be amended to take account of both the estimate adjustments and the mark-up. As previously stated, the estimate adjustments tend to be made as lump sum additions or subtractions: logically, however, they require the adjustment of the direct cost rates.

In apportioning the mark-up there are a variety of practices such as:

● marking up all items by a percentage calculated to cover overheads and profit;
● including the mark-up additions as lump sums in the preliminary section of the bill; and
● marking up the bill items by different percentages to create some element of rate loading in order to create a favourable cash flow. The effects of rate loading on cash flow is described in Chapter 12.

The preliminary section of the bill is frequently used to include site overheads, estimate adjustments and the balance of the mark-up. In some cases lump sums are included in the preliminaries and the remainder of the mark-up additions are apportioned over the bill items.

Tendering without a Bill of Quantities

In cases where tenders require only the submission of the form of tender the contractor need only submit the global sums as required. If the submitted tender is seriously being considered then the completed bill of quantities may be called for by the professional quantity surveyor. This practice is frequently used in building contracts.

Computers and Estimating

The use of computers in estimating has been adopted by some companies since the middle of the 1960's. However these early users relied on large computers and developed their own software. Around 1980 the use of computers in estimating became much more widespread and there were two central reasons for this. One was the availability of cheaper microcomputers which removed the capital constraints and the other was the development of interactive computer-aided estimating systems. The use of interactive software whereby the estimator could control each step of the calculations at a computer terminal, usually a visual display unit, gave the estimator a high degree of control of the computer system. This resulted in the development of *computer-aided* systems. This difference has revolutionised estimators' attitudes to computer system.

The Department of Civil Engineering at Loughborough University of Technology developed computer-aided estimating systems which were made commercially available under the names INTEREST C.E., meaning INTERactive ESTimating for Civil Engineering, and INTEREST BUILD, meaning INTERactive ESTimating for BUILDers. Fig. 10.4 shows an overall flow chart for the INTEREST systems.

The features of these systems are:

(a) files of supporting information for the estimators' use;
(b) a range of methods of calculating item rates;
(c) files recording all estimators' calculations;
(d) facilities for adding mark-ups; and
(e) a comprehensive reporting system.

(a) Supporting Files

The supporting files include:

(i) bill details;
(ii) cost files;
(iii) performance data files; and
(iv) operational group build-ups.

Bill details

The bill details entered by the estimating clerk or estimator's support staff include bill number, section number, page number, bill reference, and if appropriate a reference code which links the item with the data in the performance data file. This code would have been pencilled against the bill item by the estimator. These data are then available on recall for use by the estimator without having to enter it again.

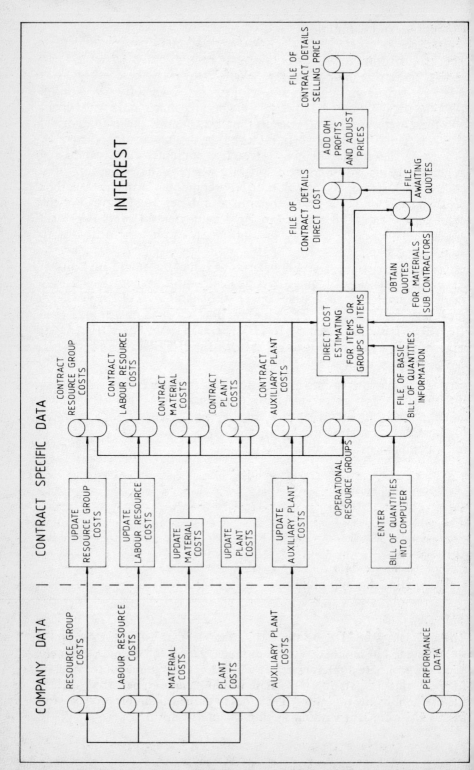

Cost files

The company data cost files contain the all-in costs for different categories of labour, different items of plant and materials prices. Within these cost files data relevant to either individual resources or to gangs may be stored.

The contract specific cost files are the company cost files transferred by the estimator for use in a specific contract. The estimator can either accept the company data, amend it to suit his own requirements for a particular contract or, as is the case with most materials, mark it as *awaiting quotes*. If the awaiting quotes facility is used then any resultant calculation of direct cost rates by the estimator will be held in the Awaiting Quotes File until the buyer or estimator supplies the quotation to the system.

Performance data files

Performance data files contain build-ups on a unit rate basis with resources and usage rates for commonly recurring items of work. These build-ups are recorded against a set of codes that enable the estimator to identify the build-up required. In the INTEREST BUILD system the codes were specially developed to suit SMM6; developments of SMM7 indicate that SMM7 will have its own codes which could be used for this purpose. In the INTEREST C.E. system the C.E.S.M.M. codes were used to store data and the computer system designed so that they could also be used in non-C.E.S.M.M. bills of quantities. Fig. 10.2 shows an example of the type of standard build-ups that can be stored in these files; in this example it is combined with two operational resource groups.

Operational group build-ups

The operational resources groups files allow for the storage of build-ups for operational resource groups, i.e. groups of resources that can be costed on an elapsed time basis rather than a usage or output basis. These build-ups can then be used in the calculation of direct rates for bill items. Fig. 10.2 shows an example of this: in this example the operational resource groups are combined with a unit rate calculation taken from the performance data file.

(b) Methods of Estimating

The range of methods available to the estimator for calculating the direct cost rates for bill items or groups of bill items are listed below.

Unit rate estimating allows the recall of recorded build-ups from the performance data file and permits modifications to the build-up if necessary. The resources and usage rates come from the performance data file, and the costs from the cost files.

Unit rate estimating provides the facility to build-up the estimate from first principles by inputting resources and usage rates. The costs of the resources come from the cost files.

Operational estimating enables the build-up of operational resource groups in the operational resource groups file and the allocation of costs to bill items.

Spot or gash rates involves supplying the labour, plant or material rates without calculation.

Sub-contractors involves supplying sub-contractor quotations.

Included provides the facility for indicating that the item has been included in another item.

Item involves supplying a lump some to an item.

A range of facilities for dealing with P.C. sub-contractors, P.C. suppliers, provisional sums, attendances and profit on P.C. sums.

(c) Files Recording the Estimator's Calculations

The estimator's build-ups for each item or group of items are recorded in the file of contract details and is available for recall by the estimator for re-working or by senior management for inspection. Any build-up that has used a resource whose cost is not firm but awaiting a quote is flagged until the quotation is supplied.

(d) Add Mark-ups

Facilities for adjusting the amount of monies in the cost categories of labour, plant, materials and own sub-contractors exist together with facilities for entering overheads as percentages or lump sums and profits as percentages are available.

(e) Reports

Fig. 10.2 shows the types of displays available on visual display unit screens for estimators' use during calculations. Printed reports available include:

- Bills of quantities giving the labour, plant and materials breakdowns in direct costs rates and rates including mark-ups. Fig. 10.5 is an example: the same listing without the labour, plant and materials breakdowns can be obtained.
- Direct cost summaries. Figure 10.6 is an example.
- Resource reconciliation reports. Figure 10.3 is an example.

```
Contract:-  A851 ROADBRIDGE                              DATE  28/10/81
    Bill Of Quantities Listing
BILL PAGE 20
BILL SECTION  2
--------------------------------------------------------------------------------
        LAB.rate  PLT.rate  DIR.rate  AUX.rate  S/C.rate  TOT.rate   Quantity      Sum
--------------------------------------------------------------------------------
1  GEN EXC SMALL AREAS MATS REUSE NE 0.25M CART 100M
         .51     3.84      0.00      0.00      0.00      4.35      40.00 M3    174.00

2  MILD STEEL REINF TO BS 4449  20 MM DIA
       73.95     0.00    262.90      0.00      0.00    336.85      14.00 T    4715.90

3  DESIGN STRUT. CONC. 30 MPA  20 MM. AGGR. OPC
        6.41     5.86     32.37       .89      0.00     45.53      78.00 M3    3551.34
                                                                   ************
                                                                   £8,441.24
                                                        TOT SECTION  2        ************
                                                                   £8,441.24
```

Fig. 10.5 Bill of Quantities Listing with labour, plant, materials and sub-contractor breakdowns.

```
Contract:-  A851 ROADBRIDGE                              DATE  28/10/81
    Bill Of Quantities Listing

                    DIRECT COST SUMMARY
********************************************************************************
PAGE  SECTION   LABOUR     PLANT    DIR.MAT.   AUX.MAT.   SUB.CON.    TOTAL
********************************************************************************
 1      1      5452.52   1685.39   14249.11    443.42      0.00    21830.43
20      2      1555.75    610.42    6205.85     59.61      0.00     8441.64
30      3      1655.73    214.90    5783.80      0.00      0.00     7654.43
31      3      1479.58    708.82    4174.90    215.99      0.00     6579.29
               ****************************************************************
SUM TOTALS    10143.58   3219.52   30413.66    729.02      0.00    44505.79
********************************************************************************
```

Fig. 10.6 Direct cost summary.

References and Bibliography

1. Institution of Civil Engineers. *Civil Engineering Standard Method of Measurement*. I.C.E., 1976.
2. The Royal Institution of Chartered Surveyors. *Standard Method of Measurement of Building Works* (Sixth Edition). The National Federation of Building Trades Employers, 1979.
3. The Royal Institution of Chartered Surveyors. *Standard Method of Measurement of Building Works: Fifth Edition*. The National Federation of Building Trades Employers, July 1968.
4. Standard Method of Measurement Development Unit. *SMM7: Proposals for Discussion*. The Royal Institution of Chartered Surveyors and the National Federation of Building Trades Employers, May 1981.
5. Department of Transport. *Method of Measurement for Road and Bridge Works*. HMSO, 1977.
6. The Institution of Civil Engineers. *Civil Engineering Procedure*. I.C.E., 1979.
7. National Joint Consultative Committee for Building. *Code of Procedure for Single Stage Selective Tendering, 1977*. RIBA Publications, 1977.
8. Estimating Practice Committee of the Institute of Building. *Code of Estimating Practice*. The Institute of Building, 1979.
9. Spence Geddes and Chrystal-Smith, G. (Ed.) *Estimating for Building and Civil Engineering Works*. Newnes-Butterworth, 1977.
10. Enterkin, H. and Reynolds, G. *Estimating for Builders and Surveyors*. Heinemann, 1978.
11. Davis, Belfield and Everest (Chartered Quantity Surveyors). *Spon's Architects' and Builders' Price Book*. E. & F. N. Spon, 1979.
12. Wheatley, N. R. (Ed.) *Laxton's Building Price Book*. Kelly's Directories Ltd., 1980.
13. Griffiths, G. H. (Ed.) *Griffiths' Building Price Book*. Barton Publishers, 1980.
14. Chrystal-Smith, G. (Ed.) *Hutchins' Priced Shedules*. G. H. Lake & Co. Ltd., 1980.
15. Baldwin, A. and McCaffer, R. *Computer-Aided Estimating and Tendering for Civil Engineering Works*. Unpublished paper, Loughborough University of Technology, 1981.
16. McCaffer, R. and Sher, W. Computer-Aided Estimating – an Interactive Approach. *Building Technology and Management*, February 1981.
17. McCaffer, R. and Sher, W. *Management Control from Computer-Aided Estimating*. Paper delivered at CIOB Estimating Seminar, Loughborough, 26th March 1981.
18. McCaffer, R. Computer-aided estimating – its evolution,

difficulties and future. *The Practice of Estimating.* The Chartered Institute of Building, 1981.

19. Hamlyn-Harris, H. *A Review and Critical Appraisal of Commercially Available Computer-Aided Estimating Systems for Builders and Civil Engineers.* M.Sc. Project Report, Loughborough University of Technology (Supervisor: R. McCaffer), 1979.

20. McCaffer, R. *Increasing Efficiency – Will the computer help?* Paper delivered at The Institute of Building Estimating Seminar, Sheffield, 1980.

21. Civil Engineering Construction Conciliation Board for Great Britain. *Working Rule Agreement.* F.C.E.C., 1981.

22. National Joint Council for the Building Industry. *National Working Rules for the Building Industry.* 1981.

23. Harris, F. and McCaffer, R. *Construction Plant: Management and Investment Decisions.* Granada, 1982.

24. McCaffer, R. and Baldwin, A.N. *Estimating and Tendering for Civil Engineering Works.* Granada, 1984.

CHAPTER 11

COMPETITIVE BIDDING

Summary

Review of the historical attempts to develop theories to aid bidding, the accuracy of estimating and its effect, some measures of a company's eagerness to win.

Introduction

Competitive bidding based on tender documents prepared by the client's professional advisors is still the most common method of distributing the construction industry's contracts among the contractors willing to undertake the work. Variations such as negotiated contracts and package deals form only a proportion of the contracts offered to the industry. The acceptance by the majority of clients, mainly central and local government, that competitive bidding is fair and will produce the lowest possible commercially viable tender price in the prevailing market conditions, ensures that this form of work distribution will continue for a long time. The random nature of bidding process also ensures that contracting companies will be unable to plan their company's activities with much certainty; that many contracts will be tendered for with unrealistically low prices and that the preoccupancy of most contractors with claims will also continue.

From the contractor's viewpoint competitive bidding has the appearance of roulette: sometimes he wins when he thinks his price is high; sometimes he loses when his price is dangerously low, and he has a wry smile for the apparent 'winner'. Often when a contractor obtains a contract he resorts to claims to ensure that the achieved mark-up is positive because the original tender was based on a low cost estimate. It is not surprising therefore that the subject of 'competitive bidding' has attracted investigations and research by both the contracting companies themselves and a variety of academics. Disappointingly the results of these investigations and efforts to remove some of the uncertainty from bidding are not conclusive. However, a study of the work will give a better understanding of where the uncertainty arises and guidance on how to live with this inherent uncertainty. Participation in the bidding game described in Chapter 15 will further reinforce some of the points made in this chapter. This chapter is divided into three parts: Part 1 reviews the historical work in bidding and describes the earlier attempts to predict the outcome of bidding competition; Part 2 discusses the accuracy of estimating and its effect on a contractor's success in bidding and achieved mark-ups; and Part 3 outlines the various ways in which some of the theories are put to use and reports on more recent research.

Part 1: A Brief Review of Bidding Strategy

Background

The subject of bidding strategy has interested various researchers in America and Europe since the mid-1950s. The aim of most of these workers has been the development of a 'probabilistic model' which will predict the chances of winning in the type of competitive bidding that is common in the construction industry. These probabilistic models have attempted to give guidance to bidders by producing statements of the type: 'If you bid at a mark-up of 12% you have a 30% chance of winning this contract.' Following on from these calculations of probability previous workers have attempted to derive a mark-up which purports to represent the 'optimum mark-up', that is the mark-up which in the long term will produce the maximum profit. The optimum mark-up theories so far devised have not taken into account the varying success a company might experience in filling its available capacity or budgeted turnover. Therefore recent work has suggested using the probability calculations as a means of predicting the overall success ratio (number of jobs won/number of bids submitted) to control work acquired, by raising mark-ups when the order book is full and work is plentiful and by reducing mark-up when the market and order book are depressed.

Review

The basic assumption of all the calculations is that a relationship exists between the tender sum and the 'probability', or 'chance', of winning the contract. The aim of the probabilistic models is to express this numerically.

In entering a bidding competition it is assumed that the contractor first estimates his costs and then adds a mark-up to cover profit (or a mark-up to cover contribution, i.e. profit and company overheads). If the contractor is really desperate to win he could submit a bid at something less than cost! If this bid was low enough then it would have a 100% chance of winning. Just as at the lower end there exists this bid with 100% chance of winning there also exists at the other extreme a bid with no chance of winning (say cost plus 50% mark-up). Between these two extremes there exists a continuum of bids with associated probabilities which measure the chance of winning. This concept was first introduced in 1956 by Friedman (ref. 1) and has been referred to by almost all other researchers since then, including Park (ref. 2), Statham and Sargeant (ref. 3), Gates (ref. 4), Morin and Clough (ref. 5), Whittaker (ref. 6) and Rickwood (ref. 7).

The method of deriving the relationship between bids and chances of winning depends on the collection and manipulation of historical data as follows:

(*a*) We collect data on bids submitted by a particular competitor on past contracts in which we have competed with him.

(*b*) We divide the competitor's *bid* by our *estimated cost* in each case.

(*c*) We group this data and plot a histogram (or frequency distribution) as shown in Fig. 11.1. This histogram now represents a picture of this competitor's historical performance against us. From this histogram it can be readily seen that with mark-ups of 10% there were six out

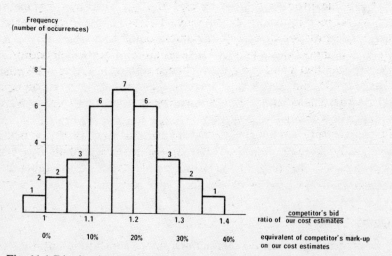

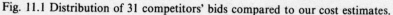

Fig. 11.1 Distribution of 31 competitors' bids compared to our cost estimates.

of 31 (i.e. 19·5%) occasions when this competitor would have had bids lower than us, or conversely 25 out of 31 (i.e. 80·5%) occasions when we would have had bids lower than this competitor. To use this as a guide to the chances of beating this competitor in a future competition assumes that this competitor's future mark-up policy is consistent with previous behaviour.

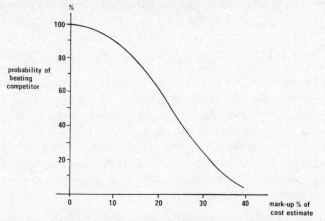

Fig. 11.2 Probability of beating competitor *v.* mark-up.

Usually this histogram is converted into a cumulative frequency curve, as shown in Fig. 11.2, with scales that show a direct relationship between our intended mark-up and the chances of beating that particular competitor.

If such a record as Fig. 11.2 can be generated for a particular competitor then the same process can be carried out for all major competitors likely to be met by a single company. Therefore a collection of such behaviour records for all major companies could exist.

In most competitions a contractor faces more than one competitor, and the knowledge that you have a 25% chance of beating 'A', a 40% chance of beating 'B' and a 15% chance of beating 'C' etc. is obviously unsatisfactory since the question that you are trying to answer is, 'What is the chance of winning the contract?'

Friedman (ref. 1) was the first to suggest a 'model', or expression, which combined these probabilities and predicted the probability of winning a contract, knowing the previous performance of the other competitors. Freidman's model was:

Probability of winning a contract at a given mark-up competing against a number of known competitors

= probability of beating competitor 'A' × probability of beating competitor 'B' × probability of beating competitor 'C' ... etc.

To deal with the bidding situation of unknown competitors Friedman and later Park (ref. 3) suggested aggregating *all* competitors' bids into a distribution similar to Fig. 11.1. Thus the historical behaviour represented by this 'picture' is that of a 'typical bidder' and not of any particular bidder.

To predict the probability of winning a contract against a known number of unknown competitors, Friedman suggested the following:

Probability of winning against *n* unknown competitors for a given mark-up

= (probability of beating one 'typical' competitor)^n

Other writers criticised Friedman's work and suggested alternative models which dealt with the points raised. The most notable was Gates (ref. 4), who in various papers published during the 1960s criticised Friedman's work on theoretical ground and offered his own solution which is again based on the collection of historical data and the creation of a distribution of competitors' bids against our estimates. In Gates's model, probability of winning a contract at a given mark-up against a number of known competitors

$$p = \frac{1}{[(1 - p_A)/p_A] + [(1 - p_B)/p_B] + [(1 - p_C)/p_C] + \ldots + 1}$$

where p_A = probability of beating A
p_B = probability of beating B
p_C = probability of beating C

For the case of unknown competitors, the Gates model becomes:

$$p_n = \frac{1}{n[(1 - p_{typ})/p_{typ}] + 1}$$

where p_n = probability of beating *n* unknown competitors
p_{typ} = probability of beating a typical competitor.

Friedman's and Gates's models give different answers, and debate over the years has attempted to solve this conflict with several writers offering their own solutions. Among them was Whittaker (ref. 6), whose model attempts to take account of managerial judgement by including a guess at the general expected level of bids in his calculations. This acknowledges that mathematics is unlikely to supersede judgement entirely. Fine, (ref. 8) has suggested the 'low competitor' model on the strength of the argument that the only competitor one is interested in beating is the lowest competitor. The low competitor model is based on a collection of historic data of the lowest competitor in each competition entered. Thus a histogram (Fig. 11.3) is produced, this time not for a particular contractor but for the lowest competitor in each competition. The attraction of this model is that it does not require a complicated expression to combine individual probabilities, instead the probability of winning is read off the computed distribution (compare with Fig. 11.2). The disadvantage appears to be the large number of competitions that need to be entered before a 'stable' distribution is achieved, i.e. a distribution which does not change dramatically with each added item of data. To collect a large set of data requires time during which the mark-up policy of competitors may change.

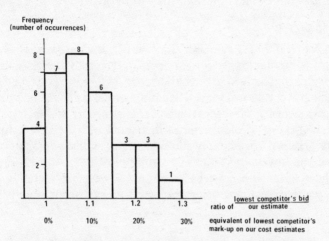

Fig. 11.3 Distribution of 31 lowest competitors' bids compared to our cost estimates.

Among those who have attempted to resolve the Friedman–Gates differences is Rickwood (ref. 7), who concluded that the Friedman model was more correct when the cost estimates used by competitors was the same and the variability in bids was due only to mark-up differences. He also concluded that the Gates model was more correct when the mark-up used by competitors was the same and the variability in bids was due to variations in cost estimate only. The statistical reasons for this are not explained here.

Rickwood proposed a compromise which was no more than a weighted average of the probability predicted by Friedman and that by Gates. The weighting given to each depends on the amount of variability due to estimates and the amount of variability due to mark-ups. However, as yet this has received no practical testing.

Whittaker (ref. 6) analysed a number of contracts relating to building projects and produced an 'overall distribution' of bids which was uniform in shape. Given that you could estimate the mean bid accurately (to within ±2%) the Whittaker distribution, or model, will tell you the probability of any particular bid being the winning bid. Whittaker reports that in tests he has shown a significant improvement when compared to bidding unsupported by his model. Curtis and Maine (ref. 9) emerged as the major critics of Whittaker's work on the grounds of the method of aggregating all contracts, irrespective of the number of bidders, in order to obtain his distribution. They also dispute the claim made by Whittaker that mean bids can be estimated using 'managerial judgement' with the required accuracy of $\pm 2\%$. Curtis and Maine (ref. 10) put forward as an alternative to Friedman and Gates a model based on conditional probabilities, but pointed out that they were of the view that such models were too simple in treating the cost estimate and the mark-up as independent variables.

McCaffer (ref. 11), sympathising with the approach of Whittaker, undertook a similar analysis. He took account of Curtis and Maine's criticisms and produced distributions of bids for roads and building works which were shown to be virtually normal distributions with standard deviations of 8·4% for roads contracts and 6·3% for buildings contracts. The use of these overall distributions, or the distribution for contracts grouped together by the number of bidders, makes it possible to predict the lowest bid from an estimate of the mean bid. Figure 11.4 shows the relationship between mean and lowest bids actually recorded and the predicted values, using 'expected values' from statistical tables,

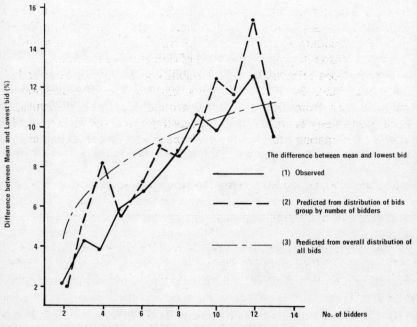

Fig. 11.4 Average difference between mean and lowest bid.

for the variances calculated for the analysis of building contracts. It must be emphasised that such figures would need to be compiled for each type of contract in each area, and that the figures shown are not necessarily universally applicable. McCaffer (ref. 15) has also attempted to predict the mean tender price, which it is accepted should be an easier task than predicting the less stable lowest bid by means of a price library and inflation indices. The method relied on the compilation of a library of prices for standard items of work, the updating of the prices to time-now using inflation indices, the statistical analyses of selected prices and the use of these statistics to simulate the price of a future tender. The accuracy of this method was shown to be about a standard deviation of 8% for roads contracts, which compares favourably with the accuracies of other methods recorded by McCaffer (ref. 15). This article records accuracies of estimating for regression models of standard deviations ranging from 5% to 20%. The accuracy of traditional estimating by the designer and clients' professionals is recorded in the same article as ranging from a standard deviation of 12% for buildings to 21% for road works. An accurate estimate of either the mean or the lowest bid could provide the contractor submitting a bid with a reasonable measure of the probability of winning.

The more recent references to the accuracy of the estimate as being the main controlling variable in determining winning bids have been by Fine (ref. 8), Whittaker (ref. 6) and Barnes and Lau (ref. 12). Barnes and Lau noted the accuracy of estimating in the process plant industry and expressed the view that it was impossible to obtain feedback of the effect of different bidding and pricing policies from observing the real situation. The main reason they give is the level of estimating inaccuracy.

Observations relating the high variability in output of labour and plant have been made by Fine and others, and the resulting question is: If output varies from 50% to 200% around the mean of 100%, how accurate can any estimator be in forecasting the cost of a contract? The effects of estimating accuracy are explored in part 2 of this chapter.

Part 2: The Importance of Accuracy in Estimating

The Effect of Estimating Inaccuracies

In the estimating process the estimating department is required to make several assessments, partly based on recorded data, partly based on experience, partly based on hunches. Typical examples of these assessments are:

(i) The likely outputs or performance standards of the various trades and of the selected plant (and even the choice of plan for the job)

(ii) An assessment (translated into cost terms) of the ease or difficulty of carrying out the various work items which make up the contract

(iii) The likely trend in material costs over the period of the contract

(iv) The likely trend in wage rates over the period of the contract

(v) The weather conditions etc.

Different estimators will obviously assess the effects of the above and other variables differently, hence a number of estimators are liable to produce a range of estimates.

The cost that the estimator is trying to produce (at least in theory) is the most likely cost of his company of executing the particular contract. This leaves the tendering panel to add profit margins which represent an adequate return commensurate with the risk involved. In general building where there is not a large element of highly specialised work and where there is a number of contractors of similar efficiencies, especially in areas where staff and labour move from company to company, a simplification assumes that the 'likely cost' of a contract to each company is similar. Clearly in specialist work, or where the methods of construction vary, the likely cost of a contract will be different from company to company.

Assuming that a contract has a 'likely cost', the range of estimates produced by each company will be 'likely cost' $\pm A\%$, where $A\%$ represents the accuracy of the estimators' prediction of likely cost. This simplification can be used to explain partially why contractors' achieved profit/turnover is significantly less than the average of the profit margins added to the cost estimates at the tender stage. The explanation rests on the margin lost in competition, which is discussed below.

The margin lost in competition

$$\text{Cost estimate range} = \text{likely cost} \pm A\%$$

where $A\%$ is a measure of the accuracy of present estimating methods. To calculate the tender, contractors add a mark-up to their cost estimate, i.e.

$$\text{Tender} = \text{cost estimate} + \text{applied mark-up}$$

In the competitive tendering process the winning tender is usually the lowest. Therefore the estimator who produces the lowest estimate, say likely cost minus $A\%$, gives his company the best chance of winning the contract. This supports the cliché, 'The estimator who makes the biggest mistake wins the contract.' The attendant cliché, 'What we lose on the swings we make on the roundabouts,' is unsupported because the estimator who produces the highest estimate, say likely cost plus $A\%$, gives his company very little chance of winning the contract, and it is probable that most winning tenders will have cost estimates which are low in the range likely cost $\pm A\%$.

Figure 11.5 shows the range of possible cost estimates as a uniform distribution (a simplification used for demonstration purposes) and all competitors adding the same mark-up (another simplification used for demonstration purposes) and the resulting distribution of winning bids.

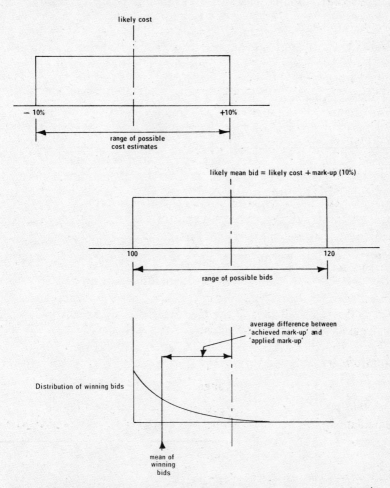

Fig. 11.5 Demonstration of how the estimate of the average amount lost in competition is derived (assuming a uniform distribution of bids).

The difference between the mean of the winning bids and the mean of all the bids is the average margin lost in competition.

Thus the winning tender based on a cost estimate which is probably less than the likely cost usually results in the mark-up achieved on the contract being less than the mark-up included in the tender. Over a large number of contracts the average difference between mark-up included in tenders and achieved mark-up is the average difference between the likely cost and the estimated costs. This average difference has been called the 'breakeven mark-up'.

If a contractor did not wish to make a profit but wanted merely to break even and attempted to do so by adding a zero profit mark-up to his tenders, he would, because of estimating inaccuracies, make a net loss over a number of contracts. In order to break even in the long term he would have to apply a profit mark-up greater than zero to compensate for differences between the likely cost and estimated costs of his winning tenders. The mark-up needed to break even depends on (1) the general level of estimating accuracy and (2) the number of competitors.

For example, with estimating inaccuracies of say ±10% and with five competitors, a mark-up of the order of 7% would be needed to break even in the long term. Any long-term achieved profit margins in this situation would be the excess over the 7% breakeven mark-up included in tenders. If a contractor included, say, 10% profit margins in his tenders the likelihood is that the average achieved profit margin would be of the order of 3%.

In an industry where the achieved mark-up (or profit/turnover ratio) is low – 'Even efficient firms which are almost household names complain of margins on turnover of under 2%' (*Construction News*, leader article,

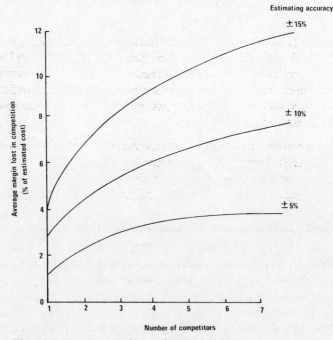

Fig. 11.6 Average margin lost in competition.

3 May, 1973) – although the applied mark-up at the tender stage is considerably higher, the margin lost in competition offers some explanation of the difference between achieved and applied mark-ups and demonstrates the likely existence of estimating inaccuracies.

To reduce the amount lost to competition and hence increase achieved mark-up, contractors need to improve their estimating accuracy and/or seek tendering situations with fewer competitors. Figure 11.6 gives a graphical representation of the margin lost in competition based on the assumption of uniform distributions and the stated estimating accuracies.

The Effect of Improving the Accuracy of Estimating

If a contractor could improve his estimating accuracy he would have to ask himself several questions, namely:

1. If I improve the accuracy of my estimating, shall I still be successful in obtaining contracts?
2. If I improve the accuracy of my estimating, what will be the effect on my profits?
3. If I derive any benefit from improving the accuracy of my estimating, will these benefits remain if the rest of the competition make similar improvements?

In an attempt to obtain answers to these questions, or at least a guide as to the likely answers, a simulation program was produced and the key results were checked by analytical means. The details of this program are not described here, but briefly it combines the factors that determine a contractor's ability to secure contracts with the resulting achieved profit margins. The factors included were:

(i) The estimating accuracy of the contractor whose record is being considered (referred to as contractor E)
(ii) The general estimating accuracy of his competitors
(iii) The average applied profit margin of contractor E (the profit margin he includes in his tenders)
(iv) The average applied profit margins of his competitors
(v) The number of competitors he meets when tendering.

Using different ranges of values for the factors listed, the results obtained gave some insight to the likely effects on achieved profit margins and a contractor's ability to secure contracts.

Results typical of those obtained for the full range of situations simulated are described below, and show something of the effect of improving estimating accuracy.

Situation 1

This situation is the assumed existing set of conditions against which any change will be compared. The level of estimating accuracy and of average mark-ups are purely assumptions.

Assumptions Contractor E and four others have estimating accuracies of likely cost $\pm$ 10%· On average, all contractors include a profit margin of 10% in their tenders.

Results All contractors win one contract in every five they tender for. The average achieved profit margin is 3%. The average difference between applied and achieved profit margins is the average difference between likely cost and the estimated cost of the winning tenders.

This means that contractor E's average profit/turnover is 3% and his success ratio (i.e. number of contracts won/number of tenders submitted) is 1:5. The success ratio is a measure of the contractor's ability to obtain contracts.

Situation 2

In this situation contractor E has improved his estimating accuracy and maintains the same average applied profit margin as in situation 1. His competitors maintain their existing accuracies and profit margins. In this situation the questions being asked are:

(a) What would be the effect on the contractor's ability to obtain contracts (i.e. the effect on his success ratio)?

(b) What will be the effect on his profit margins?

Assumptions Contractor E has an estimating accuracy of likely cost $\pm 5\%$. The four other contractors have estimating accuracies of likely cost $\pm 10\%$. On average, all contractors include a profit margin of 10% in their tenders.

Results Contractor E is less successful in securing contracts and now only wins between one in 10 and one in 11 of the contracts he tenders for. The average achieved profit margin on the contracts he wins is approximately 8%. By doubling his estimating accuracy contractor E has vastly improved the profit margins he achieves; but because his ability to secure contracts is lessened, his turnover will be reduced if he continues to submit about the same number of tenders.

The answers to the two questions are: (a) his ability to secure contracts has been reduced from 1:5 to 1:11; (b) the average profit margin has increased from 3% to 8% which, taken together, give a marginal increase in company profits.

Notwithstanding the increase in profits the decline in ability to secure contracts, which in turn affects contractor E's turnover, is unsatisfactory. However, two solutions are offered: either to compensate by increasing the number of tenders submitted, if a sufficient amount of work is available; or to reduce the applied mark-up. The effect of reducing the mark-up is studied in situation 3.

Situation 3

In this situation contractor E reduces his applied profit margin in order that his ability to secure contracts is the same as in situation 1 (i.e. a success ratio of 1:5). The question is: What effect will this have on company profit?

Assumptions Contractor E has an estimating accuracy of likely cost $\pm 5\%$ and on average includes a profit margin of 7·5% in his tenders. The four other contractors have estimating accuracies of $\pm 10\%$ and on average include a profit margin of 10% in their tenders.

Results Contractor E wins one contract in every five he tenders for (same as in situation 1). The average achieved profit margin of the contracts he wins is in excess of 6% (compare with 3% of situation 1).

The conclusions so far and the answers to questions (1) and (2) are: (1) if a contractor unilaterally improves his estimating accuracy and maintains the same average mark-up his ability to win contracts is substantially reduced. (2) If the contractor reduces his average applied profit margin in order to improve his ability to secure contracts his average achieved profit margin will still be substantially higher than before.

The third question, whether any benefits would remain if contractor E's competitors also made similar improvements, was studied in situations 4 and 5.

Situation 4

In this situation the other four contractors have also improved their estimating accuracies and have also reduced their applied profit margins.

Assumptions All five contractors have estimating accuracies of likely cost $\pm 5\%$ and on average include profit margins of 7·5% in their tenders.

Results Contractor E and the other contractors win one contract in every five they tender for. The average achieved profit margin is just over 4%.

For Contractor E this is still an improvement when compared with the original situation 1 (i.e. 3%) but is a deterioration from the situation where he alone has improved his estimating accuracy (cf. situation 3, i.e. 6%).

Situation 5
In this situation all contractors' estimating accuracies remain at the new improved level and their applied profit margins return to the level that existed originally.

Assumptions All five contractors have estimating accuracies of likely cost $\pm 5\%$ and on average include a profit margin of 10% in their tenders.

Results Contractor E and the other contractors win one contract in every five tendered for. The average achieved profit margin is just in excess of $6\frac{1}{2}\%$.

For Contractor E this compares favourably with the original situation 1 (i.e. 3%) and with the situation where he alone improved his estimating accuracy (situation 3, i.e. 6%). (In Situation 3, it will be recalled, contractor E had reduced his applied profit margin from 10% to $7\frac{1}{2}\%$.)

The answer to question (3) is that profit improvements do remain even when competitors make similar improvements to estimating accuracy.

Finally the situation was considered where not all competitors had made similar improvements to estimating accuracies.

Situation 6
In this situation four contractors (including E) have improved their estimating accuracies, the fifth has not.

Assumptions Four contractors (including E) have estimating accuracies of $\pm 5\%$. The fifth contractor has an estimating accuracy of $\pm 10\%$. All five have on average an applied profit margin of 10%.

Results The ability of contractor E to obtain contracts is slightly reduced from 1:5 to 1:6. The average achieved profit margin is $5\frac{1}{2}\%$. This compares favourably with the original achieved margin of 3% but less favourably with situation 5, where all contractors have improved their accuracy. Nevertheless, substantial profit improvements remain.

The other results from the range of situations tested give similar patterns of results. If the original estimating inaccuracy was assumed to be greater, the increase in achieved profit margins on improving the estimating accuracy was also greater. If the original estimating inaccuracy was assumed to be smaller, then the increase in the achieved profit margin on improving the estimating accuracy was also smaller.

Conclusions

The general conclusions drawn from this study are:

1. The achieved profit margin will be increased if the accuracy of estimating is improved.
2. If the estimating accuracy is improved and the contractor wishes to maintain the same turnover, he will need to (*a*) reduce his applied profit margin or (*b*) increase the number of tenders he submits or (*c*) make some reduction in his applied profit margin and also increase the number of tenders he submits.
3. The achieved profit margins will still be greater than the original profit margins when all contractors improve their estimating accuracy. This assumes that contractors fix their mark-up without reference to the current profitability of the company. However, the competitive nature of the industry would probably cause contractors to cut their margins once enhanced profitability had been achieved. It is difficult to assess this effect but at least one residual benefit would remain, namely the reduction in the number of loss-making contracts.
4. There are serious consequences for any contractor who allows the accuracy of his estimating to deteriorate.

Part 3: Some Ways of Using the Existing Theories

Number of Bidders

The theories relating to the margin lost in competition, highlights the point that the greater the number of bidders, the lower the winning bid is likely to be in relation to the 'likely cost'. The advice is simple and is to avoid the bidding competitions with a higher number of bidders. Figure 11.4 shows the average difference between the mean bid and the lowest bid actually recorded; where the same effect can be seen that with a high number of bidders the lower is the winning bid relative to the mean bid.

A disturbing piece of evidence is in Fig. 11.7 (taken from ref. 11), which shows the average of lowest bid/designer's estimate and average of mean bid/designer's estimate. It was expected that the average of lowest bid/designer's estimate would fall off as the number of bidders increased; the designer's estimate took no account of the number of bidders and this fall-off is consistent with the theory relating to the margin lost in competition. However, there is no such explanation for the fall-off of average of mean bid/designer's estimate with increasing number of bidders; the number of bidders should not have affected this statistic. This fall-off can only be explained as a manifestation of price cutting when competition is fierce. Thus there seem to be two possible mechan-

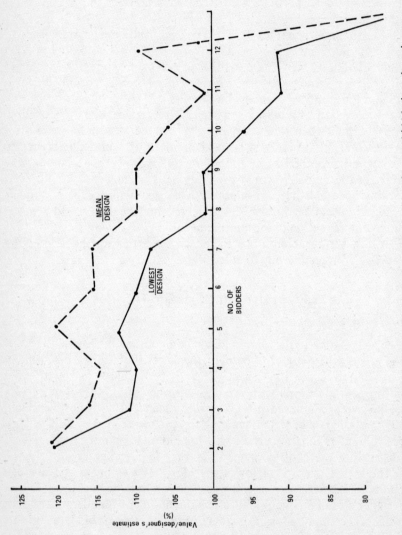

Fig. 11.7 Average of lowest bid/designer's estimate and average of mean bid/designer's estimate plotted against N, the number of bidders. (From ref. 11.)

isms forcing down the price of the lowest bid when there are many competitors, one being due to estimating variability and the other being price cutting.

Differences Between Contractors' Average Bids

Many of the approaches described in part 1 of this chapter, such as creating distributions of competitors' bids in comparison with the contractor's own cost estimates, have failed through lack of data. All statistical analyses of competitors' behaviour will fail if insufficient data exist. However, the data requirements of these distributions are specifically restricted to competitions which the contractor enters. This excludes all other competitions which the contractor's competitors enter and so excludes a substantial source of data.

The difficulty of using data from other bidding competitions is in converting this information into some meaningful standard which can then be used for comparison. The most common method of 'standardising' bids from other contracts is to divide each bid by the mean bid to obtain the ratio known as 'mean standardised bid'. There are valid theoretical reasons why this ratio should not be of much value because of the variability of the divisor, the mean bid. Nevertheless, there is also some evidence that demonstrates the usefulness of these mean standardised bids (ref. 11).

If the mean standardised bid is calculated for each contract a known contractor has entered and the average 'mean standardised bid' is calculated for that known contractor, some measure of the overall performance of this contractor in relation to the others, in particular your own company, can be obtained. Table 11.1 shows the average mean standardised bid for a number of contractors together with the observed success ratio (number of jobs won/number of jobs bid). The fifth column in the table also shows the result of a statistical test to determine if each contractor's list of bids could be regarded as a list of random numbers, or if a disproportionate number of low or high bids occurred. This table shows that the average mean standardised bid is a good indicator of success rate and low bidders. This analysis makes use of data from any bidding competition whether your own company is involved or not. The meaningfulness of the results improves as the data available increase.

Differences Between Contractors' Behaviour Patterns

Column 5 in Table 11.1 indicates that some contractors have more low bids than is normally expected and some have more high bids. It also indicates that the majority have a reasonable share of high and low bids. A study of observed bids for some contractors (ref. 11) revealed that there are occasions when contractors who in the long term have equal

Table 11.1 Correlation of 'Average Mean Standardised Bid' and 'Success Rate'. (An extract from ref. 11)

Company identifier (for anonymity this has been replaced by letter)	No. of bids submitted by company in the analysis	Average of mean standardised bid	Success rate (No of winners / No. submitted) (%)	*Statistical test for randomness
A	45	0·954	44·4	Low
B	30	0·971	6·6	Low
C	32	0·978	25·0	Low
D	46	0·983	21·7	R
E	63	0·984	20·6	R
F	21	0·990	23·8	R
G	27	0·991	14·8	R
H	22	0·991	22·7	R
I	66	0·992	13·6	R
J	65	0·997	16·9	R
K	39	0·997	17·9	R
L	27	0·998	11·1	R
M	36	0·998	16·6	R
N	41	1·001	24·3	R
O	25	1·004	20·0	R
P	21	1·005	4·7	R
Q	23	1·006	8·7	R
R	78	1·008	5·1	R
S	26	1·011	7·6	R
T	22	1·018	4·5	R
U	43	1·03	4·6	High
V	29	1·033	6·9	High
W	21	1·050	9·5	High

* Low: A disproportionate number of 'low bids'. High: A disproportionate number of 'high bids'. R: A random mixture of 'low' and 'high' bids.

shares of high and low bids have phases of varying length when they display a run of low bids or high bids. These phases when identified help differentiate the less serious competitors from the more serious.

This approach can be improved upon by calculating the cumulative sum of (bid—mean bid)/mean bid and plotting the results, as shown in Fig. 11.8. This value has been given the name the *cusum* value. An analysis of this type for some 600 contracts involving almost 400 contractors (ref. 11) showed that there were only 15% of cases when the winning bidder had a rising graph preceding his winning bid. Conversely there

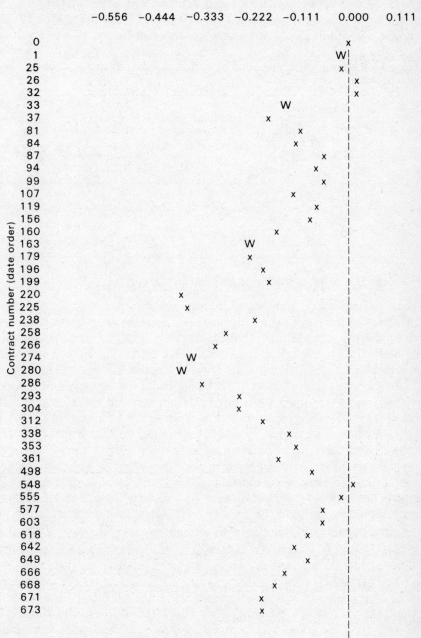

Fig. 11.8 Cusum plot for one contractor.

were 85% of cases when the winning bidder had a declining graph. Table 11.2 summarises the number of occasions a winning bid was preceded by a drop of one, two, three, four or five steps (a step being a previous bid, each bid being taken in date order). The production of such graphs is useful in identifying work-hungry competitors.

Table 11.2 Winning bids preceded by 2, 3, 4 or 5 decrements in a contractor's cusum value.

No. of times a winning bid was preceded by M decrements in the contractor's cusum value (%)	No. of decrements (i.e. previous bids)
85	2
75	3
69	4
65	5

Success Rates Sensitivity to Changes in Mark-up

There is obviously a relationship between mark-up and success rate. Increases in the mark-up will reduce success rate. Sometimes the advice given is to increase the applied mark-up and compensate for the reduced success rate by bidding for more contracts. This advice may have a firm theoretical basis but can only be applied if there are the extra contracts available and should only be applied if the sensitivity of success rate to changes in mark-up is known. The latter can be calculated, and Fig. 11.9 shows the graphs of success rate against changes in mark-up for one contractor. Repeating this for a number of contractors (ref. 11) showed that each had a different sensitivity of success rate to changes in mark-up. This is thought to reflect the different skills in market judgement. Changes in the mark-up policy of different companies would clearly lead to different outcomes. The outcome for a particular company should be examined before any unconsidered action is taken.

Other variables that should be studied are:

1. The bidding success rate with different sizes of contract
2. The bidding success rate with different types of contract
3. The bidding success rate in different regions
4. Achieved mark-up versus job size
5. Achieved mark-up versus job type

Attention to (4) and (5) recommended as a warning against being too successful in obtaining unprofitable jobs.

Contractor CC   Frequency 86

Mark-up (%)	No. of wins	Percentage wins	1	2	3	4	5	6	7	8	9	10
−44.0	86	100.0	0	0	0	0	0	0	0	0	0	0
−43.0	85	98.8										x
−42.0	85	98.8										x
−41.0	85	98.8										x
−40.0	85	98.8										x
−39.0	85	98.8										x
−38.0	85	98.8										x
−37.0	84	97.7										x
−36.0	84	97.7										x
−35.0	84	97.7										x
−34.0	84	97.7										x
−33.0	84	97.7										x
−32.0	84	97.7										x
−31.0	83	96.5										x
−30.0	83	96.5										x
−29.0	82	95.3										x
−28.0	82	95.3										x
−27.0	81	94.2										x
−26.0	81	94.2										x
−25.0	80	93.0										x
−24.0	80	93.0										x
−23.0	78	90.7									x	
−22.0	77	89.5									x	
−21.0	76	88.4									x	
−20.0	76	88.4									x	
−19.0	76	88.4									x	
−18.0	73	84.9								x		
−17.0	72	83.7								x		
−16.0	71	82.6								x		
−15.0	71	82.6								x		
−14.0	71	82.6								x		
−13.0	71	82.6								x		
−12.0	66	76.7							x			
−11.0	64	74.4							x			
−10.0	62	72.1							x			
−9.0	60	69.8							x			
−8.0	58	67.4							x			
−7.0	54	62.8							x			
−6.0	46	53.5						x				
−5.0	37	43.0					x					
−4.0	29	33.7				x						
−3.0	20	23.3			x							
−2.0	17	19.8		x								
−1.0	13	15.1		x								
0.0	11	12.8		x								

Fig. 11.9 Sensitivity of success rate to changes in mark-up.

Advice on the Data to Collect for Analysing Competitors' Bids

If no formalised efforts have been made previously to analyse competitors' behaviour, then the starting point must be the company's own competitions. If the bids are ascertained for all competitors in each competition entered, then the relationship of the competitors' bids to your own estimate can be established, as in Fig. 11.1. Data from competitions which your company does not enter are useful because these details can always be compared with the mean bid, and Table 11.1 indicates that this comparison is also a guide to likely success rate. If sufficient data are gathered relating to your major competitors then the graphs of (bid–mean bid)/mean bid, such as Fig. 11.8, can be drawn and the times when that competitor is looking for work can be identified. However, it is strongly recommended that your own company's performance be examined as listed above and that tight control be exercised on the estimating department to avoid any possibility of a deterioration in the accuracy of estimates resulting in a serious loss-making contract.

ACKNOWLEDGEMENT: Some of the material in parts 1 and 2 of this chapter was presented at conferences sponsored by *Construction News* and published in *Estimating – the Proceedings of Two Conferences* (Editor: R. McCaffer; Northwood Publications, 1974).

References and Bibliography

1. Friedman, L. A competitive bidding strategy. *Operations Research* Vol. 4, pp. 104–12, 1956.

2. Park, W. *The Strategy of Contracting for Profit*. Prentice-Hall, 1966.

3. Statham, W. & Sargeant, M. Determining an optimum bid. *Building* Vol. 216, No. 6573, 1969.

4. Gates, M. Bidding strategies and probabilities. *Journal of the Construction Division, ASCE* Vol. 93, No. CO1, proc. paper 5159, pp. 74–107, 1967.

5. Morin, T. L. & Clough, R. H. OPBID: competitive bidding strategy model. *Journal of the Construction Division, ASCE* Vol. 95, No. CO1, proc. paper 6690, pp. 85–106, 1969.

6. Whittaker, J. D. *Managerial Judgement in a Competitive Bidding Model*. Ph.D. thesis, City University, 1970.

7. Rickwood, A. K. *An Investigation into the Tenability of Bidding Theory and Techniques*. M.Sc. project report, Loughborough University of Technology, 1972.

8. Fine, B. Various unpublished papers based on work of the Costain O.R. Group.

9. Curtis, F. W. & Maine, P. W. Viewpoints: competitive bidding, *O.R.Q.* Vol. 25, No. 1, p. 179.

10. Curtis, F. W. & Maine, P. W. Closed competitive bidding. *Omega* Vol. 1, No. 4, 1973.

11. McCaffer, R. 'Contractors' Bidding Behaviour and Tender Price Prediction'. Research papers not yet published. Department of Civil Engineering, Loughborough University of Technology, 1976.

12. Barnes, N. M. L. & Lau, K. T. Bidding strategies and company performance in process plant contracting. *Third International Cost Engineering Symposium* London, 1974. Association of Cost Engineers.

13. Armstrong, K. *The Development and Appraisal of Computerised Estimating System.* M.Sc. thesis, Loughborough University of Technology, 1972.

14. Moyles, B. F. *An Analysis of the Contractor's Estimating Process.* M.Sc. thesis, Loughborough University of Technology, 1973.

15. McCaffer, R. Some examples of the use of regression analysis as an estimating tool. *The Quantity Surveyor* Vol. 32, no. 5, 1975.

CHAPTER 12

CASH FLOW FORECASTING

Summary

The need for cash flow forecasting, the requirements of a cash flow forecasting system, some practical suggestions to simplify cash flow forecasting and measuring interest charged on capital lock-up.

The Need for Cash Flow Forecasting by Contractors

Each year the construction industry usually experiences a proportionally greater number of bankruptcies than do other industries. One of the final causes of bankruptcy is inadequate cash resources and failure to convince creditors and possible lenders of money that this inadequacy is only temporary. The need to forecast cash requirements is important in order to make provision for these difficult times before they arrive. In times of high interest rates the need for cash flow forecasting is even more important, and Sandilands (ref. 1), in his *Inflation Accounting* report to government, highlighted the need to forecast cash flows in times of inflation and thus avoid an embarrassing cash deficit when replacing old equipment at new inflated costs.

There is evidence that some companies confuse profit flows with cash flows and make misleading calculations. A cash flow is the transfer of money into or out of the company. The timing of a cash flow is important. There will be a time lag between the entitlement to receive a cash payment and actually receiving it. There will be a time lag between being committed to making a payment and actually paying it. These time lags are the credit arrangements that contractors have with their creditors and debtors. It is these credit arrangements, stock levels and depreciation that make cash and profit different. The following simple example highlights this difference due to credit arrangements.

A company buys goods at £6 each and sells for £8 each; there are a number of different credit arrangements as follows:

Credit arrangement	Profit flow (£)	Cash flow (£) out	Cash flow (£) in
Buy 10 for cash Sell 10 for cash	20		20
Buy 10 on credit Sell 10 for cash	20		80
Buy 10 for cash Sell 10 for credit	20	60	

The credit arrangements cause very different cash flows. There is a need therefore for separate cash flow forecasting.

Some companies forecast their cash flows for only a few months ahead, say three or six months. This is not adequate and does not look far enough ahead. The factors which affect cash flows are the duration of new projects, the profit margin on these projects, the retention conditions, the delay in receiving payment from the client, the credit arrangements with suppliers, plant hirers and subcontractors and the phasing of the projects in the company's workload and the late settlement of outstanding claims. As many projects last one, two or three years the cash flow forecasts should also look this far ahead.

Some companies quickly point out that forecasts are guesses and therefore are probably wrong and useless and not worth the effort. However, this argument is equally applicable to estimating, which is essential to a company's operations. Cash flow forecasting is, like any forecasting, the result of calculations based on the information available at the time and a few assumptions as to what will happen. If, as is likely, the data contained in the information changes or the assumptions alter, the forecast will be in error and a new forecast is required. When a company equips itself to forecast its cash flows efficiently and without great expense it usually forecasts every quarter, and in some cases every month. This is sufficient to monitor the everchanging situation.

Contractors who undertake cash flow forecasting do so at two levels. One is at the estimating and tendering stage, when the forecast is just for the single project being estimated. The other level is the calculation of a cash flow forecast for the company, division or area; this involves aggregating cash flows for all active projects and is done regularly every quarter or every month.

These two types of forecasts require different treatments. The estimator has all the project details at the estimating stage and, because the forecast applies only to one project, the estimator can produce a carefully calculated forecast based on these details by allocating bill items to 'activities' on the pre-tender 'bar chart' or 'network'. This creates a direct link between the estimator's build-ups for each item with the pre-tender construction programme and allows the production of value versus time and cost versus time curves from which 'cash in' and 'cash out' can be calculated. This calculation is too detailed to be repeated for every active project, every quarter or every month and so contractors devise short cuts when undertaking the company or divisional cash flow forecasts. This chapter describes the principles of the calculations in cash flow forecasting and reference is made to short cuts that will allow cash flow forecasts to be made more regularly than just the one detailed forecast at the estimating stage.

The Requirements of a Forecasting System

Cash flow forecasting is strongly advisable. And for the forecasts to be meaningful they must be done regularly, and for forecasting to be done regularly the method must be simple and easy to do and yet accurate enough for the purpose. It is essential therefore to reduce the data required for cash flow forecasting to the minimum possible compatible with reliable forecasts and to streamline the necessary calculations.

The Data Needed

In construction companies the most appropriate approach is to calculate cash flows on a project basis and aggregate the cash flows from all projects and head office to form the overall company cash flow. This can be structured into divisions or areas for larger companies. The data required for a project are:

1. A graph of value *v.* time, value being the monies a contractor will eventually receive for doing the work
2. The measurement and certification interval
3. The payment delay between certification and the contractor receiving the cash
4. The retention conditions and retention repayment arrangements
5. A graph of cost *v.* time, the contractor's cost liability arising from labour, plant, materials, subcontractors and other cost headings as necessary
6. The project costs broken down into the above items

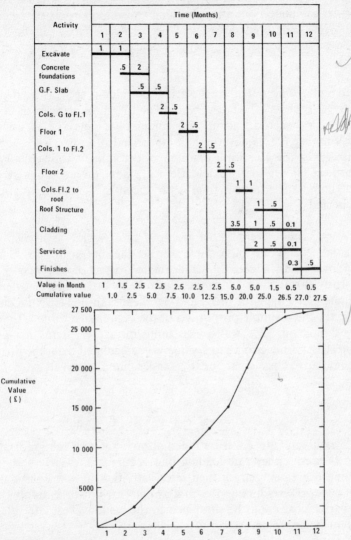

Fig. 12.1 Value *v.* time from a bar chart (values shown as £'000s).

7. The delay between incurring a cost liability under the above headings and meeting that liability

The data required for the company's head office are:

8. The head office outgoings and the time of their occurrence
9. The head office incomings and the time of their occurrence

The project-based data items 2, 3 and 4 are readily available. Item 6 can easily be calculated but after studying several contracts of the same type appropriate cost breakdowns can be derived. Item 7 should be known by the buying department. Items 1 and 5 are a little more difficult to obtain.

Value versus time   Item 1, the graph of value *v*. time, is needed in order to derive 'cash in'. This can be obtained by producing project plans, in network or bar chart form, and calculating the value of each activity and summing the value in each time period of either weeks or months. Figure 12.1 shows a simple example of the value *v*. time calculated from the project plan. Usually calculations are done on a cumulative basis and so the cumulative value *v*. time is produced by a running total over each time period.

Cost versus time   Item 5, the graph of cost *v*. time, is needed to derive 'cash out'. The contribution margin, i.e. the margin for profit and head office overheads added to the estimated direct costs, may be spread uniformly throughout the project. In other words, each bill item carries the same percentage for profit and overheads. In this case the cumulative cost *v*. time is a simple proportion of the cumulative value *v*. time figures. For example, if 12% was added uniformly to all items for profit and overheads and the cumulative value was calculated from the project plan, the cumulative costs would be 0·89 times cumulative value

$$\text{Value} = \text{cost} + 12\% = 1\cdot12 \times \text{cost}$$

Therefore

$$\text{Cost} = \text{value}/1\cdot12 = 0\cdot89 \times \text{value}$$

Alternatively the contribution margin may not be uniformly distributed because either rate loading had occurred and early activities were carrying a greater margin than later activities, or some setting-up costs were adversely reducing the margin on early work. In this case the cumulative cost could be produced in the same way as the value *v*. time from the project plan by costing each activity.

Although the cash required by a project is dependent on several factors, one of the crucial factors is the margin achieved by the project. It is important to have a realistic assessment of this margin. Chapter 11 explains at least one reason why applied mark-up (or margin) and achieved mark-up (or margin) are different, with the latter on average being less. The historical record of the company should be used as guidance. The management game in Chapter 15 further emphasises this point. It is also important to separate out claims when assessing the achieved margin. If, for example, a project had an applied mark-up of

10% and achieved this eventually in the form of 5% from the monthly measurements and 5% through claims, the cash flow would be substantially worse than an achievement of 10% through the monthly measurements. In these cases it is suggested that the margin used in the cash flow calculations is 5% and the claims income be treated as a lump sum coming at a predicted future date, say the end of the contract.

A suggested simplification

The production of cumulative value v. time and cost v. time figures based on project plans is time-consuming because it requires every project in the forecast, i.e. every active or new project in the company's workload, to be represented by a network or bar chart. However, it is possible to bypass the 'plan' stage and use 'standard' cumulative value v. time curves that adequately represent each project type. These cumulative value v. time curves, presented in percentage terms (see Fig. 12.2), can be obtained from certification records of past projects. Hardy (ref. 2) demonstrated that, within a company, projects of the same type had similar shapes of cumulative value v. time when expressed in percentage terms. To make a standard curve from a library unique to a specific project the time scale has to be multiplied by the project's estimated duration and the value scale by the project's estimated value.

When the contribution margin is uniformly spread throughout the project, the cumulative cost v. time is easily derived from the standard cumulative value curve. When contribution is not uniformly spread some

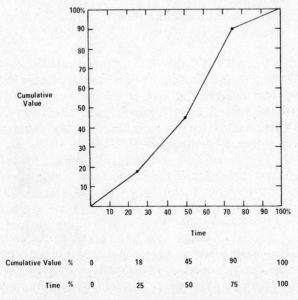

| Cumulative Value % | 0 | 18 | 45 | 90 | 100 |
| Time % | 0 | 25 | 50 | 75 | 100 |

Fig. 12.2 Cumulative value v. time in percentage terms.

calculation is necessary before the cumulative cost *v.* time is produced. However, if the information as to how the contribution is distributed throughout the project is obtained from the estimating department or the tendering panel, the cumulative cost *v.* time figures in percentage terms can be produced without a project plan. McKay (ref. 3) demonstrated that this approach of using standard curves did not lead to loss of reliability in the eventual cash flow forecast.

The calculations The calculations are set out in Table 12.1; a time period of one month is used, but weekly time periods could be used if necessary.

Table 12.1 is made up as follows. Row 1 is the cumulative value derived as previously discussed. Row 2 is the cumulative value less the retention (in this example retention is assumed to be 10%). Row 3 is the value less retention (row 2) shifted by an amount equal to the payment delay between valuation and the contractor receiving his money. Row 4 is the cumulative retention repayments inserted at the time they would be received, in this case half at one month after practical completion and half six months after practical completion.

The cost headings in Table 12.1 are treated individually. The cumulative costs for the total project are shown in row 5. The proportion of costs due to labour is calculated and inserted in row 6, for materials in row 8, for plant in row 10 and for subcontractors in row 12. This can be extended to as many cost headings as required. The proportions of the cost breakdown vary throughout the contract period and this variation can be taken into account; however, the introduction of such a refinement increases the calculations required, and the increase in the accuracy of the forecast is not commensurate with the extra effort.

Rows 7, 9, 11 and 13 of Table 12.1 shift the cost liabilities shown in rows 6, 8, 10 and 12 by an amount equal to the average delay between incurring the cost liability and making the payment. For labour this is taken as zero because labour is usually paid after one week's delay, which is less than one month – the smallest time unit in the example. For plant, materials and subcontractors the delay is taken as one month. Row 14 is the cumulative cash out and is the sum of rows 7, 9, 11 and 13. Row 15 is the cumulative cash flow from row 3 plus row 4 less row 14.

Another suggested simplification

Much of the calculating effort goes into reckoning the cash out due to each individual cost heading. This can be particularly tedious if the exercise is based on time periods of one week instead of one month. The simplification is to calculate a weighted average payment delay for all cost headings, the weighting being the percentage of cost due to that heading.

Table 12.1 Cash flow forecasting calculations

Time (months) (£)

	1	2	3	4	5	6	7	8	9	10	11	12	13	18
1. Cumulative value	1 000	2 500	5 000	7 500	10 000	12 500	15 000	20 000	25 000	26 500	27 000	27 500	27 500	27 500
2. Cumulative value less retention	900	2 250	4 500	6 750	9 000	11 250	13 500	18 000	22 500	23 850	24 300	24 750	24 750	24 750
3. Cumulative payment received from certification		900	2 250	4 500	6 750	9 000	11 250	13 500	18 000	22 500	23 850	24 300	24 750	24 750
4. Cumulative retention payment													1 375	2 750
5. Cumulative cost	920	2 300	4 600	6 900	9 200	11 500	13 800	18 400	23 000	24 380	24 840	25 300	25 300	25 300
6. Cumulative labour costs (30%)	276	690	1 380	2 070	2 760	3 450	4 140	5 520	6 900	7 314	7 452	7 590	7 590	7 590
7. Cumulative labour payments	276	690	1 380	2 070	2 760	3 450	4 140	5 520	6 900	7 314	7 452	7 590	7 590	7 590
8. Cumulative materials cost (20%)	184	460	920	1 380	1 840	2 300	2 760	3 680	4 600	4 876	4 968	5 060	5 060	5 060
9. Cumulative materials payments		184	460	920	1 380	1 840	2 300	2 760	3 680	4 600	4 876	4 968	5 060	5 060
10. Cumulative plant cost (30%)	276	690	1 380	2 070	2 760	3 450	4 140	5 520	6 900	7 314	7 452	7 590	7 590	7 590
11. Cumulative plant payments		276	690	1 380	2 070	2 760	3 450	4 140	5 520	6 900	7 314	7 452	7 590	7 590
12. Cumulative Subcont. cost (20%)	184	460	920	1 380	1 840	2 300	2 760	3 680	4 600	4 876	4 968	5 060	5 060	5 060
13. Cumulative Subcont. payments		184	460	920	1 380	1 840	2 300	2 760	3 680	4 600	4 876	4 968	5 060	5 060
14. Cumulative cash out (7) + (9) + (11) + (13)	276	1 334	2 990	5 290	7 590	9 890	12 190	15 180	19 780	23 414	24 518	24 978	25 300	25 300
15. Cumulative cash flow (3) + (4) — (14)	−276	−434	−740	−790	−840	−890	−940	−1 680	−1 780	−914	−668	−678	+825	+2 200

For example, the figures tabulated below show the contract costs as a percentage of the total cost, broken down into four main groups. The delay experienced between the incurring of a cost liability and the making of a payment is also shown for each of these groups. Using this percentage cost as a weighting, the weighted average payment delay is calculated as 5·1 weeks.

Cost group	Costs as percentage of total cost	Delay between incurring a cost liability and making payment	Calculation of weighted average payment delay
Labour	30	1 week	30% × 1 = 0·3
Plant	30	8 weeks	30% × 8 = 2·4
Materials	20	6 weeks	20% × 6 = 1·2
Subcontractors	20	6 weeks	20% × 6 = 1·2
		Total, i.e. weighted average payment delay	= 5·1

This weighted average delay applied to the total cost gives cash out figures which are accurate over the duration of the contract except during the first few weeks and the last few weeks. A comparison between the accuracy of using individual delays for each cost heading and the accuracy of weighted average is given in ref. 8.

The Company Cash Flow

Each project is treated as above and the cash flows from each project summed together and then added to the company's head office cash flows to produce the company cash flow. The head office cash flows are treated separately in the following way.

(a) The head office outgoings are entered at the time the outgoings occur. These outgoings are, for example, rent and rates, telephones, office equipment hire charges, payments to shareholders, tax, directors' fees etc.

(b) The head office incomings are treated in the same way. The incomings are derived from selling head office services; also any claims or retentions unsettled from past projects may have the expected amount entered in head office incomings.

Table 12.2 Input data required for one period

```
HARDY - MCKAY LTD   TRIAL /     TRIM/HMK CASHFLCW FORECASTING  F202  PAGE   6

P1  PROJECT CODE   2
P2  PROJECT NAME     TWO
P3  RUN NUMBER      1
P4  PROJ START     27
P5  PRJ DURATION105
P6  PROJ VALUE     190000
P7  PLOT FLOW ?     0
V1  NO OF POINTS    5
     SHAPE OF VALUE CURVE  =
V2   % OF TIME        0.0  30.0  50.0  70.0 100.0
V3   % OF VALUE       0.0  14.0  44.0  82.0 100.0
C1  UNIFORM CON?    0
C3  NO OF POINTS    5
     SHAPE OF COST CURVE  =
C4   % OF TIME        0.0  30.0  60.0  80.0 100.0
     COST AS % OF
C5   TOTAL VALUE      0.0  39.0  44.0  82.0  86.0
M1  OVERMEASURE?    0
U1  UPDATING ?      0
E1  COST CAT NO.    4
                          % OF COST    DELAY
E2  LABOUR                   30.0         1
E2  MATERIALS                20.0         9
E2  PLANT                    30.0        11
E2  SUB-CONTRACTORS          20.0        13
I1  RETENTION       10.0
I2  MAX RETENT £      8000
I3  VAL INTERVAL445
I4  FIRST VAL       4
I5  PAY DELAY       2
I6  NO. REP STEP    2
I7  REPAY  50.0 %       DELAY =    2
I7  REPAY  50.0 %       DELAY =   26
```

The summation of head office outgoings and incomings added to the cash flows of all projects give the company cash flow.

Computers and Cash Flow Forecasting

The preceding calculations are a little daunting if they are to be done for all the company's projects every three months. It was to meet this problem that Professor Geoffrey Trimble of the Department of Civil Engineering, Loughborough University of Technology, developed a computer program capable of undertaking the preceding calculations. Table 12.2 shows the type of input required for one project and Table 12.3 shows the resulting output for a project. Figure 12.3 shows the company cash flow, which is the summation of the cash flows from all projects and company head office.

The computerised method described has been used by a number of companies for regularly forecasting the company's cash flows. To reduce the effort required, some companies have used the full computerised method on only the contracts representing say 60% of their workload; for the others they have made further simplifications.

Table 12.3 Output produced for one project

HARDY - MCKAY LTD   TRIAL 2

PROJECT 2   TWO

TRIM/HMK CASHFLOW FORECASTING   F202   PAGE 8

RUN NO. 1

WEEK	VALUE	COST	CASH OUT	CUMULATIVE CASH OUT	CASH IN	CUMULATIVE CASH IN	NET CASH FLOW	CUMULATIVE CASH FLOW	WEEK
25JAN76	85319	75155	845	68400	0	61804	-845	-6596	79
1FEB76	88757	76000	844	69244	12714	74018	11370	4774	80
8FEB76	92105	76844	844	70088	0	74018	-844	3930	81
15FEB76	95633	77688	845	70933	0	74018	-845	3085	82
22FEB76	99071	78533	844	71777	0	74018	-844	2241	83
29FEB76	102509	79377	845	72622	12616	86634	11771	14012	84
7MAR76	105947	80222	844	73466	0	86634	-844	13168	85
14MAR76	109385	81066	845	74311	0	86634	-845	12323	86
21MAR76	112823	81911	844	75155	0	86634	-844	11479	87
28MAR76	116261	82755	845	76000	12907	100386	12907	24386	88
4APR76	119699	83600	844	76844	0	100386	-844	23542	89
11APR76	123138	87038	844	77688	0	100386	-844	22698	90
18APR76	126576	90476	845	78533	0	100386	-845	21853	91
25APR76	130014	93914	844	79377	0	100386	-844	21009	92
2MAY76	133452	97352	845	80222	17191	117577	16346	37355	93
9MAY76	136890	100790	844	81066	0	117577	-844	36511	94
16MAY76	140328	104228	845	81911	0	117577	-845	35666	95
23MAY76	143766	107666	844	82755	0	117577	-844	34822	96
30MAY76	147204	111104	845	83600	13752	131329	12907	47729	97
6JUN76	150642	114542	3438	87038	0	131329	-3438	44291	98
13JUN76	154080	117980	3438	90476	0	131329	-3438	40853	99
20JUN76	156342	121418	3438	93914	0	131329	-3438	37415	100

#									Date	
101	47729	10314	145081	13752	97352	3438	126857	157428	27JUN76	
102	44291	-3438	145081		100790	3438	128295	158514	4JUL76	
103	40853	-3438	145081		104228	3438	131733	159509	11JUL76	
104	37415	-3438	145081		107666	3438	135171	160485	18JUL76	
105	33977	3167	145081	6605	111104	3438	138609	161771	25JUL76	
106	37144	-3438	151686		114542	3438	142047	162857	1AUG76	
107	33706	-3438	151686		117980	3439	145485	163942	8AUG76	
108	30267	-3438	151686		121419	3438	148923	165028	15AUG76	
109	26829	905	156029	4343	124857	3438	152361	166114	22AUG76	
110	27734	-3438	156029		128295	3438	155800	167200	29AUG76	
111	24296	-3438	156029		131733	3438	156161	168285	5SEP76	
112	20858	905	156029		135171	3438	156885	169371	12SEP76	
113	18325	-3438	160372	4343	138609	3438	157247	170457	19SEP76	
114	14887	-3438	160372		142047	3438	157601	171542	26SEP76	
115	11449	-3439	160372		145485	3438	157971	172628	3OCT76	
116	8011	5068	160372	5429	148923	3430	158333	173714	10OCT76	
117	4572	-362	165801		152361	362	158695	174800	17OCT76	
118	9640	-362	165801		155800	362	159057	175885	24OCT76	
119	8916	-362	165801		156161	362	159419	176957	31OCT76	
120	8554	-362	170143	4342	156885	362	159780	178057	7NOV76	
121	12534	3980	170143		157247	362	160142	179142	14NOV76	
122	12172	-362	170143		157601	362		180228	21NOV76	
123	11810	-362	174486	4343	157971	362		181314	28NOV76	
124	15429	-362	174486		158333	362		182399	5DEC76	
125	11448	3981	174486		158695	362		183485	12DEC76	
126	15067	-362	174486		159057	362		184571	19DEC76	
127	14706	-361			159419	361		185657	26DEC76	
128	14344	-362			159780	362		186742	2JAN77	
129					160142			187828	9JAN77	
130								188914	16JAN77	

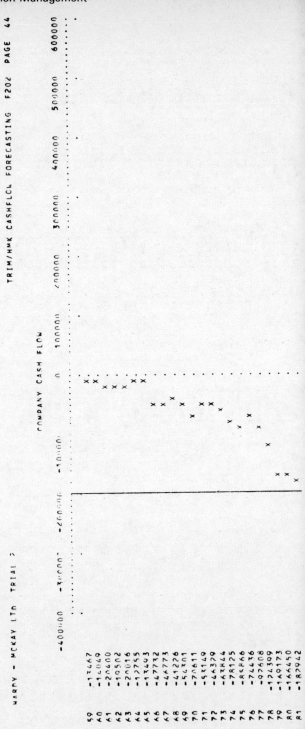

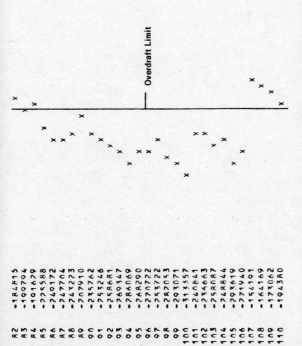

Fig. 12.3 Cash flow forecasts for company with overdraft limit marked.

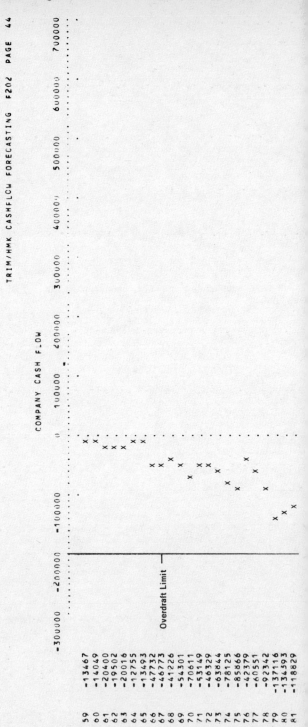

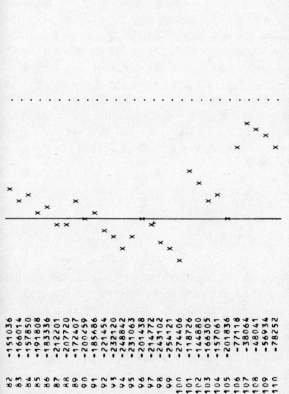

Fig. 12.4 Retention rate now 7% instead of 12% in new project. Client pay delay now 2 weeks instead of 8 weeks.

Equipped with this computation capability it becomes a matter of routine to forecast cash requirements every quarter. Also the effect of starting a new project can be studied at the estimating and tendering stage before any commitment is made. For example Fig. 12.3 shows a graph of the company's cumulative cash flow, i.e. the current account balance, if a new project was undertaken on the payment conditions, retention arrangement and start date currently being negotiated. The limit of the company's overdraft is also shown.

Figure 12.4 shows the effect of negotiating certain changes in these contractual arrangements.

Capital Lock-up

The negative cash flows experienced in the early stages of projects represent locked up capital that is supplied from the company's cash reserves or borrowed. If the company borrows the cash it will have to pay interest charged to the project; if the company uses its own cash reserves it is being deprived of the interest-earning capability of the cash and should therefore charge the project for this interest lost. A measure of the interest payable is obtained by calculating the area between the cash-out and the cash-in curves shown as the finance area in Fig. 12.5. The area is in units of £ × weeks (or months) because the vertical scale is in pounds and the horizontal scale in time (weeks or months). This compound measure, say 5000 £ × months, represents the volume of borrowing from the extremes of £5000 for one month to £1 for 5000 months. This measurement has been given the name of *captim*, standing for capital × time. A simple interest calculation is all that is required to convert captim into an interest charge, e.g. captim of 25 000 £ × months, annual interest rate of 15%,

$$\text{Interest payable} = \frac{\pounds 25\,000 \times \text{months}}{12\,\text{months/year}} \times 15\% \text{ p.a.}$$

$$= \pounds 312 \cdot 50$$

This calculation can be done on the negative captim alone, assuming that the cash released by the project does not earn interest, or the interest earned by the positive captim is subtracted from the interest paid on the negative captim. It is likely that the interest paying rate will be different and probably greater than the interest earning rate. The use of this captim measure enables the effect of interest charges to be evaluated.

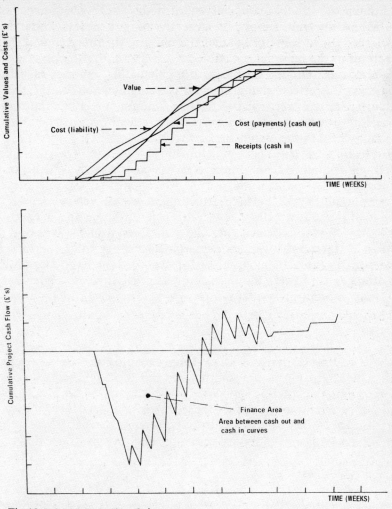

Fig 12.5 Cash-out and cash-in curves.

The Factors that affect Capital Lock-up

The factors that affect the capital lock-up for an individual project or contract are as follows.

Margin

The margin, whether profit margin or contribution (profit plus head office overheads) margin, is amongst the most important because it determines the excess over costs and it is this excess that controls the capital lock-up. Quite simply, the larger the margin, the less capital that is locked up: conversely, the smaller the margin, the more capital that is locked up in the contract.

The margin that should be used in calculating contract cash flows should be the 'effective' margin that is being achieved at the time of executing the contract. This 'effective' margin is neither the margin included at the tender stage nor the margin achieved at the end of the contract when all the claims are settled.

For example, if the tender panel included a margin of 9% and due to variations and other client interference the costs rose by 4%, this would reduce the 'effective' margin to only 5%. Even if an astute contractor recovered another 6% in claims, making his overall achieved margin at the end of the contract 10%, the 'effective' margin at the time of executing the contract and thus determining the cash flows, would still be only 5%.

Most contractors use the tender margin when calculating contract cash flows and this leads to an optimistic forecast. Although the 'margin' is an important factor in determining a contract's cash flow the tender margin is usually chosen for market reasons rather than cash flow reasons.

Retentions

In the U.K. the sysem of retentions simply reduces the 'effective' margin during the execution of the contract and the effect of retentions can be included in the calculations as shown in this chapter. In times of very low margins the retention can reduce the 'effective' margin to zero or less. As retentions are fairly standard in public sector contracts there is little scope for negotiation to reduce retention and improve cash flows.

Claims

As explained above under the section on 'Margins', claims can return a contract to its original intended level of profit. However, as the settlement of claims is normally subject to some delay the actual settlement does not improve a contract's cash flow and the circumstances giving rise to a genuine claim are likely to worsen a contract's cash flow.

The settlement of claims is, of course, important to the company's cash flow and therefore it is important that claims are settled as quickly as possible.

Front End Rate Loading

Front end rate loading is the device whereby the earlier items in the 'bill' carry a higher margin than the later items. This has the effect of improving the 'effective' margin in the early stages of the contract while keeping the overall margin at a competitive level. It is in these early stages that capital lock-up is at its worst. The degree to which front end rate loading can be done depends on the client's awareness.

Overmeasurement

Overmeasurement is the device whereby the amount of work certified in the early months of a contract is greater than the amount of work done. This is compensated for in later measurements. Thus, overmeasurement has the same effect as front end rate loading; it improves the 'cash in' in the early stages and reduces the capital lock-up.

Back End Rate Loading and Undermeasurement

Back end rate loading is the opposite to front end rate loading. Back end rate loading is the device whereby the later items in the 'bill' carry a higher margin than the earlier items. Undermeasurement is the opposite to overmeasurement. Undermeasurement is the situation whereby the amount of work certified in the early months of a contract is less than the amount actually done. Both these devices have the effect of increasing the capital lock-up and, in most circumstances, these situations are not sought by contractors. However, in index-linked price adjustment contracts these devices enhance the monies recovered from price fluctuations in times of inflation. If inflation is high in comparison to the 'cost of money' the contractor may get a better return by funding a larger capital lock-up and gaining on price fluctuations rather than minimising the capital lock-up in the more traditional way. These circumstances existed in the United Kingdom in 1975 and 1976.

Figure 12.6 gives details of a contract (based on an actual case) and demonstrates the unequal effects of inflation on the 'cash in' 'cash out' sides of a contract's cash flow. The figure shows the effect on both cash flow, (measured in terms of maximum negative cash flow) and contract profit (total value of work done minus total costs) as well as the total residual monies which take account of the 'cost of money'. The total residual monies were calculated by assuming that all monies were paid into and drawn from the same account: when the account was in deficit interest was charged at the stated rates and when the account was in surplus the account earned interest.

The calculations presented were calculated for the time periods 1971–72, 1972–74, 1973–75 and 1975–77 representing different rates of inflation. The interest rates used were representative of those existing during the same time periods. The calculations in each time period were performed twice, once assuming front end rate loading (or overmeasurement) and also assuming back end rate loading (or undermeasurement).

Fig. 12.6 A comparison of the effects of rate loading, inflation and interest rates on a contract's cash flow and profitability.

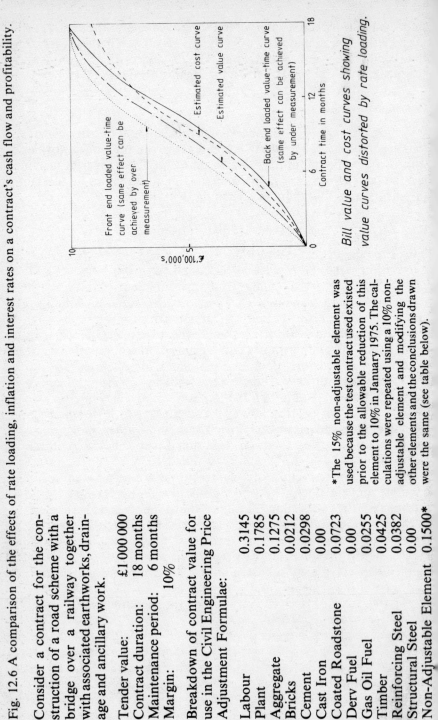

Bill value and cost curves showing value curves distorted by rate loading.

Consider a contract for the construction of a road scheme with a bridge over a railway together with associated earthworks, drainage and ancillary work.

Tender value: £1 000 000
Contract duration: 18 months
Maintenance period: 6 months
Margin: 10%

Breakdown of contract value for use in the Civil Engineering Price Adjustment Formulae:

Labour	0.3145
Plant	0.1785
Aggregate	0.1275
Bricks	0.0212
Cement	0.0298
Cast Iron	0.00
Coated Roadstone	0.0723
Derv Fuel	0.00
Gas Oil Fuel	0.0255
Timber	0.0425
Reinforcing Steel	0.0382
Structural Steel	0.00
Non-Adjustable Element	0.1500*

*The 15% non-adjustable element was used because the test contract used existed prior to the allowable reduction of this element to 10% in January 1975. The calculations were repeated using a 10% non-adjustable element and modifying the other elements and the conclusions drawn were the same (see table below).

Contract time span (Base month)	Earned on +ve cash flow	Paid on -ve cash flow	NON adjustable element	Front or back loading	Total value of work done	Total cost of contractor
April '71– Sept '72 (Jan '71)	8%	10%	15%	Front	1,054,079	960,817
			15%	Back	1,060,797	960,817
Aug '72– Jan '74 (Jun '72)	8%	12%	15%	Front	1,108,555	1,041,988
			15%	Back	1,125,861	1,041,988
Dec '73– May '75 (Nov '73)	12%	14%	15%	Front	1,129,699	1,065,129
			15%	Back	1,168,427	1,065,129
			15%	Front	1,111,528	1,036,105
Nov '75– March '77 (Aug '75)	12%	16%	15%	Back	1,145,560	1,036,105
			10%	Front	1,118,078	1,036,105
			10%	Back	1,154,110	1,036,105

Note: (1) The original bill value plus additions due to The Price Adjustment Formulae.
(2) The estimated cost plus the increases for inflation, based on the indices.
(3) The total monies remaining after all receipts are received, payments made, interest paid on negative cash flows and earned on positive cash flows.

Using the contract described above as an example, this table compares the effect of front-end loading (and/or overmeasuring early monthly certificates) and back-end loading (and/or undermeasuring early monthly certificates) and shows the periods when, due to inflation, back-end loading would have produced bigger 'total residual monies'. Note that two sets of figures are given for the 1975–77 time period (in both cases exclusive of productivity deductions), to show that reducing the non-adjustable element used in the Civil Engineering Price Adjustment Formula from 15% to 10% only exaggerates the result.

The results presented in Figure 12.6 show that when the rate of inflation was high, as in 1973–75 and 1975–77, and the cost of money relative to inflation was low then back end rate loading and/or undermeasurement in the early stages produced the better return despite the adverse cash flows. When the reverse was true, as in 1971–72, and the cost of money was greater than or near to the rate of inflation, then front end rate loading or overmeasurement produced the better return.

Thus only when inflation is very high, which is generally difficult to predict, and borrowing limitations are not critical, can the approach of back end rate loading be countenanced at the tender stage. However, monthly over- or undermeasurement gives a contractor a flexibility of policy over the duration of a contract such that changes can be made quickly in response to predicted movements in the inflation indices and money markets. The effectiveness of this policy also depends on the client's awareness or lack of it.

Delay in Receiving Payment from Client

The time between interim measurement, issuing the certificate and receiving payment is an important variable in the calculation of cash flows. Although 'monies out' goes to many destinations, e.g. labour, plant hirers, materials suppliers and subcontractors, the 'monies in' comes from only one source – the client. Thus, any increase in the delay in receiving this money delays all the income for the contract with a resulting increase in the capital lock-up. The time allowed for this payment is specified in the contract and normally interest is charged if payment is late. This may act as an incentive to the client but if he is slow in paying it is the contractor who has to find the cash.

Delay in paying Labour, Plant Hirers, Materials Suppliers and Subcontractors

The time interval between receiving goods or services and paying for these is the credit the contractor receives from his suppliers. A one-week delay is normal in paying labour and anything between three to six weeks is normal in paying plant hirers and materials suppliers. Any increase in these would reduce the capital required to fund a contract. However, these items evolve as part of the normal commercial trading arrangements and any increase in these times may undermine commercial confidence in the company. Hence, these factors are not usually seen as suitable for controlling capital lock-up in a contract.

Company Cash Flow

The additional key factor that affects the company cash flow is the timing of contract starts. If several new contracts start within a few weeks of each other then the maximum negative cash flow for each contract may occur at around the same time and the cumulative effect of several contracts demanding cash can cause difficulties.

Conclusion

Cash flow forecasting provides a valuable early warning system to predict possible insolvency. This enables preventative measures to be considered and taken in good time. Examples of the actions available are:

  (i) Not taking on a new contract if, when the contract is included in the cash flow forecast, the company's projected cash requirements are much more than the overdraft limit
 (ii) Renegotiation of overdraft limits supported by reliable forecasts
(iii) The adjustment of the work schedules of existing contracts
(iv) The negotiation of extended credit with some suppliers
 (v) Accepting suppliers' full credit facilities even if it means temporarily losing some discounts

The calculations described are not impossible manually but computer aids provide greater calculating capability and make it simpler to include all the company's projects in a regular forecast.

Experience has shown that the discipline of reviewing all projects for cash flow forecasting has a rewarding spin-off in that the attention of senior management is attracted to projects requiring their action. Another byproduct includes total current workload figures which are useful as a guide to the intensity of tendering efforts required. This aspect is described by Trimble (ref. 6).

In a cash flow forecasting system it may be useful to set up a funding account for the plant department and pay the depreciation recovered from internal hire into the funding account for replacement. This will alert the company to the danger of replacement costs exceeding the sum of depreciation.

References and Bibliography

1. Sandilands, F. E. P. *Inflation Accounting*. Report of the Inflation Accounting Committee. HMSO, 1975.

2. Hardy, J. V. *Cash Flow Forecasting for the Construction Industry*. M.Sc. project report, Department of Civil Engineering, Loughborough University of Technology, 1970.

3. McKay, I. B. *Cash Flow Forecasting by Computer*. M.Sc. project

report, Department of Civil Engineering, Loughborough University of Technology, 1971.

4. Kerr, D. *Cash Flow Forecasting.* M.Sc. project report, Department of Civil Engineering, Loughborough University of Technology, 1973.

5. Construction News Report. 'Taking the tedium from cash flow forecasting.' *Construction News* 9 March 1973.

6. Trimble, E. G. 'Financial control – the forward look.' *Construction News* 17 January 1974.

7. Trimble, E. G. & Kerr, D. 'How Much Profit from Contractors Goes to the Bank?' *Construction News* 7 March 1974.

8. Trimble, E. G. *A comparison of the Effect of Using Individual Payment Delays for Cost Headings and a Weighted Average Payment Delay Applied to All Costs.* Internal paper, Department of Civil Engineering, Loughborough University of Technology, 1975.

9. Pike, J. J. *Contract Cash Flow and Inflation.* M.Sc. Thesis, Loughborough University of Technology, 1979.

10. Harris, F. and McCaffer, R. *Worked Examples in Construction Management.* Granada, 1978.

CASH FLOW FORECASTING EXERCISES

Exercise 1

The programme for the construction of a small workshop building is displayed in the form of a precedence diagram, shown in Fig. 12.7. The value of the work contained in each activity has been calculated from the rates contained in the bill of quantities and listed in Table 12.4. The contractor undertaking this project would like you to prepare graphs of cumulative cost and monies received to date against time for activities starting

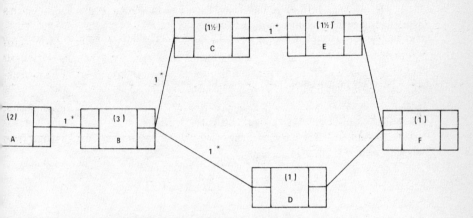

Fig. 12.7 Diagram for cash flow forecasting exercise No. 1.
* The amount of overlap between finish of previous activity and start of next.

as early as possible in order that he may have a clearer picture of the financial implications of this contract. From these graphs calculate the net profit if interest is charged at 8% p.a. on outstanding monies. The gross profit margin is 10% of contract value and retention is 5% up to a maximum limit of £3000. Measurement is made monthly with a payment delay of one month. Half of the retention is paid on practical completion and the remaining half six months later. To simplify the calculation you may assume that all costs must be met a half month after they are incurred.

What is the maximum amount of cash the contractor needs to execute this contract and when does he require this amount?

Table 12.4 Data for cash flow forecasting exercise No. 1

	Activities	Duration in months	Value (£)
A	Excavation	2	9 000
B	Concrete bases	3	12 000
C	Erect frames	$1\frac{1}{2}$	18 000
D	Concrete floor slab	1	15 000
E	Fix cladding	$1\frac{1}{2}$	6 000
F	Install plant	1	20 000

Rate of work throughout any activity is uniform.

Exercise 2

Table 12.5 is the contractor's budgeted cost liabilities for a contract. The contractor will add a contribution mark-up of 8% to the estimated cost of each item in the bill of quantities. The contract conditions allow for monthly measurements to be made and payment of the amount certified less 10% retention is made one month later. The retention money is repaid six months after the practical completion of the project. The weighted delay between incurring a cost liability and making payment may be calculated from the information given in Table 12.5, which is the percentage cost and the delay associated with each cost element

If the current interest rate on borrowed capital is 14% p.a., what reduction in the contractor's budgeted contribution will occur due to interest charges? What is the maximum amount of cash needed to execute the contract? (Each month may be assumed to be $4\frac{1}{3}$ weeks.)

Table 12.5 Data for cash flow forecasting exercise No. 2

Cost element	Percentage of total cost	Payment delay (weeks)
Labour	25%	1·12
Plant	25%	8·20
Materials	50%	4·00

Month No.	1	2	3	4	5	6	7	8	9
Cost of work executed in month (£'000)	3	3	4	6	6	8	6	4	2

Exercise 3

Table 12.6 shows a contractor's project budget and profit distribution for a newly awarded contract. The conditions of contract allow interim measurements to be made monthly and payment of the amount certified less 10% retention paid to the contractor one month later. Half the retention is released on practical completion and the other half is released six months later. The client is anxious to reduce administrative costs and has proposed to the contractor that measurements be made every two months, again with a delay of one month before the contractor receives payment. The contractor is equally anxious to reduce administrative costs but wishes to assess the financial implications. To assist him to do this, prepare graphs of cumulative cash out and receipts for both monthly and two-monthly measurements. (All graphs to be on the

Table 12.6 Data for cash flow forecasting exercise No. 3

Month No.	1	2	3	4	5	6	7	8	9	10
Value of work each month (£000's)	3	4	5	8	8	8	7	6	5	2
Profit (percentage of value)	15%	15%	10%	10%	10%	10%	10%	10%	5%	5%

same sheet.) An average payment delay of one month between the contractor's cost liability and the outward cash flow may be assumed.

From these graphs, calculate:

(a) The maximum amount of capital needed to execute the project with monthly and two-monthly interim measurements.
(b) The interest charge of the *extra* finance needed, given that the cost of capital is 15% per annum.

CHAPTER 13

ECONOMIC ASSESSMENTS

Summary

Interest relationships, present worth, equivalent annual costs, DCF yield, inflation, accuracy of future estimates, sensitivity and risk analysis, tax allowances and worked examples.

Introduction

Economic assessments, or investment appraisal techniques, form the basis for answering two main questions: Which proposed scheme is the most economic? Are any of the proposed schemes profitable enough?

This chapter briefly describes investment appraisal techniques and gives examples appropriate to the construction industry. The essential difference between traditional economic calculations and those of modern investment appraisal is the latter's recognition of the effect of the time value of money: that is, the effect of interest rates on the method of assessment. While current use of these techniques has been predominantly by the industry's clients or their professional advisors for appraising the feasibility of projects, there are a number of applications that are useful to contractors.

1. *The economic comparison between different items of plant or methods*   Many of these comparisons relate to the short term and therefore require no more than a straight comparison of cost. At site level the engineer will be constantly appraising the different methods possible without involving interest rates in such comparisons. This is entirely

valid since most site operations are of short duration and the effect of interest calculations is minimal. On choices of method relating to activities of long duration, that is several years, or in selecting between items of plant which will operate for several years, then the principles of modern investment appraisal should be used.

2. *Recovery of capital invested in plant through either external or internal hiring*   It is sometimes alleged that the contractor's projects make capital which is subsequently reinvested in plant which is then run on a breakeven basis. It is essential that all capital, including the capital invested in plant, earns an adequate return.

3. *Assessing the replacement age of plant items*   Although in some cases the mechanical performance of plant determines when it should be replaced, in other cases the economic factors prevail. The techniques of modern investment appraisal can be used to identify the age range at which the plant should be replaced.

4. *Decisions relating to frequency of maintenance*   The principles of sensitivity analysis described in this chapter can be used to determine the effect on the economic viability of the plant items. Sensitivity analysis is also useful for determining the utilisation rate below which it is uneconomic to keep an item of plant.

5. *The effect of corporation tax and development grants on the economics of plant ownership*   A plant item can be seen as an investment leading to a series of returns; these returns will be subject to corporation tax and the effect of this will reduce the plant items return on capital. In some regions development grants may operate and these will improve the plant items' return on capital.

The material presented in this chapter will provide the theoretical basis for all the above calculations. The chapter will be of interest to engineers who spend some time with consulting engineers (usually preparing for their professional interview). However, the specific items that will help contractors' staff to answer the problems set out above are as follows:

(*a*)   For economic comparison of long duration construction methods and choice between plant items – present worth and equivalent annual cost techniques. These techniques are also useful in determining the form of ownership, e.g. hire or buy or lease.

(*b*)   For capital recovery of capital invested in plant – capital recovery factors as tabulated in Appendix 13.1 and explained in this chapter. Also, Chapter 7 deals with plant hire rates in a manner that requires knowledge of interest calculations; exercises based on this knowledge appear at the end of Chapter 7. The rate of return on any investment is now commonly measured by DCF yield; the calculation of DCF yield and the meaning of this measure of profitability are fully explained.

(*c*) For determining the economic replacement age of plant items – equivalent annual costs used to find the balance between increasing repair and maintenance costs and decreasing resale values. An example is given in this chapter.

(*d*) For frequency of maintenance – sensitivity analysis producing sensitivity graphs. Maintenance is just one factor in determining the costs of running an item of plant. The effect of this one factor on the rate of return can be determined by producing a sensitivity graph from calculations based on a range of different maintenance costs. An example of the sensitivity of rate of return to the utilisation factor is given in Fig. 13.4b. The utilisation factor is of crucial importance to the profitability of most hired plant.

The sensitivity analysis can be extended from the effects of variability in one factor into a risk analysis where the variability of all the factors that affect plant profitability can be studied. These factors would include maintenance cost, utilisation rate, hire rate, capital cost, resale value, fuel and running costs etc. This chapter describes the principles of both sensitivity and risk analyses.

The contents as set out explain the basis of these calculations and where appropriate gives suitable examples.

Interest

The major difference between modern investment appraisal and historical rule-of-thumb methods of appraising projects is the recognition that interest rates are now substantial enough to warrant being included in the appraisal. The inclusion of interest calculations results in the need to know when cash transactions take place. A cash flow is the transfer of money out of (negative cash flow) or into (positive cash flow) the project in question at a known or forecast point in time. Knowledge of the amount and time of cash flows representing a project permit the use of modern investment appraisal techniques. Previously, ignoring interest calculations, a choice between two pumping schemes might be made on say the initial investment, which could lead to installing the smallest pump possible. Or the choice could be made on the total projected expenditure taking the initial investment plus the projected annual running costs times the number of years the scheme would operate. This could lead to installing the largest pump possible. Neither method of appraisal is satisfactory since the first ignores running costs and the second exaggerates their effect. To balance the effect of initial sums and the future running costs, the time value of the money involved must be taken into account through interest rates representing the cost of capital. The cost of capital is the interest rate paid for borrowing capital; to a company it is a weighted average of the dividends paid to shareholders for equity capital and interest paid on loans (p. 59 of ref. 8, gives an explanation).

The manipulations of cash sums and interest rates are achieved by the use of the tabulated factors given in Appendix A13.1 at the end of this chapter. This appendix gives only the factors for 10% and 15%, but the factors for other interest rates can be calculated and the expressions needed are also given.

The use of the tables can be described by six short examples which are given in the same order as the factors are tabulated.

1. *Compound amounts*
If a sum of money, £1000, is invested in an account for some years, say five, at an interest rate of 10%, the amount that can be withdrawn at the end is

$$£1000 \times 1 \cdot 6105 = £1610 \cdot 50$$

The factor $1 \cdot 6105$ is obtained from the tables.

2. *Present worth*
This is the inverse of the compound amount. If a sum of money, £1610·50, is required in five years time, what amount has to be invested today to generate this amount if interest is 10%?

$$£1610 \cdot 5 \times 0 \cdot 620 \, 92 = £1000$$

The factor $0 \cdot 620 \, 92$ is obtained from the tables.

The £1000 is called the present worth of £1610·50 in year 5, as it is the today's equivalent of £1610·50 in year 5. Having £1000 today is the same as having £1610·50 in five years because the £1000 could earn £610·50 of interest in five years. This provides a convenient way of comparing two different sums of money occurring at different times.

3. *Compound amount of a regular or uniform series*
As example 1 gave the amount generated by investing one sum for a specified period at a given interest rate, this factor gives the amount generated by investing a regular sum each period for a specified number of periods at a given interest rate. Each sum earns interest for a different time period. It would be possible to use factor 1 to calculate the amount generated by each individual sum and finally add them all together. The compound amount factor for a regular series does the

calculation in one step. Thus investing £100 each year for six years at an annual rate of 15% will generate a total amount of £875·30, viz.

$$£100 \times 8·753 = £875·30$$

where 8·753 is obtained from the tables.

4. *Sinking fund deposit*
This factor allows the calculation of the amount needed to be invested each period in order to generate a specified amount at some future date. It is the amount required to be regularly deposited in a sinking fund to pay off a debt. For example, if £500 was owed in five years time, the amount that would have to be deposited each year is £81.90 provided 10% can be obtained

$$£500 \times 0·163\ 79 = £81·90$$

where 0·163 79 is tabulated. Note that £81·90 is less than the £100 per year needed if no interest was earned.

5. *Present worth of a regular or uniform series*
As factor 2 calculated the present worth of an individual or lump sum this factor calculates the present worth of a regular series. Thus the present worth of £100 each year for five years given an interest rate of 15% is £335·21

$$£100 \times 3·3521 = £335·21$$

where 3·3521 is tabulated. That is, £335·21 is the equivalent today of £100 each year for the next five years; or £335·21 is the amount needed to be invested today to pay £100 each year over the next five years, provided an interest rate of 15% can be obtained.

This factor provides a method of comparing different regular series in combination with different lump sums. Together with factor 2 this factor provides the basis for the comparison of different projects on a present worth basis.

6. *Capital recovery*
This factor calculates the amount to be recovered each period from an investment in order that the invested capital and a specified return can be recovered. If £500 is invested the amount that must be recovered each year for the next five years to ensure a return of 10% is £131·90

$$£500 \times 0·263\ 79 = £131·90$$

where 0·263 79 is tabulated. This factor is useful in calculating plant hire capital recovery.

Economic Comparisons

The object of economic comparison is to compare the cash flows that will result from one course of action with the cash flows that will result from another course of action. An example is in comparing the cost of buying an item of plant with leasing it. Or comparing two or more different plant arrangements, for say, a pumping scheme where the initial capital expenditure and running costs are different. The only difficulty in comparing such cash flows is that they occur at different times. It is necessary, therefore, to manipulate the cash flows into a form that can be compared. The most popular is the *present worth* method of comparison and an alternative method is that of comparing expenditures on a basis of *equivalent annual costs*. The present worth method simply converts all cash flows to time now. Equivalent annual costs allocates the initial capital investment to each year of operation.

Present Worth

The typical use of present worth is to compare two (or more) schemes each with a different initial investment and different running costs. For example, consider schemes 1 and 2 and the cash flows estimated at today's prices pertaining to buying and operating an item of equipment.

	Scheme 1	*Scheme 2*
Initial plant cost	£5000	£4000
Running cost	£500 p.a.	£800 p.a.
Life	6 years	6 years

If interest rates are 10%, the present worth of these schemes are

Scheme 1   Present worth = £5000 + £500(4·3552)
$$= £7177·60$$
Scheme 2   Present worth = £4000 + £800(4·3552)
$$= £7484·16$$

The factors were obtained from the tables.

Thus since scheme 1 has the smaller present worth it is said that scheme 1 is the more economic. What is being compared is the £1000 extra initial investment of scheme 1 with the £300 extra running costs in scheme 2. In other words, is £1000 now more or less than £300 each year for the next six years with obtainable interest rates being 10%? From previous calculations £1000 now is £306·56 less than £300 each year for six years.

The above comparison is valid because both schemes have the same life. However, if two schemes of different lives are being compared it is necessary to take steps to have an analogy that presents two schemes of the same life. For example, compare scheme 1 from above and scheme 3 below.

Scheme 3

Initial plant cost	£3000
Running cost	£500 p.a.
Life	3 years

The present worth of scheme 1 is £7177·60; the present worth of scheme 3 is £3000 + £500(2·4868) = £4243·40. However, this £4243·40 represents only three years of service whereas £7177·60 represents six years of service. It is necessary to consider a replacement for scheme 3, and since all these estimates have been made at today's prices the replacement costs the same as the first plant item. The present worth of scheme 3 and its replacement becomes

$$\text{Present worth scheme 3 and replacement}$$
$$= £4243·40 + £4243·40(0·751\ 31)$$
$$= £7431·51$$

where 0·751 31 is the present worth factor at year 3. Figure 13.1 sets out the reasoning for this calculation. Clearly 6 years and 3 years have been

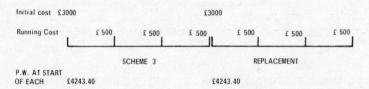

Fig. 13.1 Relationship between total present worth and the present worth of the scheme and its replacement.

chosen to illustrate the above. If 6 years and 4 years were being considered, then one replacement of the 6-year scheme and two replacements of the 4-year scheme would produce two schemes of the same life.

Present worth example

As a further example, the following cash flows pertain to buying and running an item of plant and the alternative of hiring it. The present worth (P.W.) calculations are based on an interest rate of 10%.

	Buying	*Hiring*
Initial cost	£8000	
Running cost	£800 p.a.	£2100 p.a.
Life	7 years	

P.W. of buying = £8000 + £800 (4·8684) = £11 894·72
P.W. of hiring = £2100 (4·8684)   = £10 223·64

Therefore hiring is more economical.

Equivalent Annual Costs

These comparisons are based on calculating the equivalent capital cost each year of the project. Using scheme 1 the equivalent annual cost is

$$£500 + £5000 (0·2296) = £500 + £1148$$
$$= £1648$$

The £500 is already an annual running cost, the £1148 is the annual equivalent over 6 years of £5000 at 10%. The factor used is the capital recovery factor for 10%. This, compared to the equivalent annual cost of £800 + £4000(0·2296) = £1718·40 for scheme 2, shows that as a means of differentiating between two projects the result is the same as a present worth comparison.

The equivalent annual cost for scheme 3 is £500 + (£3000 × 0·402 11) = £1706·33. Even if a replacement is considered the annual cost will still be £1706·33.

Equivalent annual cost example
The example used is the same as that for the present worth example above.

Equivalent annual cost of buying = £800 + £8000(0·2054)
= £2443·20

Equivalent annual cost of hiring = £2100

Thus hiring is more economical as the present worth comparison also showed.

Profitability Measures

The purpose of economic comparison is to differentiate between two or more projects in order to choose the least expensive. Profitability measurement applies to projects where an investment leads to a return; it is important to determine if this return is adequate. A trite example is an investment of £100 and a return of £110 compared with an investment of £1000 and a return of £1011. While the net profit is larger in the second case, the return on capital will not be satisfactory; and since capital costs money in the form of interest charges or dividends to shareholders, it is necessary to measure the return on capital and compare it to the cost of capital, thereby determining whether the return is adequate. The generally accepted way of measuring return on capital is now 'discounted cash flow yield' (DCF yield), sometimes called the internal rate of return.

DCF Yield

One definition of DCF yield is that it is the *maximum* interest rate that could be paid on borrowed capital assuming that all the capital needed to fund the project is acquired as an overdraft. An example of this definition is given below.

	Year	Project's cash flow (£)	Interest paid on borrowed capital at 8% (trial estimate) (£)	Borrowing account (£)
Investment	0	−1000		−1000
Return	1	+400	−80·00	−680
	2	+400	−54·40	−334·40
	3	+400	−26·75	+38·85

Explanation   At the outset £1000 was borrowed; in year 1 this costs £80; at the end of year 1 the account is −£1000 − £80 + £400 = −£680.

This £680 cost £54·40 in year 2, and at the end of year 2 the account is −£334·40. This −£334·40 costs £26·75 and at the end there is £38·85 remaining. The definition requires the maximum interest rate that could be paid on borrowed capital. Since charging at 8% leaves £38·85 then 8% is not the maximum interest that could be paid for borrowed capital by this project. A second trial rate would have to use a higher interest rate, as below.

Year	Project's cash flow (£)	Interest paid on borrowed capital at 10% (£)	Borrowing Account (£)
0	−1000		−1000
1	+400	−100	−700
2	+400	−70	−370
3	+400	−37	−7

Since the amount remaining is very close to zero at −£7, it can be assumed that the maximum interest rate that can be paid for capital is almost 10%. The exact rate is 9·68%.

This figure of 9·68% represents the DCF yield; it represents the maximum that could be paid for borrowed capital. If the cost of capital is greater than 9·68% then this project does not yield enough to be profitable. Measuring the maximum that could be paid for borrowed capital is a way of measuring the amount being generated by the project. The DCF yield is therefore a profitability measure.

The more usual way of calculating the yield is to use the present worth factors as tabulated in the interest tables (Appendix A13.1) and to redefine DCF as the interest rate which, if used to discount all cash flows, would produce a net present worth of zero. The above project's DCF yield would be calculated as follows.

	Project's	*First trial* *P.W. factors*		*Second trial* *P.W. factors*	
	cash flow	at 9%	P.W.	at 11%	P.W.
Year	(£)	(£)	(£)	(£)	(£)
0	−1000	1·00	−1000	1·00	−1000·00
1	+400	0·917	366·80	0·900	360·00
2	+400	0·841	336·40	0·811	324·40
3	+400	0·772	308·80	0·731	292·40
	Net present worth		+12·00		−23·20

Interpolating between 9% and 11% gives the interest rate which results in a net present worth of zero

$$\text{DCF yield} = 9 + (11 - 9) \times \frac{12 \cdot 00}{12 \cdot 00 - (-23 \cdot 20)}$$

$$= 9 \cdot 68\%$$

The graph in Fig. 13.2 shows that the DCF yield is the interest rate which gives a net present worth of zero.

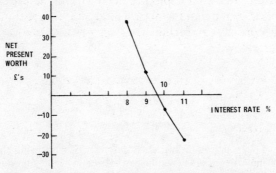

Fig. 13.2 Graph of net present worth *v.* interest rate.

Net Present Worth

Net present worth itself can be used as a means of determining whether a project is profitable enough to be considered a worthwhile investment. The interest rate used in the calculation of the net present worth is usually called the criterion rate of return. The criterion rate is the assessed cost of capital to the company plus a margin in excess of cost to allow for risk. If the project's DCF yield is greater than the criterion rate, the project's net present worth at the criterion rate will be positive. If the project's yield is less than the criterion, then the project's net present worth at the criterion rate will be negative. In the example shown below, project 1 has a positive net present worth at the criterion rate of 15%, project 2 does not. Therefore in selecting projects this method is useful in rejecting the unprofitable ones.

Example   criterion rate 15%

	Project 1		Project 2	
	Cash flow			*Cash flow*
Year	*(£)*	*Year*		*(£)*
0	−4000	0		−4000
1	+2000	1		+1700
2	+2000	2		+1700
3	+2000	3		+1700
Net present worth	+566·40			−118·56

Limitation of Net Present Worth

It is inadvisable to depend exclusively on net present worth to select between different projects. Figure 13.3 shows two projects. If the criterion

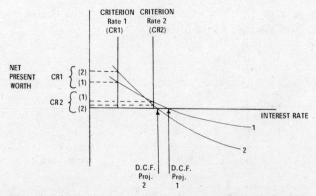

Fig. 13.3 Net present worth *v.* interest rates showing the differing order of net P.W. that can be obtained from different interest rates.

rate was C.R.1, project 2 would, at that rate, have the largest net present worth. If the criterion rate was C.R.2, project 1 would, at that rate, have the largest net present worth. Since project 1 has the largest yield, it would be inappropriate to use the single calculation of net present worth at rate C.R.1 and imply that project 2 has the largest yield.

Limitation of DCF Yield

DCF yield calculations under some cash flow patterns, can have two or more interest rates which both produce a zero net present worth. These patterns are the ones which have large negative flows in the cash flow stream at times other than at the beginning. Examples are open-cast coal mining and quarrying work where expensive land reinstatement is required at the end of the project and also when, due to tax time-lags, a negative tax bill occurs at the end of a project. The solution is a dual rate calculation, and most computer packages which are available to undertake investment appraisal calculations offer the dual rate calculations as a facility.

The dual rate method introduces a second interest rate, an earning rate, assumed to be the rate at which interest can be earned on capital in a safe investment. The calculations proceed to find the maximum paying rate, as before for the fixed earning rate. Merret and Sykes (ref. 1) quote a set of cash flows which have zero net present worths for interest rates of zero, 20% and 40%. The dual rate approach produces a unique yield for a given earning rate. The example below illustrates the calculations. The paying rate calculated by the dual rate method must always be quoted with the earning rate used in the calculation.

Year	Cash flows (£)	Paying rate 10% (found by trial and error) (£)	Earning rate 5% (known) (£)	Borrowing account (£)
0	−2000			−2000
1	+1000	−200		−1200
2	+1000	−120		−320
3	+1000	−32		+648
4	+1000		+32·40	+1680·40
5	−1765		+84·02	−0·58

(NB. 0·58 taken as nearly zero.)

An alternative offered by Merret and Sykes (ref. 1) for when the negative amount occurring at the end of cash flow stream is not large is to discount the negative amount by one year and add it to the previous year's cash flows, and to repeat until a positive amount is obtained. This allows the single rate calculations to be undertaken and is the method used in the example involving corporation tax later in this chapter.

Other Methods of Project Evaluation

The methods of DCF yield or net present worth have largely replaced other methods of project evaluation or project selection. Among the other methods that exist are payback period and average annual rate of return.

Payback period

This involves calculating how long it takes for a project to repay its original invested capital. The shorter the payback period the greater is the likelihood that the project will be profitable. Projects 1 and 2 below are examples of projects with payback periods of 4 years and 2·67 years respectively, therefore project 2 is to be preferred to project 1. The weakness in this method is that it does not take account of the cash flows that occur after the payback period.

Example

	Project 1		Project 2
Year	Cash flow (£)	Year	Cash flow (£)
0	−8000	0	−8000
1	+1000	1	+3000
2	+1000	2	+3000
3	+3000	3	+3000
4	+3000	4	+1000
5	+3000	5	+1000
	Payback period 4 years		Payback period 2·67 years

Average annual rate of return

This method involves calculating the average return and expressing it as a percentage of the invested capital. For project 1 above, the average annual return is

$$\frac{1000 + 1000 + 3000 + 3000 + 3000}{5}$$

$$= £2200$$

which is 27·5% of £8000. Therefore the average annual rate of return is 27·5%. The weakness of this method is that it does not discriminate between the timings of the cash flows. This is illustrated by the fact that project 2 above also has an average annual rate of return of 27·5%;

although it is already known and simple inspection will show that project 2 is clearly the more profitable project, because of the timing of the cash flows. The average annual rate of return does not identify this.

Payback period and average annual rate of return should only be used in conjunction with other more discriminating methods of evaluation.

Inflation

So far it has been assumed that the forecasts of future costs and revenues have been at today's prices. Clearly it is easier to forecast at today's prices since this removes at least one more variable from the forecast, although it also brings into question whether this is a valid approach. However, the effect of inflation can be taken into account when undertaking present worth and yield calculations.

Present Worth

In calculating present worths for the purposes of comparing the costs of alternative projects the effects of inflation can be allowed for in three ways:

 (i) by ignoring inflation;
 (ii) by adjusting the estimated cash flows; and
 (iii) by adjusting the interest rate used to discount the future cash flows.

(i) Ignoring inflation
If the purpose of calculating present worths is simply to compare proposals and to select the most economic, and if the inflation rate assumed is small, then this comparison will not be affected dramatically by the inclusion of inflation. If small allowances for inflation are added into each proposal under consideration the effect will be to increase the present worth of each proposal and the ranking of the proposals is likely to remain unaltered.

(ii) Adjusting cash flows
The simplest way to allow for inflation in present worth calculations is to take the cash flows estimated at today's (i.e. year zero) prices and adjust them for an assumed inflation rate.

As an illustration consider Scheme 1 in the original example of economic comparisons. The cash flows estimated at year zero prices and those adjusted for an assumed rate of 8% inflation each year are:

Scheme 1		Scheme 2	
Cash flows at year zero prices		Cash flows adjusted for an annual inflation rate of 8%	
Year	Cash flows (£)	Year	Cash flows (£)
0	5 000.00	0	5 000.00
1	500.00	1	540.00
2	500.00	2	583.20
3	500.00	3	629.86
4	500.00	4	680.24
5	500.00	5	734.66
6	500.00	6	793.44

The present worth of the original Scheme 1 was £7 177.60 calculated at an interest rate of 10%. The present worth of Scheme 1 adjusted for an annual inflation rate of 8% is £7 814.76. This present worth is larger because it represents the capital required to be invested now, at 10%, to pay for the initial investment of £5 000.00, the running costs of £500.00 per year and also the extra costs due to inflation as represented in the adjusted cash flows. If the cash flows for Scheme 2 were adjusted similarly for inflation and the present worth calculated then comparison of the present worths for the two inflation-adjusted proposals would be possible.

(iii) Adjusting the interest rate
In the example above, the inflation adjustment simply increased the cash flows by 8% each year. The adjustment was made as follows, 'd' representing the inflation rate (d = 0.08 for 8%).

	Scheme 1	Scheme 1	Scheme 1	
Year	Original cash flows (£)	Adjusted cash flows (£)	Original cash flows: inflation adjustment (£)	
0	5 000.00	5 000.00	5 000.00	
1	500.00	540.00	$500.00 \times (1 + d)^1$	
2	500.00	583.20	$500.00 \times (1 + d)^2$	
3	500.00	629.86	$500.00 \times (1 + d)^3$	
4	500.00	680.24	$500.00 \times (1 + d)^4$	
5	500.00	734.66	$500.00 \times (1 + d)^5$	
6	500.00	793.44	$500.00 \times (1 + d)^6$	

The present worth for each adjusted cash flow is calculated by multiplying the adjusted cash flow by the present worth factor as, for example, for year 4:

Year	Cash flow	Present worth factor
4	$£500 \times (1 + d)^4 \quad \times$	$\dfrac{1}{(1 + i)^4}$

where 'i' is the interest rate.

This can be generalised for any year as:

Year	Cash flow	Present worth factor
n	$£500 \times (1 + d)^n \quad \times$	$\dfrac{1}{(1 + i)^n}$

This calculation can be simplified by substituting $(1 + d)^n (1 + e)^n$ for $(1 + i)^n$ where 'd' is the inflation rate and 'e' is calculated so that:

$$(1 + i)^n = (1 + d)^n (1 + e)^n$$

$$\text{giving } (1 + e) = \frac{(1 + i)}{(1 + d)}$$

$$\text{and } e = \frac{(1 + i)}{(1 + d)} - 1.$$

Using this substitution the present worth calculation becomes:

Year	Cash flow	Present worth factor
n	$£500 \times (1 + d)^n \quad \times$	$\dfrac{1}{(1 + d)^n (1 + e)^n}$

The elements $(1 + d)_n$ cancel and the calculation is reduced to:

$$£500 \times \frac{1}{(1 + e)^n}$$

This is the same as the calculation of present worth on the original cash flows except that the interest rate used is 'e' instead of 'i'. The effect of inflation has, therefore, been accommodated by adjusting the interest rate. If i were 10% and d were 8% then:

$$e = \frac{(1 + 0.1)}{(1 + 0.08)} - 1 = 0.01852 = 1.85\%$$

If the present worth of the original cash flows were calculated using an interest rate of 1.85% the present worth would be £7 814.76, which is the same as that achieved by adjusting the cash flows themselves. Adjusting the interest rate is a quicker method of achieving the same effect. The 1.85% calculated is measuring the interest earned in excess of the inflation rate.

If 'i' were 10% and 'd' were 10% then 'e' would be zero and the present worth including inflation would be simply the sum of the original cash flows. If 'i' were 10% and 'd' were 15% then 'e' would be −4.34% and the present worth factors would be greater than unity.

This method of adjusting the interest rates is the most common method employed in allowing for inflation in economic comparisons.

Yield Calculations

If the cash flows used to calculate the D.C.F. yield were estimated at present day prices then this yield would not reflect the effect of inflation. If the cash flows were adjusted for inflation then the yield calculated would be larger than the yield calculated on the original cash flows by an amount equivalent to the inflation rate. The example presented here shows the original example used with a yield of 9.68% on the original cash flows and the original cash flows adjusted for inflation at the rate of 8% per annum which gives a yield of 18.45%.

Year	Original cash flows £	Year	Cash flows adjusted for inflation at 8% per year £
0	− 1 000.00	0	− 1 000.00
1	+ 400.00	1	+ 432.00
2	+ 400.00	2	+ 466.56
3	+ 400.00	3	+ 503.88
	Yield = 9.68%		Yield = 18.45%

The yield calculated on the *uninflated cash flows* is called the real yield or real rate of return because it contains no effects from inflation and the yield calculated on the *inflated cash flows* is called the apparent yield or apparent rate of return because it appears larger than it actually is, due to inflation. The relationship between the real rate (i_r), the apparent rate (i_a) and the inflation rate (i_d) is similar to the relationship used in the present worth calculations and is:

$$(1 + i_a) = (1 + i_r)(1 + i_d)$$

Most proposed investments are appraised on estimates based on today's or year zero prices and the rate of return calculated and used to judge a proposal's viability is therefore normally the real rate of return. It is assumed that as the project is executed inflation will push up both the costs and the revenues so that the achieved apparent rate will become larger than the originally calculated real rate; also, when the effects of inflation are removed the achieved real rate will be at or near the original value. However, if inflation pushes up costs more than revenues the apparent rate may not be sufficiently large to give the original real rate. The cash flows recorded as projects are taking place are normally based on the transactions that occur at current prices and thus the recorded cash flows have inflation included as a matter of course. The yield calculated on these recorded cash flows, therefore, is the apparent rate of return. It is therefore important to distinguish whether the cash flows are based on constant, year zero, prices or current prices when interpreting the calculated yield.

If, for example, the apparent yield calculated on recorded cash flows were 18.8% and the rate of inflation were 10% then the real rate of return would be 8%. Or, if the apparent rate calculated on recorded cash flows were 14.5% and the inflation rate were 10% the real rate would be only 4.09%. The most frightening example is if the apparent rate, calculated on recorded cash flows, were only 8.0% and the inflation rate were 10% the real rate would be −1.8%, that is, a *negative* return.

Accuracy of Future Estimates

The predicted cash flows used in economic appraisals of projects will be subject to error as is any estimate. Accepting that these errors exist,

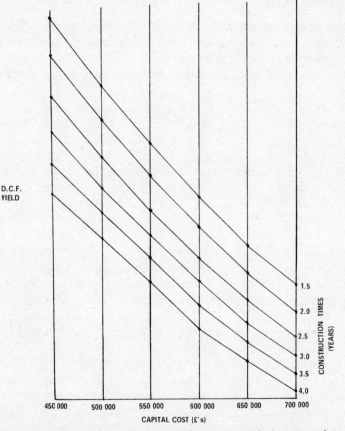

Fig. 13.4a Sensitivity chart of DCF yield, capital cost and construction times from Table 13.1.

Table 13.1 Thirty combinations of construction time and construction cost

Construction time (years)	Construction cost (£)					
1·5	450 000	500 000	550 000	600 000	650 000	700 000
2·0	450 000	500 000	550 000	600 000	650 000	700 000
2·5	450 000	500 000	550 000	600 000	650 000	700 000
3·0	450 000	500 000	550 000	600 000	650 000	700 000
3·5	450 000	500 000	550 000	600 000	650 000	700 000
4·0	450 000	500 000	550 000	600 000	650 000	700 000

appraisal techniques can be extended to evaluate the effect of these errors and produce forecasts of yields in probabilistic terms. The two main techniques are known as sensitivity analysis and risk analysis.

Sensitivity Analysis

This technique requires the DCF yield (or present worth) to be calculated for different values of the cost and incomes estimates. If a hotel was being constructed and the effect on the DCF yield of two variables 'construction cost' and 'construction time', was being examined, the

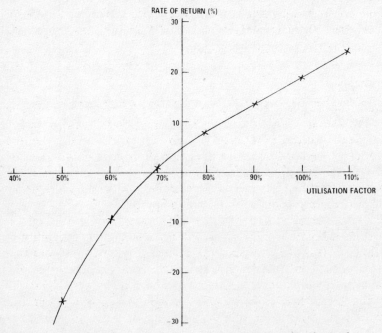

Fig. 13.4b Sensitivity of rate of return to the utilisation of an item of plant.

DCF yield can be calculated for different estimates of the construction cost and time. Table 13.1 shows 30 different combinations of construction cost and time, and Fig. 13.4a shows the 30 different yields resulting from using these 30 different estimates of cost and time. The graph is known as a sensitivity chart and demonstrates how sensitive DCF yield is to changes in the two variables examined. For example, if the duration was increasing due to a lack of proper planning and site control, the reduction in DCF yield could be predicted. If the construction cost was increased in order to finish more quickly, the loss in DCF yield due to increased cost could be predicted and the improvement in DCF yield due to reduced construction time could also be predicted. Whether the increase in cost and reduction in duration leads to an improved DCF yield can be seen from these graphs. It is possible to draw on the graph a line representing the criterion rate of return and thus identify the cost and time combinations that will produce an acceptable return.

Figure 13.4b shows a sensitivity graph of rate of return v. utilisation rate for an excavator. (This graph is reproduced from ref. 10 and is the result of an analysis on a specific item of plant; it is not generally applicable to all plant items.) The limitations of this technique are that it can only cope with a limited number of variables on one graph and that it does not identify the probability of the various combinations occurring. It is unlikely that the smallest construction time would occur with the smallest construction cost; sensitivity graphs do not identify this. The process of risk analysis extends the calculations to include more variables and to take in the above probabilities.

Risk Analysis

Risk analysis requires a 'model' of the cash flows that are used in the DCF calculation. This model consists of breaking down the cash flows until a level of detail is reached whereby estimates for the element can be produced. Figure 13.5 shows such a cash flow model for a proposed small factory. The project being modelled is to buy some land, build a factory, buy equipment, produce electronic goods and sell them. The model has been kept simple for illustration purposes.

The estimates produced for each element are not just single sums, unless the cash flow is known and will not change; the variability of the cash flow for that element is also estimated. Figure 13.6 shows such an estimate for the construction cost. It is in the form of a histogram because risk analysis requires that weights or relative likelihood of the cash flow occurring be attached to the estimates. What the estimates in Fig. 13.6 are reflecting is an expectation that the construction cost will most likely be £500 000; the estimator has given this a 50% chance. The estimator allows for the possibility that the construction cost will be as low as

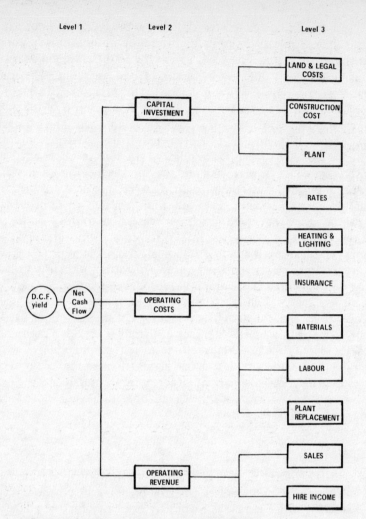

Fig. 13.5 Cash flow model for proposed factory.

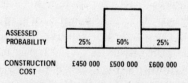

Fig. 13.6 Estimates of construction cost and the variability of the cost.

£450 000, but only gives this a chance of 25%, and similarly acknowledges that the cost could be as high as £600 000.

Those who are new to this type of cash flow modelling with probabilities attached to estimates typically have two reactions, one is to
declare such estimating as impossible and the other is to say it is not
detailed enough to reflect the real world. In answer to the first point the
argument usually takes the line that estimates have to be made; that
estimates almost by definition will be in error and that if the normal
estimating process produces £500 000 then it is no great step to
examine estimates above and below this. If the element being estimated
is too general for this treatment it can always be broken down into smaller
elements. The answer to the second criticism is that if the estimates are
made more detailed, as in Fig. 13.7 the effort required to produce such
detailed estimates may outweigh the information to be gained from the
analysis. A balance between too much detail and too broad an approach
must be found and this will depend on the specific case being analysed.
Figures 13.6 and 13.7 may imply that estimates of variability are always
symmetrical about a mean, but this is not so and Fig. 13.8 shows an
estimate of variability that is skewed.

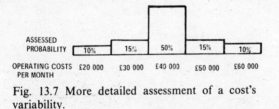

Fig. 13.7 More detailed assessment of a cost's
variability.

Risk analysis requires that estimates for each element be made in the
form above. Estimates are only made for the smallest, most detailed
elements in the model since the other elements can be calculated. The
elements to be estimated in Fig. 13.5 are those shown in level 3.

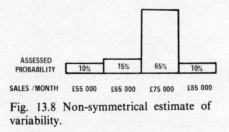

Fig. 13.8 Non-symmetrical estimate of
variability.

There are 11 elements in level 3 and if five estimates were made for
each element then a total of 5^{11}, or 48 828 125, different cash flows
and hence yields could be calculated for this small model. Even with a

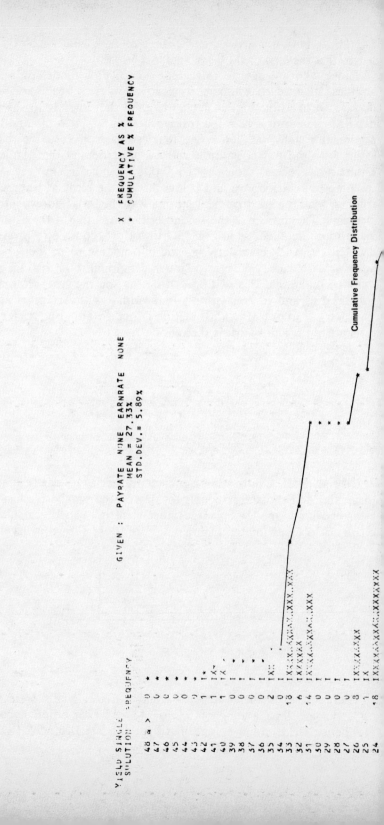

GIVEN : PAYRATE NONE EARNRATE NONE
MEAN = 27.33%
STD.DEV.= 5.89%

X FREQUENCY AS %
* CUMULATIVE % FREQUENCY

Cumulative Frequency Distribution

Fig. 13.10 Simulation output.

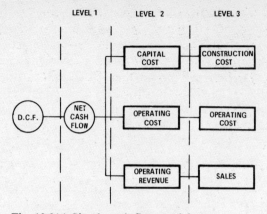

Fig. 13.9(a) Simple cash flow model.

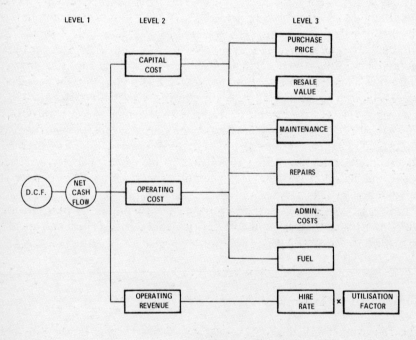

SIMPLE CASH FLOW MODEL FOR
A PLANT HIRE OPERATION

Fig. 13.9(b) Simple cash flow model for a plant hire operation.

computer this would take a long time and the expense is unthinkable. Therefore, instead of calculating all these different combinations, the computer packages available (and to do such calculations without a computer is also unthinkable) select random estimates for each element. Each random selection will be weighted according to the probabilities attached to the estimates. To explain the random process further, examine the very simple model shown in Fig. 13.9a. The elements in level 3 have estimates as shown in Figs. 13.6, 13.7 and 13.8. The total number of possible cash flows are

3 (from Fig. 13.6) × 5 (from Fig. 13.7) × 4 (from Fig. 13.8) = 60

The first selection takes a construction cost at random from Fig. 13.6. In every 100 selections 25 of these will be £450 000, 50 will be £500 000 and 25 will be £600 000. This single selection made at random will be used as the capital cost element when calculating the cash flows. Similarly with the operating cost a random selection will be made from Fig. 13.7. This selection will not have any relationship with the selection for construction cost or sales. The sales figure will be selected from Fig. 13.8. These three selections will be used to calculate the net cash flow and hence the DCF yield. This yield is just one of the 60 possible yields. If this process was repeated 10 times a representation of all the possible yields and the variability of these yields would be obtained. Similarly with the larger example in Fig. 13.5, if the process of random selection and calculation of yield was done say 200 or even 500 times a representation of the possible yields and its variability would be obtained. The results of such an analysis is usually presented in a histogram form as shown in Fig. 13.10. The cumulative curve allows the calculation of the probability of achieving a certain yield. This requires a more sophisticated definition of criterion rate of return. Previously it was a simple rate, say 15%; now it has to have a probability attached – say the criterion becomes 15% provided there is an 85% chance of achieving 15% or better.

Figure 13.9b shows a similar simple cash flow model for plant hiring, which illustrates that the principles of risk analysis described can equally be applied in this case.

Some Worked Examples

The following worked examples are presented as a guide to potential users of these techniques. The examples are

1. A DCF yield calculation allowing for corporation tax and development grants

2. A replacement calculation based on minimising the equivalent annual costs
3. A present worth calculation showing the effect of changes in interest rate

Further examples relating to plant hire calculations are given in Chapter 7.

Table 13.2 DCF example including corporation tax

Year	Investment in plant (£)	Net revenue (£)	Corporation tax at 35% payable on previous year's profits (£)	Plant tax allowances (£)	Tax saved by allowances (£)	Tax paid (£)	Net cash flow (£)
0	120 000			30 000	10 500	−10 500	−104 500.00
1		30 000		22 500	7 875	−7 875	37 875.00
2		30 000	10 500	16 875	5 906.25	4 593.75	25 406.25
3		30 000	10 500	12 656.25	4 429.69	6 070.31	23 929.69
4		30 000	10 500	9 492.19	3 322.27	7 177.73	22 822.27
5		20 000	10 500	7 119.14	2 491.70	8 008.30	11 991.70
6		12 000	7 000	5 339.35	1 868.77	5 131.23	6 868.77
7		10 000	4 200	4 004.52	1 401.58	2 798.42	7 201.58
8		6 000	3 500	3 003.39	1 051.19	2 448.81	3 551.19
9			2 100			2 100.00	−2 100

Note: It is assumed that the tax saving of £10 500 can be taken in year 0 because the company offset this tax saving against its other profits. Capital purchases are added to a company 'pool' and resale values deducted in order to calculate capital allowances. As this case has no resale value there are still effectively capital allowances after disposal which have been ignored.

	Trial interest rate 8%			Trial interest rate 9%		
Year	Net cash flow with discounting of −£2 100 (£)	P.W. factors at 8% (£)	P.W. (£)	Net cash flow with discounting of −£2 100 (£)	P.W. factors at 9% (£)	P.W. (£)
0	−109 500	1.0	−109 500	−109 500	1.0	−109 500
1	37 875	0.925	35 034.38	37 875	0.917	34 731.38
2	25 406.25	0.857	21 773.16	25 406.25	0.841	21 366.66
3	23 929.69	0.793	18 976.24	23 929.69	0.772	18 473.72
4	22 822.27	0.735	16 774.37	22 822.27	0.708	16 158.17
5	11 991.70	0.680	8 154.36	11 991.70	0.649	7 782.61
6	6 868.77	0.630	4 327.33	6 868.77	0.596	4 093.79
7	7 201.58	0.583	4 198.52	7 201.58	0.547	3 939.26
8	1 551.99	0.540	838.07	1 551.99	0.501	777.55
	Net present value +£576.43			Net present value −£2 176.86		

* By discounting −£2 100 from year 9 at 8% and adding to the cash flow for year 8.

Interpolating to find the interest rate which gives a net present worth of zero

$$\text{DCF yield} = 8 + 1 \times \frac{576.43}{576.43 - (-2\ 176.86)} = 8.21\%$$

An Example Demonstrating the Inclusion of Corporation Tax

A company with annual profits of over £1 million purchases and installs a new item of plant. The plant is classed as industrial plant and attracts tax allowances of 25% written down. The cost of equipment, which has no resale value, and the net revenue are shown in columns 1 and 2 of Table 13.2. If corporation tax rate is 35% what is the net of tax DCF yield? A tax time-lag of one year exists. The minimum rate of return the company expects to earn on its capital is 5%.

Cash flows from Table 13.2 have a negative sum, −£2 100 in year 9. Before discounting by the trial interest rates it is necessary to discount £2 100 by one year at the minimum return and add it to the +£3 551.19 of year 8. This produces a positive cash flow and permits a single rate calculation.

Including an Investment Grant

If the plant item in the previous example was installed in a region which attracted an investment grant of say 20%, the cash flows would become as shown in Table 13.3. An investment grant lag of one year exists.

Table 13.3 DCF example including development grant

Year	Invest- ment in plant (£)	Net revenue (£)	Develop- ment grant 20% (£)	Corporation tax at 35% on previous year's profits (£)	Plant tax allowance (£)	Tax saved by allowance (£)	Tax paid (£)	Net cash flow (£)
0	120 000				30 000	10 500	−10 500	−109 500.00
1		30 000	24 000		22 500	7 875	−7 875	61 875
2		30 000		10 500	16 875	5 906.25	4 593.75	25 406.25
3		30 000		10 500	12 656.25	4 429.69	6 070.31	23 929.69
4		30 000		10 500	9 492.19	3 322.27	7 177.73	22 822.27
5		20 000		10 500	7 119.14	2 491.70	8 008.30	11 991.70
6		12 000		7 000	5 339.35	1 868.77	5 131.23	6 868.77
7		10 000		4 200	4 004.52	1 401.58	2 798.42	7 201.58
8		6 000		3 500	3 003.39	1 051.19	2 448.81	3 551.19
9				2 100			2 100.00	−2 100.00

With the investment reduced by the amount of the grant and the returns the same, the DCF yield will be higher.

Example Determining the Optimal Replacement Age based on Minimum Equivalent Annual Costs

The purchase price of a small electricity generating plant is £20 000. The operating costs based on the annual average estimated hours of operation are £800 in the first year, when manufacturers' warranties operate, and £1200 in the second year, rising by £300 each year thereafter. The resale value of the plant can be assumed to be as predicted in Table 13.4. The cost of capital is 15%.

Table 13.4 Predicted Resale Values

Year	Predicted resale values
1	£18 000
2	£16 000
3	£15 000
4	£12 000
5	£8 000
6	£5 000
7	£2 000

The calculations involve determining the equivalent annual cost of keeping the generator for one year and for two years and for three years etc. See Table 13.5.

The optimal replacement age is three years because this produces the minimum equivalent annual costs.

The calculations in Table 13.5 are seeking the balance between rising running costs and declining resale values. The method adopted is self-explanatory from the headings in the table.

Example showing the effect of interest rates on
Present Worth calculations

A pumping scheme being developed has three different possible systems of pumps and pipework. If the life of the scheme is 20 years, which scheme should be recommended as the most economic?

Scheme	Pipe diameter	Installation cost	Annual running cost
A	500 mm	£18 250	£7250
B	600 mm	£20 200	£4600
C	750 mm	£24 000	£4000

Using 15% to represent the cost of capital

Scheme A

$$\begin{aligned}
\text{Present worth of installation cost} &= £18\,250 \\
\text{Present worth of £7250 each year} & \\
\text{for 20 years} = 7250\,(6{\cdot}2593) &= £45\,379{\cdot}93 \\
\hline
\text{Total present worth} &= £63\,629{\cdot}93
\end{aligned}$$

Table 13.5 Calculating the optimal replacement age

Year	A Purchase price (£)	B Capital recovery factors at 15% (£)	C Equivalent annual costs of purchase price (A × B) (£)	D Running costs (£)	E P.W. factors at 15% (£)	F P.W. of running costs (D × E) (£)	G Sum of P.W. of running costs (£)	H Equivalent annual cost of P.W. of running costs (B × G) (£)	I Equivalent annual costs of purchase price and running costs (C + H) (£)	K Resale value (£)	L P.W. of resale (K × E) (£)	M Equivalent annual costs of P.W. of resale (L × B) (£)	N Equivalent annual costs of purchase running and resale (I − M) (£)
0	20 000				1.0								
1		1·150	23 000·0	800	0·869	695	695	799·25	23 799·25	18 000	15 642·00	17 988·30	5 810·95
2		0·615	12 300·0	1 200	0·750	900	1 595	980·93	13 280·93	16 000	12 000·00	7 380·00	5 900·93
3		0·437	8 740·0	1 500	0·657	985	2 580	1 127·46	9 867·46	15 000	9 855·00	4 306·64	5 560·82
4		0·350	7 000·0	1 800	0·571	1 027	3 607	1 262·45	8 262·45	12 000	6 852·00	2 398·20	5 864·25
5		0·298	5 960·0	2 100	0·497	1 043	4 650	1 385·70	7 345·70	8 000	3 976·00	1 184·85	6 160·85
6		0·264	5 280·0	2 400	0·432	1 036	5 686	1 501·10	6 781·10	5 000	2 160·00	570·24	6 210·86

Scheme B

Present worth of installation cost	= £20 200
Present worth of £4600 each year for 20 years = 4600 (6·2593)	= £28 792·78
Total present worth	= £48 992·78

Scheme C

Present worth of installation cost	= £24 000
Present worth of £4000 each year for 20 years = 4000 (6·2593)	= £25 037·20
Total present worth	= £49 037·20

Therefore at 15% scheme B is the most economical.
Repeating the calculations at 10%

Scheme A

Present worth of installation cost	= £18 250
Present worth of £7250 each year for 20 years = 7250 (8·5135)	= £61 722·88
Total present worth	= £79 972·88

Scheme B

Present worth of installation cost	= £20 200
Present worth of £4600 each year for 20 years = 4600 (8·5135)	= £39 162·10
Total present worth	= £59 362·10

Scheme C

Present worth of installation cost	= £24 000
Present worth of £4000 each year for 20 years = 4000 (8·5135)	= £34 054·00
Total present worth	= £58 054·00

At 10% scheme C is the more economic.

The difference between these two calculations is the interest rate. Scheme C requires an extra investment of £3800 in comparison to B. The saving in running costs is £600 per year. When the interest rate is at 15% the savings in running costs are not sufficient to justify the extra expenditure, i.e. the extra expenditure can earn more than £600 per year. When the interest rate is only 10% the extra expenditure cannot earn more than £600 per year and would therefore be better employed earning this saving.

References and Bibliography

1. Merret, A. J. & Sykes, A. *The Finance and Analysis of Capital Projects*. Longman, 1963.

2. Merret, A. J. & Sykes, A. *Capital Budgeting and Company Finance*. Longman, 1966.

3. National Economic Development Council. *Investment Appraisal*. HMSO, 1971.

4. Alfred, A. M. & Evans, J. B. *Discounted Cash Flow – Principles and Short-cut Techniques*. Chapman & Hall, 1965.

5. Wright, M. G. *Discounted Cash Flow*. McGraw-Hill, 1967.

6. Institution of Civil Engineers. *An Introduction to Engineering Economics*. ICE, 1969.

7. Pilcher, R. *Appraisal and Control of Project Costs*. McGraw-Hill, 1973.

8. Savage, C. I. & Small, J. R. *Introduction to Managerial Economics*. Hutchinson, 1970.

9. Harris, F. & McCaffer, R. *Construction Plant: Management and Investment Decisions*. Granada, 1982.

10. Pace, M. *A Cost Reporting System for Construction Plant Management*. M.Sc. project report, Department of Civil Engineering Loughborough University of Technology, 1972.

11. Department of Trade and Industry. *Incentives for Industry in the Areas for Expansion*. HMSO, 1975.

12. Harris, F. & McCaffer, R. *Worked Examples in Construction Management*. Granada, 1978.

13. Pritchard, N.E. *Corporation Tax*. 8th Ed. Polytechnic Publishers Ltd, 1984.

APPENDIX A13.1.

Tabulations of Interest and Time Relationships

Terms

i Rate of interest per period (usually years)

n Number of time periods

Table A13.1 Interest tables for 10%

Year or period (n)	$(1+i)^n$ Compound amount of a single sum	$\dfrac{1}{(1+i)^n}$ Present value of a single sum	$\dfrac{(1+i)^n - 1}{i}$ Compound amount of a uniform series	$\dfrac{i}{(1+i)^n - 1}$ Sinking fund deposit	$\dfrac{(1+i)^n - 1}{i(1+i)^n}$ Present worth of a uniform series	$\dfrac{i(1+i)^n}{(1+i)^n - 1}$ Capital recovery
1	1·100 0	0·909 09	1·000	1·000 00	0·909 0	1·100 00
2	1·209 9	0·826 44	2·099	0·476 19	1·735 5	0·576 19
3	1·330 9	0·751 31	3·309	0·302 11	2·486 8	0·402 11
4	1·464 0	0·683 01	4·640	0·215 47	3·169 8	0·315 47
5	1·610 5	0·620 92	6·105	0·163 79	3·790 7	0·263 79
6	1·771 5	0·564 47	7·715	0·129 60	4·355 2	0·229 60
7	1·948 7	0·513 15	9·487	0·105 40	4·868 4	0·205 40
8	2·143 5	0·466 50	11 435	0·087 44	5·334 9	0·187 44
9	2·357 9	0·424 09	13·579	0·073 64	5·759 0	0·173 64
10	2·593 7	0·385 54	15·937	0·062 74	6·144 5	0·162 74
11	2·853 1	0·350 49	18·531	0·053 96	6·495 0	0·153 96
12	3·138 4	0·318 63	21·384	0·046 76	6·813 6	0·146 76
13	3·452 2	0·289 66	24·522	0·040 77	7·103 3	0·140 77
14	3·797 4	0·263 33	27 974	0·035 74	7·366 6	0·135 74
15	4·177 2	0·239 39	31·722	0·031 47	7·606 0	0·131 47
16	4·594 9	0·217 62	35·949	0·027 81	7·923 7	0·127 81
17	5·054 4	0·197 84	40·544	0·024 66	8·021 5	0·124 66
18	5·559 9	0·179 85	45·599	0·021 93	8·201 4	0·121 93
19	6·115 9	0·163 50	51·159	0·019 54	8·364 9	0·119 54
20	6·727 4	0·148 64	57·274	0·017 45	8·513 5	0·117 45
21	7·400 2	0·135 13	64·002	0·015 62	8·648 6	0·115 62
22	8·140 2	0·122 84	71·402	0·014 00	8·771 5	0·114 00
23	8·954 3	0·111 67	79·543	0·012 57	8·883 2	0·112 57
24	9·849 7	0·101 52	88·497	0·011 29	8·984 7	0·111 29
25	10·834 7	0·092 29	98·347	0·010 16	9·077 0	0·110 16
26	11·918 1	0·083 90	109·181	0·009 15	9·160 9	0·109 15
27	13·109 9	0·076 27	121·099	0·008 25	9·237 2	0·108 25
28	14·420 9	0·069 34	134·209	0·007 45	9·306 5	0·107 45
29	15·863 0	0·063 03	148·630	0·006 72	9·369 6	0·106 72
30	17·449 4	0·057 30	164·494	0·006 07	9·426 9	0·106 07
35	28·102 4	0·035 58	271·024	0·003 68	9·644 1	0·103 68
40	45·259 2	0·022 09	442·592	0·002 25	9·779 0	0·102 25
45	72·890 4	0·013 71	718·904	0·001 39	9·862 8	0·101 39
50	117·390 8	0·008 51	1 163·908	0·000 85	9·914 8	0·100 85

Tables are reproduced from the examination tables of Loughborough University of Technology, Department of Civil Engineering.

Table A13.1 Interest tables for 15%

Year or period (n)	$(1 + i)^n$ Compound amount of a single sum	$\dfrac{1}{(1 + i)^n}$ Present worth of a single sum	$\dfrac{(1 + i)^n - 1}{i}$ Compound amount of a uniform series	$\dfrac{i}{(1 + i)^n - 1}$ Sinking fund deposit	$\dfrac{(1 + i)^n - 1}{i(1 + i)^n}$ Present worth of a uniform series	$\dfrac{i(1 + i)^n}{(1 + i)^n - 1}$ Capital recovery
1	1·150 0	0·869 56	1·000	1·000 00	0·869 5	1·150 00
2	1·322 4	0·756 14	2·149	0·465 11	1·625 7	0·615 11
3	1·520 8	0·657 51	3·472	0·287 97	2·283 2	0·437 97
4	1·749 0	0·571 75	4·993	0·200 26	2·854 9	0·350 26
5	2·011 3	0·497 17	6·742	0·148 31	3·352 1	0·298 31
6	2·313 0	0·432 32	8·753	0·114 23	3·784 4	0·264 23
7	2·660 0	0·375 93	11·066	0·090 36	4·160 4	0·240 36
8	3·059 0	0·326 90	13·725	0·072 85	4·487 3	0·222 85
9	3·517 8	0·284 26	16·785	0·059 57	4·771 5	0·209 57
10	4·045 5	0·247 18	20·303	0·049 25	5·018 7	0·199 25
11	4·652 3	0·214 94	24·349	0·041 06	5·233 7	0·191 06
12	5·350 2	0·186 90	29·001	0·034 48	5·420 6	0·184 48
13	6·152 7	0·162 52	34·351	0·029 11	5·583 1	0·179 11
14	7·075 7	0·141 32	40·504	0·024 68	5·724 4	0·174 68
15	8·137 0	0·122 89	47·580	0·021 01	5·847 3	0·171 01
16	9·357 6	0·106 86	55·717	0·017 94	5·954 2	0·167 94
17	10·761 2	0·092 92	65·075	0·015 36	6·047 1	0·165 36
18	12·375 4	0·080 80	75·836	0·013 18	6·127 9	0·163 18
19	14·231 7	0·070 26	88·211	0·011 33	6·198 2	0·161 33
20	16·366 5	0·061 10	102·443	0·009 76	6·259 3	0·159 76
21	18·821 5	0·053 13	118·810	0·008 41	6·312 4	0·158 41
22	21·644 7	0·046 20	137·631	0·007 26	6·358 6	0·157 26
23	24·891 4	0·040 17	159·276	0·006 27	6·398 8	0·156 27
24	28·625 1	0·034 93	184·167	0·005 42	6·433 7	0·155 42
25	32·918 9	0·030 37	212·793	0·004 69	6·464 1	0·154 69
26	37·856 7	0·026 41	245·711	0·004 06	6·490 5	0·154 06
27	43·535 3	0·022 96	283·568	0·003 52	6·513 5	0·153 52
28	50·065 6	0·019 97	327·104	0·003 05	6·533 5	0·153 05
29	57·575 4	0·017 36	377·169	0·002 65	6·550 8	0·152 65
30	66·211 7	0·015 10	434·745	0·002 30	6·565 9	0·152 30
35	133·175 5	0·007 50	881·170	0·001 13	6·616 6	0·151 13
40	267·863 5	0·003 73	1 779·090	0·000 56	6·641 7	0·150 56
45	538·769 2	0·001 85	3 585·128	0·000 27	6·654 2	0·150 27
50	1 083·657 3	0·000 92	7 217·715	0·000 13	6·660 5	0·150 13

INVESTMENT APPRAISAL EXERCISES

Exercise 1

A town built on a river is considering building an additional bridge across the river. Two proposals have been put forward for bridges at different sites. The costs of each proposal are summarised as follows:

	Bridge A	Bridge B
Initial cost of bridge	£65 000	£50 000
Initial cost of roadworks	£35 000	£30 000
Annual maintenance of bridge	£500	£900 for first 15 years
		£1100 thereafter
Structural inspection	—	£2000 at year 15
Annual maintenance of roads	£300	£250
Life of bridge	60 years	30 years
Life of roads	60 years	60 years

With the cost of money at 9%, which proposal should be adopted? Assessment of the proposals to be carried out by a comparison of their net present worths.

Exercise 2

A company are considering the installation of new process plant equipment at a cost of £59 500 spread over three years, as follows:

Year 1	£17 500
Year 2	£22 000
Year 3	£20 000

The net annual income from this plant will be £10 500.

The suppliers of the plant recommend a life of only 10 years for the equipment, but the company intend to run the plant for 13 years after the completion of the installation, and this means incurring heavy replacement and maintenance costs of £6500, £7500 and £9500 during the last three years.

Calculate the DCF yield for this project.

Exercise 3

A company with annual pre-tax profits of approximately £2 million propose to purchase an item of plant for £50 000. There is no expected resale value.

Depreciation allowance to be set against tax is 100% in the first year and an investment grant of 20% is available. Corporation tax is 50% and a time lag of one year exists before tax is paid and the grant is received.

Calculate the cash flows net of tax based on the projected revenues given and determine whether the net of tax yield is more than 15%.

Year	Net revenue
1	£15 000
2	£18 000
3	£20 000
4	£20 000
5	£10 000
6	£10 000

Exercise 4

A precast concrete company is considering purchasing a small concrete mixing plant to be used for on-site remedial work. The equipment suppliers claim that, because of the limited use the plant will be put to, the resale value will remain high and the equipment will operate efficiently for 20 years or more.

However, the precast concrete company have asked you to assess the economic replacement age.

The initial cost of the equipment is £15 000.

The operating costs of the plant, based on an average estimate of hours used each year, is £500 in the first year when manufacturer's warranties operate and £1000 in the second year, increasing by £300 per annum thereafter.

The resale value is estimated to decrease by 15% per annum compound.

In your calculations explain (do not derive) any relationship or expression used.

The cost of capital can be assumed to be 12%.

Exercise 5

(a)
A material supplier has bought quarrying rights and is free to quarry stone provided the farmland affected is reinstated afterwards. The reinstatement work involves the company in heavy capital expenditure towards the end of the project. The table shows the capital expenditure and the net revenue.

Calculate the paying rate given that the earning rate is 5% p.a. Why is the 'paying rate' a measure of the project's profitability?

Year	Capital expenditure	Net revenue
0	£500 000	
1	£300 000	£400 000
2		£200 000
3		£200 000
4		£200 000
5		£200 000
6	£180 000	

(b)
The estimate of £180 000 for reinstatement is thought to be the least reliable of all these estimates. Explain how you would deal with such an unreliable estimate in an assessment of the project's rate of return.

Exercise 6

Ten years ago an investment project was entered into by a company because the calculated rate of return on the predicted costs and revenues was a satisfactory 14% in real terms. The project did not prove to be as lucrative as expected, and the net annual revenues obtained during the project are shown below.

If over the last 10 years inflation was on average 5% per annum, what was the real rate of return to the company on the capital invested in this project?

Year		
0	Investment	£24 450
1		£4 500
2		£4 700
3		£5 000
4		£5 100
5	Net revenues	£4 900
6		£5 100
7		£5 300
8		£4 900
9		£4 800
10		£4 300

CHAPTER 14

FINANCIAL MANAGEMENT

Summary

The purpose of this chapter is to provide an understanding of capital and its effective use in a construction company so that the manager is better equipped to deal with the financial crises which inevitably occur. The sources, types and means of acquiring funds and capital are described. Examples illustrating the capital workings are given, which are later reinforced by a case study illustrating the accounts for a typical construction company. The study describes the build-up of the profit and loss account and the balance sheet, giving examples highlighting the important financial information which can be derived from such accounts.

Introduction

In 1981 there were over 96 000 companies operating in the British construction industry, of which all but 1000 employed less than 100 people. The number of bankruptcies of these smaller companies is high and the reasons are not hard to find. Many contracts are undertaken on the basis that the client pays for completed work progressively throughout the life of the project. Therefore, providing that the contractor is able to raise sufficient capital to finance possibly the first two months of the contract, he can rely on steady interim payment thereafter. However whenever the market takes a downward turn the competition for contracts becomes more fierce, resulting in underpriced tenders. Should any unforeseen difficulties then arise during the course of the contract's execution, insufficient financial resources are available to pay the creditors and bankruptcy follows. Furthermore, in times of rapid inflation those companies which carry high material stocks may run into cash flow problems because of the need to purchase the now more expensive materials out of previous earnings. In many cases such companies are in a profit-making situation in the long term, but do not have the immediate cash to pay creditors. During recent years even the larger contractor has faced such problems. A better understanding of financial control may help to avoid such problems and difficulties. (For wider treatment of this subject see references, especially Goodlad (ref. 6).)

Types of Businesses

The limited company which emerged from the nineteenth century has proved successful and is the predominant type found in the construction industry today. The significant feature is that private individuals introduce capital into the company and in so doing become shareholders, but with their personal liability limited to the amount unpaid on their shareholdings. There are two types of limited company, private and public, which are both covered by the 1948 and 1967 Companies Acts.

Private Companies

The legal procedure for forming a private company is fairly straightforward. The persons wishing to form the company must place with the Registrar of Companies:

The memorandum
The articles of association (if any)
A list of persons who have consented to be directors
A statement of the nominal share capital (Finance Act 1933)
A statutory declaration of compliance (the purpose of which is to show that all legal requirements have been met)

Also, within 14 days of registering:

The address of the registered office
Particulars of the directors and secretary

The memorandum of association contains five compulsory clauses:

(i) The name of the company (which must end with the word limited).
(ii) The objectives of the company – these can be drawn so wide that they may include almost any legitimate activity.
(iii) The amount of authorised share capital.
(iv) The domicile of the company.

(v) The limitation of liability of the members of the company (share-holders) signed by each subscriber in the presence of at least one witness. Each subscriber must take at least one share.

The articles of association   A company is not bound to have articles of association. However, if a company fails to register, articles will automatically be ruled by the model set to be found in Table 4 of the Companies Act.

The articles comprise the rules and regulations which govern the internal workings of the company. They cover matters such as the issue and transfer of shares, alterations to capital holdings, borrowing powers, shareholders' meetings and voting rights, the appointment and powers of directors, and the presenting and auditing of accounts.

Public Companies

When a private company reaches a certain size, the problem of obtaining additional capital for further expansion is often best achieved by increasing the shareholdings in the company. However, the number of individuals willing to invest capital in an unquoted company are likely to be few, since they cannot get a realistic valuation of their shares without the facilities of the market forces which operate on the Stock Exchange. To become a public company, therefore, involves the raising of capital via the Stock Exchange. The legal requirements for the public company are slightly more involved than for the private one. The number of directors must be at least two and the number of persons signing the memorandum at least seven, although there is no maximum limit. Additionally, as the company wishes to issue shares to the public, it must file a copy of the prospectus (a document inviting the public to subscribe to the company's share capital) with the Registrar General. (Sometimes the capital is subscribed privately by a large institution, in which case the company must file a statement in lieu of the prospectus.)

The Prospectus

A company wishing to raise capital on the London stock market, usually approaches a broker, who then lodges a letter of application setting out the particulars for which a quotation is sought. At the Stock Exchange various Committees on Quotations consider the application and judge whether the company should be allowed to advertise for subscribers. The advertisement contains all the information required by the prospectus plus other information demanded by the Stock Exchange, as follows:

(*a*) A statement of the company's previously issued capital, dividends and capital repayments, and the voting rights of the different classes of shareholders.

(b) A list of names and addresses of the company directors, auditors, secretary, bankers, brokers and solicitors.

(c) An outline history of the company.

(d) A profit statement for the last ten years, together with a summary of the previous audited balance sheet.

(e) Details from the articles of association.

(f) A summary of contracts and other work entered into during the previous two years.

(g) The views of the board of directors on the future trading and financial prospects for the company.

Stock Exchange quotations

Whenever a share issue is to be made to the public, much advice is required regarding:

(i) The price at which to issue the shares for subscription.

(ii) The type and number of shares to issue.

(iii) Any legal rights and implications.

(iv) The viability of the issue.

It is usual to engage the services of an experienced issuing house to carry out this work. The issuing house will also take on the administrative duties involved with placing the necessary advertisements and allocations of the shares. The considerable experience of issuing houses is called upon to judge the market, since if all the shares are not taken up and their market price subsequently falls, the plan to raise the necessary capital will not be fulfilled. For this reason the issuing house either underwrites the risk itself or arranges elsewhere for the share issue to be underwritten. Only reputable companies with a solid record are therefore likely to be considered by such houses. Once an agreed minimum number of shares have been taken up, the company is given a Stock Exchange quotation.

Buying and selling shares   The shares are floated on the stock market at a previously decided price called the nominal price of the share, which represents the capital to be raised by the issue. However, subsequent buying or selling of the shares is subject to the market forces operating at the time, causing the price of the share to fluctuate wildly. The reasons for this are many, but are mainly associated with the company performance and the economy as a whole. The gains or losses in the share price are independent of the company and are borne entirely by the shareholders. In general, the market share price reflects the market's valuation of the company.

Sources of Capital

The small company beginning operations will normally need to find the initial capital to start the business from private resources. Few others

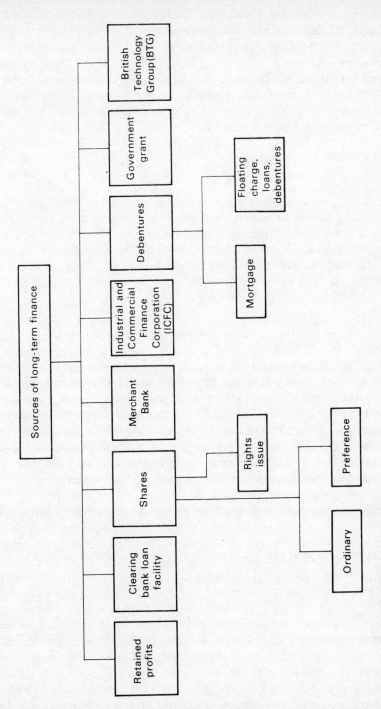

Fig. 14.1 Sources of long-term finance.

are willing to take the risks associated with an unknown enterprise. Gradually, though, as the firm prospers by ploughing back retained profits, the usual lenders of capital may then consider providing loans and investments.

Loan capital can be classified into short-term and long-term borrowings. Short-term loans usually carry lower interest rates, by virtue of the fact that repayment periods are short of the order of months, and therefore open to much less risk than loans granted over a period of years.

Long-term/Medium-term Finance

Long-term finance is that capital required for five to ten years, either to start the business or to carry out expansion programmes. Broadly the capital is used to purchase buildings, plant and equipment and to carry stocks of materials. The risks to the lender are high because of the time scale involved, consequently only established firms are generally considered by the lending institutions. Some of the more important sources of long-term capital are shown in Fig. 14.1.

Short-term Finance

The firm when established often needs short-term capital to overcome immediate cash flow problems. Materials have to be purchased, plant hired, labour and subcontractors paid and so on before payment is received for the finished product. Furthermore, capital may be required to smooth out the strains on cash flow resulting from rapid fluctuations in the market demand for the company's goods. Many sources of short-term finance are available to ease the situation, but naturally the firm must be well managed and profitable before the lending institutions will consider any loan application. The main sources are shown in Fig. 14.2; the clearing bank overdraft facility is the most important source.

Capital Sources and Institutions

The more common types are the following:

Shares
Shares are called the equity in the company. The shareholder is entitled to the residual profits in the company after all other commitments have been met. The share also entitles the holder to voting rights and is termed an ordinary share. Other forms of shareholding include; those without voting rights; preference shares, which entitle the holder to a dividend

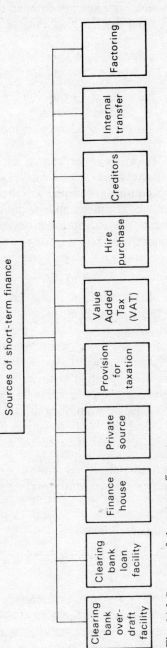

Fig. 14.2 Sources of short-term finance.

in preference to the ordinary shareholder; and cumulative preference shares, whereby a dividend is paid in full later to allow for those years when a dividend was not declared.

Debentures

These are loans made to the company. They differ from conventional loans insofar as they are offered to the market at a fixed interest rate and are repayable at a set time. The loan is either secured by the mortgage on the firm's property or simply on the basis of the company's reputation.

Debenture holders rank ahead of almost all other creditors in the case of liquidation of the firm's assets. Like other loans, debentures represent a cost to the company and as such the interest payment made to the holders is deducted from profits before allowance is made for corporation tax payments. In addition, the payments rank ahead of any dividend declared to shareholders.

Loans

Loans are not easy to obtain. Most institutions are reluctant to lend long term, particularly to construction firms. They often request the borrower to provide a proportion of the finance from internal resources. Merchant banks tend to demand higher rates of interest than the clearing banks since they are normally dealing with a large loan. Their role is not great in the construction industry but such institutions are gradually becoming more involved with the large contractor who has interests in package deals and speculative ventures, both at home and increasingly overseas. In the main, however, the bulk of construction firms must rely on good relationships developed with one of the clearing banks.

The Industrial and Commercial Finance Corporation (ICFC)

Founded in 1945 and a subsidiary of Finance for Industry (which is owned by the major clearing banks and the Bank of England), ICFC helps mainly small businesses with loans and equity, but never more than £1 million at a time.

Rights issue

Shareholders are offered new shares in exchange for their present holdings. Any not taken up are put up for sale; e.g. a company with shares holding a nominal value of say £2, offers its shareholders three new shares at £0·90 each in exchange. The market price of the new share is now likely to fall, but of course the shareholder has more shares to take account of this.

Provision for Corporation Tax
Payment of this tax is usually made one year in arrears. The cash therefore remains in the business during that time and acts as a valuable source of short-term funds.

Cash from creditors
Delayed payments to creditors and prompt ones from debtors, if handled with care, ease cash flow problems. The construction industry is well suited for this sort of financial arrangement since completed work is paid for by the client in monthly stages.

Retained profits

The Control of Capital

Liabilities

The capital in a business is that money invested by shareholders, money loaned by individuals or institutions and retained profits. The capital represents a liability on the company and is used to purchase its assets. Short-term liabilities, sometimes called *current liabilities*, include creditors, short-term loans and provisions for taxation and are not usually included with the capital employed for analysis purposes.

Assets

Fixed assets
The fixed assets are the buildings, land, plant and equipment etc. permanently retained in the business for the purpose of facilitating the use of the working capital.

Current assets
Current assets include material stocks, work in progress, cash at the bank, debtors and short-term investments. They are the assets locked up in the working capital cycle.

Working capital
Working capital comprises the liquid or near-liquid assets needed to lubricate the daily transactions of the business. It is represented by the difference between current assets and current liabilities, and is locked up in a continuous cycle as shown in Fig. 14.3. Working capital should not be confused with capital employed, described later.

Example – illustrating working capital requirements   A precast concrete manufacturer is considering whether to increase production. In order to do so, a new and fully equipped factory is required at an estimated cost of £450 000. The value of the increase in turnover is projected to be £2 000 000 p.a. broken down as 40% materials, 35% wages and other production costs, 15% administration, the remaining 10% representing profit. On average the concrete units take two weeks to produce, after which they are put into store until fully cured and ready for sale. The average period between completion of manufacture and sale is two

The Working Capital Cycle

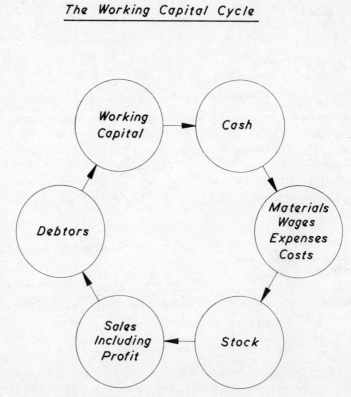

Fig. 14.3 The working capital cycle.

months, and two months credit is allowed to customers. Three months supply of raw materials will be kept in stock at all times, for which suppliers customarily allow one and a half months credit.

Problem   Determine the capital required to equip the new business, plus the working capital to finance the normal transactions.

New capital requirements		£
Buildings and equipment		450 000
		450 000

Working capital requirements
Materials (40% of £2 millions = £800 000

	Time factor	
Materials held in stock	3 months	
Materials held in production	$\frac{1}{2}$ month	
Finished goods held before sale	2 months	
Credit to purchasers	2 months	
	$7\frac{1}{2}$ months	
Less credit from suppliers	$1\frac{1}{2}$ months	
	6 months	

$\therefore$ Materials $= \dfrac{6}{12} \times 800\,000$ 400 000

Labour (35% of £2 millions is £700 000)

	Time factor	
Production period	$\frac{1}{2}$ month	
Selling period	2 months	
Credit to purchaser	2 months	
	$4\frac{1}{2}$ months	

$\therefore$ Labour $= \dfrac{4\frac{1}{2}}{12} \times 700\,000$ 262 500

Administration/selling (15% of £2 millions is £300 000)

$= \dfrac{4\frac{1}{2}}{12} \times 300\,000$ 112 500

£775 000

Total new capital requirement   £1 225 000

The capital raised for the purchase of the building is needed on a long-term basis. But that required to ease the cash flow situation generated by the normal trading processes has to be financed with internal sources of capital or with short-term loans, for which a bank overdraft facility is the more usual source.

Capital Gearing

Capital gearing is defined as the ratio of fixed return capital to ordinary share capital.

If a company can confidently expect to make a reasonable profit in most years, then it is wise to raise some of its capital by means of debentures and/or preference shares at a fixed interest payment, so providing an improved yield for the ordinary shareholder as demonstrated in the following examples:

Fixed return capital (F.R.C.) – preference shares, debentures, and loans
Company X is high-geared while Company Y is low-geared.

	Company X (£)	Company Y (£)
10% Debentures	10 000	100 000
5% Preference shares	6 000	300 000
Ordinary shares	4 000	1 600 000
TOTAL F.R.C.	£16 000	£400 000
TOTAL Ordinary shares	4 000	1 600 000

$$\text{Capital gearing Ratio} \quad \frac{16\,000}{4\,000} \times 100\% = 400\% \qquad \frac{400\,000}{1\,600\,000} \times 100 = 25\%$$

Leverage

The question of capital gearing is extremely important when considering the injection of new finance into the company. The following example illustrates how high gearing can raise the yield on ordinary shares. (Assume 15% profit earned on capital employed.)

	Period 1 (£)	Period 2 (£)
Ordinary shares @ £1 each	2 000	1 000
1000 10% Debentures @ £1 each	—	1 000
	£2 000	£2 000
Disposable profit	£300	£300
Interest on debentures	—	£100
Profit	£300	£200
Corporation tax (say 50%)	£150	£100
Profit available to ordinary shareholders	£150	£100
Profit per share	7·5p	10p
Gearing ratio	— (low)	100% (high)

Note: A fall of £200 in profits would entirely eliminate the yield on the ordinary shares for the highly geared company. It is unwise to gear up highly if profits are likely to fluctuate wildly from year to year, since debentures have to be paid irrespectively. Furthermore, when the average profit is good, but fluctuates over a period of years, the preference shareholder is entitled to only a fixed interest payment, while the ordinary shareholder gains in the good years. This is overcome by means of cumulative preference shares, on which a dividend is paid to cover all the years when full payment was not possible.

The Company Accounts

Since the 1967 Companies Act, all limited companies are required to file their annual accounts with the Registrar of Companies. To ensure that these accounts give a true and fair view of the company's trading position, they are subjected to an annual audit by an independent firm of professional accountants appointed by the Dept. of Trade. The Act requires the company to present to its shareholders a balance sheet, and profit and loss account, which clearly separates the assets, liabilities and trading results for the period of one year just past.' The balance sheet represents a 'photograph' of the company's trading position at a given point in time.

In practice the exercise takes many weeks to complete and is therefore only the accountants' forward projections of the trading position to that time. In addition, current discussion may lead to the implementation of inflation accounting in line with the recommendations of the Sandilands Report.

The profit and loss account

The company accounts are kept in a ledger, using the double entry bookkeeping convention. The figures record each and every money transaction entered into by the business, from which a profit and loss statement is derived.

Example A construction company works on five contracts during the year ended 31 December 1981. The trading position of each contract is given in Tables 14.1 and 14.2.

Analysis The information is interpreted to give the profit and loss account (Table 14.3) and the balance sheet (Table 14.4).

Table 14.1 Company trading position at 31 December 1981

Description	Contract (£)				
	A	B	C	D*	E*
Plant hired	2 500	1 500	1 000	500	500
Materials used	10 000	12 000	7 500	9 000	5 000
Wages and salaries incurred	7 500	6 000	2 500	2 000	1 000
Value of completed work	25 000	24 000	14 000	—	—
Work certified and paid for	25 000	24 000	8 000	—	—

* Contracts D and E are incomplete at the end of 1981.

Table 14.2 Details of the trading position

Item	£
(a) Value of company fixed assets of land and buildings as at 31 December 1980	15 000
(b) Materials purchased and delivered to contracts	44 500
(c) Payments completed in respect of:	
(i) Overhead expenses on contracts	3 000
(ii) Salaries and overheads at head office	6 000
(iii) Wages and salaries on contracts	18 000
(d) Payments completed in respect of creditors	49 000
(e) Price of plant and equipment purchased during year (depreciation allowance on plant and equipment is 10% p.a.)	5 000
(f) Cash at bank as at 31 December 1981	2 500
(g) Depreciation of buildings (3⅓% p.a.) on:	15 000
(h) Opening stock of materials at 31 December 1980	500

Notes:

1. Work on site not yet completed is valued at 50% added to wages, materials and plant costs incurred.

2. The capital employed in the business is represented by

   £21 500 – ordinary shares at £1 each
   £5 000 – 7% debentures at £1 each
   £10 000 – 10 000 5% preference shares at £1 each

3. Corporation tax is set at 50%. (Corporation tax will be treated simply as a straightforward deduction from profits. In fact the payment of tax is quite complex as governed under the new Advanced Corporation Tax Act.)

Table 14.3 Profit and Loss statement for 1981

Tabulated revenue account year ended 31 Dec. 1981	£	£
Sales	25 000	
	24 000	
	14 000	
	——— 63 000	
Work in progress	9 000	
	500	
	2 000	
	5 000	
	500	
	1 000	
	———	
	18 000 × 1·5 27 000	
Value of production		£90 000
Materials used	10 000	
	12 000	
	7 500	
	9 000	
	5 000	
	——— 43 500	
Wages incurred	7 500	
	6 000	
	2 500	
	2 000	
	1 000	
	——— 19 000	
Plant hire	2 500	
	1 500	
	1 000	
	500	
	500	
	——— 6 000	
Overhead expenses on sites	3 000	
Cost of production		£71 500
Production profit		£18 500
Head office overheads and salaries	6 000	
Trading profit		£12 500
Depreciation of Plant and buildings	1 000	
Net profit (before tax)		£11 500
Interest on 7% debentures	350	
		£11 150
Corporation tax (say 50%)	5 575	
Profit after tax		£5 575
Proposed dividend	2 500	
Transfer to general reserve	3 000	
Balance C/F		£75

Table 14.4 Tabulated Balance Sheet at 31 December 1981

(a)

Balance Sheet as at 31 Dec. 1981					As at Dec 31 1980
			Dep'n		
EMPLOYMENT OF CAPITAL		£	£	£	£
Fixed assets					
Buildings		15 000	500	14 500	
Plant and equipment		5 000	500	4 500	
		20 000	1 000	19 000	(15 000)
Current assets					
Cash at bank			2 500		(—)
Stock of materials	45 000				
Less used	43 500				
			1 500		(500)
Work in progress			27 000		(28 250)
Debtors: Contract C	14 000				
Less paid	8 000				
			6 000		(5 000)
				37 000	33 750
				56 000	48 750
Current liabilities					
Creditors: Equip.	5 000				
Plant hire	6 000				
Mat.	45 000				
	56 000				
Less paid	49 000				
			7 000		(5 500)
Wages and salaries on site	19 000				
Less paid	18 000				
			1 000		(500)
Proposed dividend			2 500		(150)
Interest due on loans			350		(700)
Bank overdraft			(—)		(250)
Corporation tax liability			5 575		(150)
				16 425	(7 250)
				£39 575	£41 500

(b)

	1981	(1980)
CAPITAL EMPLOYED	£	£
Share Capital authorised and issued		
21 500 ord. shares @ £1 ea.	21 500	(21 500)
10 000 5% pref. shares @ £1 ea.	10 000	(10 000)
5 000 7% debentures @ £1 ea.	5 000	(10 000)
Reserves		
General	3 000	(—)
Capital	—	(—)
Profit and loss account	75	(—)
	£39 575	(£41 500)

Note: In practice it is usual for corporation tax payments to be paid approximately one year in arrears, in which case the tax liability for 1981 would appear as part of the capital employed and not as a current liability as shown.

The Balance Sheet

The 1948 Companies Act requires all companies to produce a yearly balance sheet showing: (1) the capital invested in the business and its classification; (2) how the capital is being employed by the business. The presentation is either in (*a*) tabular form, showing the employment of the capital with deductions made for current liabilities followed by the classification of the capital employed, or (*b*) liabilities shown on the left-hand side and the assets on the right of the page. In each case the opposing sets of figures must balance exactly (Table 14.5).

Common Terms Used in the Accounts

Debtor   Monies owed to the business by others who have received goods or services.

Creditor   Monies owed by the business to others for goods and services supplied.

Depreciation   The assets of the business wear out in producing the goods and finally have to be replaced. The loss in value each year represents a cost on the business to be taken out of the profits and in theory is set aside to replace the asset when worn out. Buildings, however, sometimes appreciate. At present, tax is not payable on the increase in value until the asset is sold, at which time the company is liable for capital gains tax. The usual way to cover such future payments is to create a capital reserve fund.

General reserve   Profits which are not distributed to shareholders are allocated to the general reserve and as such are reinvested into the business. If the general reserve grows large relative to other capital employed in the business, either the shareholders are given free shares or the nominal price of the existing shares is increased, whereby the general reserve is proportionately reduced. Such action removes any confusion that the general reserve can be declared as a dividend. (The general reserve, remember, has probably already been spent, but must remain as a liability on the balance sheet.)

Dividend   The dividend is that proportion of profits distributed to shareholders after all other commitments have been met.

Interpreting Balance Sheet Information

The flow of funds
It is becoming more common for the presentation of the annual accounts to include, with the balance sheet and profit and loss account information, an analysis of the source and application of funds.

Table 14.5 Alternative presentation of the balance sheet

Balance sheet as at 31 December 1981

Liabilities	£	£
Share capital authorised and issued		
21 500 ord. shares @ £1 each		21 500
10 000 5% pref. shares @ £1 each		10 000
5 000 7% debentures @ £1 each		5 000
General reserve		3 000
Profit and loss account		75
		39 575
Current liabilities		
Creditors	56 000	
Less paid	49 000	
		7 000
Wages		1 000
Proposed dividend		2 500
Interest on loans		350
Corporation tax liability		5 575
		16 425
		£56 000

Assets	£	£	£
Fixed assets			
Buildings	15 000	500	14 500
Plant and equipment	5 000	500	4 500
	20 000	1 000	19 000
Current assets			
Cash at bank			2 500
Stock			1 500
Work in progress			27 000
Debtors			6 000
			37 000
			£56 000

Example Show details of (*a*) the source and application of funds, and (*b*) the working capital changes, using the information given for the company in Tables 14.3 and 14.4 for the year ended 31 December 1981.

Internal sources of funds	£
Profit before tax	11 500
Add: depreciation	1 000
Decrease in work in progress	1 250
Increase in creditors	1 500
Wages and salaries	500
	£15 750

Application	
Dividends, loan interest and tax paid for 1980	1 000
Increase in debtors	1 000
Purchase of new equipment	5 000
Decrease in debenture holdings	5 000
Increase in stocks	1 000
Reduction of overdraft at bank	250
	£13 250
Increase in cash at bank	£2 500
Cash at bank	£2 500

Working capital = current assets − current liabilities

Dec. 1981 = £37 000 − £16 425 = £20 575
Dec. 1980 = £33 750 − £7 250 = £26 500

Drop in working capital in 1981 = £5 925

Ratio Analysis

Working capital ratios Changes in working capital must be observed fairly regularly. A sudden demand for payment by creditors may cause severe cash flow problems, even though an adequate profit is being made. Two tests are commonly applied:

(1981)   (1980)

1.   Current ratio (C.R.) $= \dfrac{\text{Current assets}}{\text{Current liabilities}}$

$$\text{C.R.} = \frac{37\,000}{16\,425} = 2 \cdot 25 \qquad \text{C.R.} \frac{33\,750}{7\,250} = 4 \cdot 65$$

2.
$$\text{Acid test (A.T.)} = \frac{\text{Cash and debtors}}{\text{Current liabilities}}$$

$$\text{A.T.} = \frac{8\ 500}{16\ 425} = 0\cdot5 \qquad\qquad \text{A.T.} = \frac{5\ 000}{7\ 250} = 0\cdot7$$

Most accountants look for ratios of 2:1 and 1:1 respectively. In 1980 in the example the current assets were running too high, but the C.R. test was only corrected in 1981 because of the large tax liability. A look at the acid tests shows that little cash is available to meet this liability. A better policy would be to reduce the large amount of work in progress and thereby increase the cash balances.

Profitability and operating ratios

1.
$$\frac{\text{Net profit before tax}}{\text{Turnover}} = \frac{11\ 500}{90\ 000} \times 100 = 12\cdot5\%$$

2.
$$\frac{\text{Net profit before tax}}{\text{Capital employed}} = \frac{11\ 500}{39\ 575} = 29\cdot2\%$$

(The primary ratio)

3.
$$\frac{\text{Turnover}}{\text{Capital employed}} = \frac{90\ 000}{39\ 575} = 2\cdot3$$

(The turnover ratio)

The *turnover ratio* can provide telling information about the capital structure of a company. For example, the firm which purchases most of its plant and equipment will tend to have a much lower ratio than the firm which has a hiring policy, and furthermore it possesses assets which are not easy to convert into a more liquid form in times of crisis.

Other ratios

$$\frac{\text{Debtors}}{\text{Turnover}} \times 12 = \frac{6\ 000}{90\ 000} \times 12 = 0\cdot8 \text{ months}$$

Customers are given three weeks credit.

$$\frac{\text{Creditors}}{\text{Purchases}} \times 12 = \frac{7\ 000}{50\ 000} \times 12 = 1\cdot7 \text{ months}$$

Suppliers give six weeks credit.

The ratios indicate that the company is applying a sensible policy with respect to both its creditors and customers, and is in fact using suppliers' credit as a short-term form of finance.

A deeper investigation into a company's affairs may yield important information regarding productivity. Typical ratios are:

(a) $\dfrac{\text{Turnover}}{\text{Number of employees}}$ $\dfrac{\text{Profit}}{\text{Number of employees}}$ $\dfrac{\text{Plant and equipment value}}{\text{Number of employees}}$

(b) Profit and dividends related to shareholdings.

Inflation Accounting

In the early 1970s it became obvious that increased inflation rates made the historical system of accounting unsatisfactory and disadvantageous to the commercial sector of the economy. Several bodies subsequently put forward proposals for dealing with the problem (ref. 12) and in 1980 the Accounting Standards Committee published guidance notes for preparing financial accounts with inflation (ref. 13). However, these are not mandatory under the Companies Acts and taxation and other government requirements are still largely based on the historical accounts, with some exemptions allowed for stock appreciation. Inflation adjustments to the historical accounts for the Profit and Loss Statement and Balance Sheet as advised under SSAP 16* are as follows:

Adjustment of the Profit and Loss Account

SSAP 16 (Statement of Standard Accounting Practice) requires the profit and loss account to be adjusted for:

 (i) Depreciation;
 (ii) Stock changes;
(iii) Monetary working capital;
(iv) Gearing.

Example Using the information provided in the previous example, the profit and loss account shown in Table 14.3 is adjusted for inflation as follows:

Index at 31st December 1980	100
Index at 31st December 1981	115
Average index for year	109

---

* There has been considerable controversy on the nature of inflation adjustment under SSAP 16 and an Exposure Draft may shortly be published by the committee (ED38) to deal with the criticism.

(i) *Depreciation*

For simplicity the gross replacement cost of plant and non-specialised buildings is assumed to be governed by a single index. For specialised buildings the gross replacement cost may have to be valued based on expert assessment.

The depreciation charge is calculated as a fixed percentage of the gross replacement cost, the latter being determined from the *average* value of the index over the year.

		£
(a)	Average gross replacement cost of buildings in 1981	
	$= 15\,000 \times \dfrac{109}{100}$	16 350
	Current cost depreciation charge $3\frac{1}{3}\%$ p.a.	545
	Less depreciation in historical P/L account	500
	Depreciation adjustment to be deducted from historical profits	45
(b)	Average gross replacement cost of plant in 1981	
	$= 0 \times \dfrac{109}{100}$	0
	Additions during year $= 5\,000 \times \dfrac{109}{100}$	5 450
	Current cost depreciation charge 10% p.a.	545
	Less depreciation charge in historical P/L account	500
	Depreciation adjustment to be deducted from historical profits	45

(ii) *Stock changes*

The difference between the closing and opening stock of materials in times of inflation may not necessarily represent a change in the volume of materials held. Where this is so then the difference in the values should be set against profits. Thus, using the same indices as before and abstracting stock information from the balance sheet shown in Table 14.4:

(a) Historical closing stock = £1 500
    Historical opening stock = £ 500
                         £1 000

(b) The change in the *volume* of materials stock may be eliminated by considering the average current cost of the opening and closing stocks as follows:

Volume change =

$$\frac{\text{Historical cost closing stock}}{\text{Closing index number}} \times \text{Average index number}$$

$$- \frac{\text{Historical opening stock}}{\text{Opening index number}} \times \text{Average index number}$$

$$\text{Volume change} = \frac{1\,500}{115} \times 109 - \frac{500}{100} \times 109 = \text{£876}.$$

Thus the price increase element of the stocks = $1\,000 - 876 = \underline{\text{£124}}$ and is to be deducted from historical profits.

iii) *Monetary working capital (MWC)*

Monetary working capital is the financial resources tied up in trade debtors and creditors. Like stock changes, the difference between these two volumes at the start and end of the financial year may or may not represent a volume change, i.e. a real change because of the effects of inflation. Using the balance sheet information shown in Table 14.4:

a) Monetary Working Capital (MWC) = trade debtors — trade creditors

		£
Opening MWC = $5\,000 - 6\,000$		$-1\,000$
Closing MWC (including wages) = $6\,000 - 8\,000$		$-2\,000$
		$-1\,000$

b) The change in the *volume* of MWC may be eliminated by considering the average price for the period. Thus:

Volume change =

$$\frac{\text{Closing MWC}}{\text{Closing index number}} \times \text{Average index number} -$$

$$\frac{\text{Opening MWC}}{\text{Opening index number}} \times \text{Average index number}$$

$$= \frac{-2\,000}{115} \times 109 - \frac{-1\,000}{100} \times 109 = -\text{£806}$$

The price increase element of the MWC $= -1\,000 - (-806) = -\text{£194}$.

In this case the creditors exceed the debtors and the adjustment will be credit (i.e. added) to historical profits. Where debtors exceed creditors the adjustment will be a charge against profits when prices are rising, and *vice versa* when prices are falling.

iv) *Gearing*

During a period of rising prices capital borrowing represents a benefit to shareholders because its value increases while the borrowing is a fixed monetary amount. In these circumstances the adjustments made to profits for depreciation, stock changes and monetary working capital changes must be further modified in proportion to the ratio of net borrowings to net assets at their current cost values. This final adjustment would be added to profits when prices are rising and deducted when prices are falling.

Thus, using the current cost balance sheet data given in Table 14.7:

	1981 £	1980 £
Net borrowing is:		
Debentures	5 000	10 000
Taxation	5 575	150
Bank overdraft	—	250
Interest	350	700
	10 925	11 100
Cash	2 500	—
	8 425	11 100

Net borrowing is the aggregate of all liabilities, excluding proposed dividends and those included in the monetary working capital calculations.

	1981 (£)	1980 (£)
Net Operating Assets (see inflation-adjusted balance sheet, Table 14.7):		
Buildings and Plant	21 850	15 000
Cash	2 500	—
Stock	1 725	500
Work in progress	27 000	28 250
MWC	(2 000)	(1 000)
	51 075	42 750

$$\text{Average gearing proportion} = \frac{8\,425 + 11\,100}{51\,075 + 42\,750} = \frac{19\,525}{93\,825} = 20.0\%$$

Further current cost adjustment is:

	£
Depreciation	90
Stocks	124
MWC	−194
	20 × 0.20 = £4

Gearing adjustment to the P & L account is £4 added to profits.

Table 14.6 Current Cost P & L statement for 1981

	£
Sales	90 000
Net profit before interest and tax	11 500
Less current cost adjustments (see note (1))	(20)
Current cost profit	11 480
Interest on borrowings	350
	11 130
Taxation	5 575
Profit after tax	5 555
Gearing adjustment	4
Current cost profit available for distribution	5 559
Dividend	2 500
Retained current cost profit	3 059
Transfer to general reserve (see note (2))	3 075

Notes:

(1)

Depreciation	£90
Stocks	£124
MWC	−£194
	+ £20

(2) Realised Net Profit after deduction for interest, tax and dividend carried to reserves is £3 075 (as shown previously in balance sheet). The balance of £16 over the retained current cost profit represents extra monetary profit caused by inflation.

Presentation of the Balance Sheet

The recommended practice is to present both an historical cost balance sheet accompanied by a current cost balance sheet and any necessary notes. SSAP 16 recommends that the current cost balance sheet should show assets and liabilities on the following basis:

(a) Land, buildings, plant and stock, at their current value to the firm.
(b) Current assets not subject to an inflation adjustment, at their historical cost, e.g. cash.
(c) All liabilities, at their historical values.

The reserves in the current cost balance sheet should include revaluations made to the realised current cost profit shown in the profit and loss account calculated at average cost movements, plus any unrealised revaluations necessary to bring asset values up to date.

Example The balance sheet shown in Table 14.4 is adjusted for inflation as follows:

(a) *Fixed assets*
 (i) Buildings:

Gross replacement cost of buildings at 31 December 1981

$$= 15\,000 \times \frac{115}{100} \qquad\qquad 17\,250$$

Current cost depreciation charge at $3\frac{1}{3}\%$ p.a.	575
Current cost value	16 675
Historical cost value	14 500
Transfer to current cost reserve	2 175

(ii) Plant:

Gross replacement cost of plant at 31 December 1981 £

$$= 0 \times \frac{115}{100} \qquad\qquad 0$$

Additions during year $5\,000 \times \dfrac{115}{100}$ 5 750

Current cost depreciation charge at 10% p.a.	575
Current cost value	5 175
Historical cost value	4 500
Transfer to current cost reserve	675

(b) *Stocks*

Closing stock at 31 December 1981 $\dfrac{1\,500}{100} \times 115 =$ £1 725

Historical closing stock value	1 500
Transfer to current cost reserve	£225

Table 14.7 Current cost balance sheet

Employment of capital			31 Dec 1981 (inflated)	31 Dec 1981 (historical)
Fixed assets:	Replacement value	Depreciation	£	£
Buildings	17 250	575	16 675	14 500
Plant	5 750	575	5 175	4 500
			21 850	19 000

	31 Dec 1981	31 Dec 1981
Current assets:		
Cash	2 500	2 500
Stock of materials	1 725	1 500
Work in progress	27 000	27 000
Debtors	6 000	6 000
	37 225	37 000
	59 075	56 000
Current liabilities:		
Creditors	7 000	7 000
Wages	1 000	1 000
Proposed dividend	2 500	2 500
Interest due on loans	350	350
Bank overdraft	—	—
Corporation tax liability	5 575	5 575
	16 425	16 425
	42 650	39 575

	1981	1980
Capital employed		
Share capital authorised and issued		
21 500 ordinary shares @ £1 each	21 500	21 500
10 000 5% preference shares @ £1 each	10 000	10 000
5 000 7% debentures @ £1 each	5 000	5 000
Reserves		
General		
Realised	3 075	3 075
Unrealised – Buildings	2 175	—
Plant	675	—
Stocks	225	—
	42 650	39 575

Exercises

Exercise 1
The capital structures for two construction companies are given in Table 14.8, and the profits available for interest payments and dividends are given in Table 14.9.

(a) Calculate and comment upon the capital gearing ratios for each of the companies.
(b) Calculate the dividend available to the ordinary shareholders and comment upon the earnings per share in each year.
(c) What is the effect of making the preference shares cumulative?

Corporation tax is 50%

Exercise 2
The Financial Director of a construction company, after carrying out a thorough market investigation of the opportunities for work in a development area, decides to set up a division in the region. The work will be obtained by tender only, and a small management organisation is to be set up in offices purchased for £45 000. The estimate for work is built up on the following figures:

(*a*)   Labour and plant, 35%
                                                 Materials, 40%
                                                 Overheads, 15%
                                                 Profit, 10%

(*b*) All materials purchased and plant hired are given one month's credit by suppliers and three months' stock of materials is held on site at all times.
(*c*) The average time between starting a section of work and receipt of the interim payment is two months.

The working capital available is £180 000.
    Calculate the annual turnover required to justify the directors' decision to go ahead and give a summary of the new capital requirements.

Table 14.8

	Company A (£ '000)	Company B (£ '000)
Ordinary shares (50p)	155	35
7% Preference shares	45	45
10% Loan stock (debentures)	—	120

Table 14.9

Year	1	2	3	4	5	6
Profit (£)	10 000	12 000	15 000	20 000	25 000	30 000

Table 14.10

Balances as at 31 Dec 1981	£ '000
Materials purchased and delivered to site	300
Closing stock as at 31 Dec 1980	15
Materials on site as at 31 Dec 1981	10
Wages incurred	250
Salaries incurred	100
Plant and equipment purchased during year (annual depreciation 20%)	100
Work certified (as at 31 Dec 1981)	695
Work in progress	10

Exercise 3
The figures shown in Table 14.10 are balances extracted from the accounts of a construction company as at 31 December 1981.

(a) Prepare a tabulated profit and loss statement in respect of the figures.
(b) Prepare a tabulated balance sheet for December 1981, given the following information:

  (i) Value of land and buildings as at 31 December 1981 is £50 000.
 (ii) Cash at bank as at 31 December 1981 is £40 000.
 (iii) Value of work certified but not yet paid is £25 000.
 (iv) Payment completed in respect of: Materials – £295 000; Plant and equipment – £95 000; Wages and salaries – £345 000.
  (v) Authorised and issued share capital is in the form of 150 000 ordinary shares at £1 each.
 (vi) The general reserve stands at £20 000 as at 31 December 1980.
(vii) Corporation tax is paid at 50%.
(viii) Only 50% of profit after tax is to be paid as dividend to shareholders. The remainder is to be transferred to the general reserve.

Exercise 4
Calculate the important financial ratios for question 3.

Exercise 5
Typically in the construction industry the primary ratio is about 20% and the turnover ratio 5 or 6. The example given in the text shows ratios more like those of the manufacturing industry. By examining the profit and loss account and balance sheet for the example, indicate the capital arrangements which are untypical.

Exercise 6
The balance sheet for a medium-size construction company engaged in general building as at 31 December 1981 is as follows:

Employment of capital		£
Fixed assets		
Land and premises		220 500
Plant (less depreciation)		229 500
		450 000
Current assets		
Debtors	112 000	
Cash	31 000	
Stock	62 000	
Work in progress	95 000	
		300 000

Current liabilities		
Creditors	90 000	
Bank overdraft	—	
		90 000
		£660 000

Capital employed	
450 000 Ordinary shares at £1 each	450 000
75 000 8% Debentures	75 000
General reserve	135 000
Profit and loss account	—
	£660 000

During the following 12 months normal trading continued, involving the following transactions:

Net profit made before tax	£67 500
Dividend paid	£18 000
Tax paid to Inland Revenue	£30 000
Interest paid to debenture holders	£6 000
Debtors increased by	£30 000
10 000 Ordinary shares of £1 issued at a price of £1·25 per share, all cash is received	
7500 8% Debentures are redeemed	
Creditors are increased by £45 000	
£100 500 of new plant is purchased	
Annual depreciation on plant holdings is 10%	
Work in progress is decreased by	£7 500
Stock increased by	£15 000
Bank overdraft increased by	£10 500

(*a*) Show the source and application of funds during the year.
(*b*) Prepare a tabulated balance sheet for 31 December 1982.
(*c*) Calculate for the period up to 31 December 1982:

 (i) Current ratio
 (ii) Liquidity ratio (or acid test) and compare these ratios with those of the previous year.

References and Bibliography

1. Goch, D. *Finance and Accounts for Managers*. Pan Books, 1971.
2. Sizer, J. *An Insight into Management Accounting*. Pelican, 1969.
3. Wolkstein, H. W. *Accounting Methods and Controls for the Construction Industry*. Prentice-Hall, 1969.
4. Coomes, W. E. *Construction Accounting and Financial Management*. McGraw-Hill, 1958.
5. Jones, J. R. *Construction Management in Principle and Practice: Finance and Control of Cost*. Longman, 1971.
6. Goodlad, J. B. *Accounting for Construction Management*. Heinemann, 1974.
7. Gobourne, J. *Cost Control in the Construction Industry*. Newnes-Butterworth, 1973.
8. Nedved, S. C. *Builders Accounting*. Newnes-Butterworth, 1973.
9. Paish, F. W. *Business Finance*. Pitman, 1965.
10. Rockley, L. E. *The Non-Accountant's Guide to the Balance Sheet*. Business Books, 1973.
11. Sandilands, F. E. P. *Inflation Accounting*. Report of the Inflation Accounting Committee. HMSO, 1975.
12. The Accounting Standards Committee. *Guidance Notes on SSAP 16. Current Cost Accounting*. London, 1980.
13. The Institute of Chartered Accountants. *Current Cost Accounting, SSAP 16*. London, March 1980.
14. Mason, R. J. and Harris, F. C. *Predicting company failure in the construction industry*. *Proceedings Part I*. Institution of Civil Engineers. May, 1979.
15. Jones, D. W. and Harris, F. C. Company acquisitions and business performance in the construction industry. *Construction Papers*. Chartered Institute of Building. January, 1982.

SECTION THREE

CHAPTER 15

CONTRACTORS' MANAGEMENT GAME

Summary

A management game which specifically relates to the construction industry, demonstrating the relationships between estimating accuracy, bidding success, overhead recovery, cash flow and company profits. The game's instructions and supporting computer programs and a simplified manual version of the game.

Chapters 10, 11, 12 and 14 provide useful background and theory to this game.

Introduction

This chapter describes and lists the supporting computer programs for a management game which specifically relates to the construction industry. The game was originally created for use in undergraduate and post-graduate teaching within the Department of Civil Engineering, Loughborough University of Technology. Later the game described here or its variants, have been used in short courses offered by Loughborough's Department of Civil Engineering and attended by middle and senior executives from industry. Delegates at an international conference and company executives in their own company have also participated in the game or simulation. The game is presented here in two forms; one is the full computerised version designed to be played over several days or weeks usually as part of a larger educational or training programme. The other form is a very basic shortened manual version which can be played in one session of an hour to an hour and a half. This second version is useful in demonstrating many of the main points of the larger game and has been used as an introduction to the full game.

This chapter is in three parts:

Part 1 – Contractors' Management game
      The instructions as issued to the game's participants for the full computerised version

Part 2 – Contractors' Management Game
      The game operator's instructions and program listing

Part 3 – Bidding Game
      The simplified manual version

Part 1 – Contractors' Management Game

Description and Instructions to Participants

Basic Aims and Purpose

The game is designed to demonstrate the problems of overall control of a contracting company whose entire turnover is made up of contracts obtained by tendering in the type of competitive market found in the construction industry.

Briefly, control of a contracting company means preparing targets for turnover and profit and forecasting cash requirements, monitoring the company performance against these standards and taking the necessary corrective action. The game allows up to 20 companies to 'operate' within their 'market' for a simulated period of five years facing the problems of control already outlined and hopefully finding solutions to some of these problems.

The purpose of the game is to give participants a feel for:

(a) The problem of constantly revising targets and plans

(b) The problem of allowing for overheads when workload differs from the forecast

(c) The problem of cash restraints on growth

(d) The problem of overhead commitments when trying to reduce the size of your company

(e) The bidding situation where the actions and estimates of other companies thwart your own plans

(f) The pressure to reduce mark-ups when an insufficient number of contracts are being won

Background

The majority of building and civil engineering contracts in the UK construction industry are offered jobs through a process of competitive tendering. This is the process whereby the client or his representative prepares the contract documents including drawings, specifications and bills of quantities, and arranges that two or more contractors submit a tender or price for the contract. Based on this tender and other relevant information the client is free to choose which contractor should be awarded the contract.

A contractor who is tendering has to prepare an estimate for the cost of the work based on the client-prepared contract documents and any other investigations he wishes to make. To this cost estimate the contractor adds a mark-up which is an allowance for profit and company overheads not directly associated with the particular job. The sum of estimate and mark-up is the tender, or bid.

Tender = estimate of contract costs +
mark-up (includes profit margin and allowances for company overheads)

The actual cost of executing the contract incurred by the successful contractor will be at variance with his original estimate. The contribution, i.e. the margin remaining for company overheads and profit, is the tender value less the actual cost

Contribution = tender − actual cost

Company profit is the sum of the contributions from all contracts won less the company's overheads

Company profit = contributions from all contracts won −
company's overheads

Usually such a figure as this would be related to some time period, for example one year.

Almost all contracts in the construction industry allow a series of interim payments to be made to the contractor. The amount of these interim payments is based on a valuation of the work already completed less a retention held by the client until the completion of the contract. Typical retentions in the UK construction industry are 5% to 10% of contract value. Typical achieved profit margins are less than 10% and are often less than 5% of contract value. Thus it is not unusual for a company to find all its 'profits' locked up in retentions. The resulting adverse cash flow problems may in the real situation be offset by negotiating favourable credit conditions with materials suppliers and plant hire companies. However, frequent cash problems arise in the industry as demonstrated by the high bankruptcy rate.

Game Features

In the game each of the participants plays the role of a company. Each company obtains all its work through the competitive process. In the real world situation, while many companies are dependent on the competitive market for most of their work, few rely on it completely and make up the remainder of their turnover with negotiated contracts or other diversifications.

The game does not attempt to simulate the estimating procedures of a contractor, but enters the process with control decisions on such questions as 'Do we want this job and, if so, at what figure are we prepared to tender?' These important decisions are made against a background of uncertainty, the uncertainty arising from the difficulties in predicting the behaviour of competitors and the knowledge that the cost estimate is inaccurate.

The cash flows of a company in the game are calculated given predetermined retention conditions, payment delays from clients and credit limits from suppliers. Although these important variables in controlling cash flow are fixed, the company in the game has control of its cash flow through the number of contracts it takes on, the turnover mix (i.e. the turnover made up of all small short jobs or large jobs of long duration) and the profit levels at which the company operates.

Game Description and Information Flow

The game is computer-based and allows up to 20 teams to manage their own contracting companies over a simulated five years. Decisions are required every quarter. The frequency of the 20 decision periods is restricted by computer turnround and the time needed between decisions for analysis. Operating at two periods per week the game can be played within 10 weeks, but much faster rates of play have been achieved. Restricted manual versions of the game have been played during the course of an afternoon.

The main control information available to companies is the 'state of company' report (see Table 15.6); this report is described in detail later.

At the start companies are given the 'state of company' report, information on the 'state of the market' and a list of jobs on offer during the next period. The jobs on offer are described in terms of the particular company's cost estimate and the job duration in quarters. Each company's cost estimate is drawn from a distribution whose mean is 'likely cost' and whose range is 0·9 of 'likely cost' to 1·1 of 'likely cost'. 'Likely cost' is the notional 'true cost'. Thus by drawing estimates from this range, estimating inaccuracies of $\pm 10\%$ are being assumed.

The decisions each company has to take are:

How many jobs shall we bid for?
Which jobs will these be?
What mark-up should we apply to each job?

The information is collected using the form shown in Fig. 15.2. With this information from all companies the tenders for all jobs are calculated and listed (Table 15.4). The company with the lowest tender is awarded that particular contract.

The 'state of company' report is now updated with the new contracts and costs etc. added.

Each company receives his new 'state of company' report and a list of jobs for the next period.

Information Available to Companies

Market information
An analysis of the value of the contracts which were available over the last two years are given, as shown in Fig. 15.1. An indication as to the rate of growth or contraction of the market is given and reviewed annually.

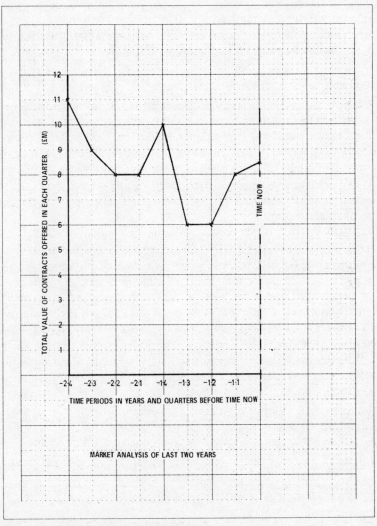

Fig. 15.1 Market analysis of last two years.

CONTRACTORS' MANAGEMENT GAME BIDDING FORM

To be completed and returned to:
R. McCaffer,
Department of Civil Engineering,
University of Technology,
Loughborough, Leics. LE11 3TU.

GAME PARTICIPANTS MUST COMPLETE ONE FORM EACH PERIOD

1. Game Name _____

2. Company No. [   ]

3. Period [   ]

4. Are any jobs being bid for this period

Yes	
No		*

5. If YES answer all remaining questions.

   If NO answer question 6 if appropriate
   sign form and return.

6. Companies are allowed to change their "size"
   if required every second period (i.e. the "even"
   period). If change is permitted this period do
   you wish to alter the size of your company

Yes	
No		*

   If YES by what percentage (limited to range

   ± 10%) [   ]

   * delete as necessary

LOUGHBOROUGH UNIVERSITY OF TECHNOLOGY
DEPARTMENT OF CIVIL ENGINEERING

7. Enter total number of jobs being bid for this period
   [1 | 2]

8. For each job being bid for enter the job number in
   Cols. 1 and 2 (jobs with single number only e.g. 4
   should be entered in Col. 2) and the mark up in
   Cols. 3 to 8 (use the existing decimal point when
   entering mark up)

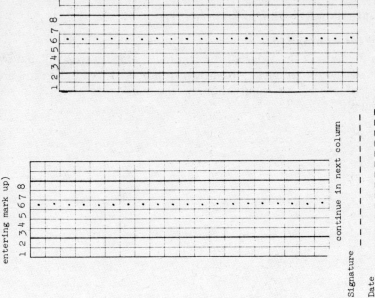

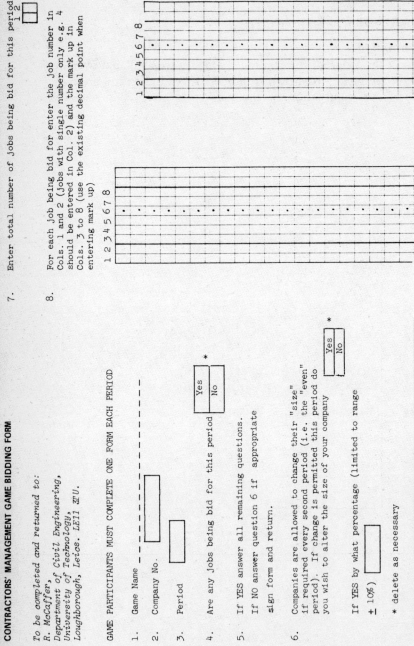

Signature _____

Date _____

continue in next column

Fig. 15.2 Contractors' management game bidding form.

Table 15.1 Company estimates for jobs on offer next period

COMPANY NO. 9 ESTIMATES FOR JOBS ON OFFER IN PERIOD 2.3

JOB NO.	ESTIMATE	DURATION
1	143638.	3.0
2	98503.	4.0
3	74917.	4.0
4	127955.	3.0
5	59028.	5.0
6	57781.	7.0
7	90162.	5.0
8	110374.	6.0
9	176813.	6.0
10	402836.	5.0
11	339938.	7.0
12	163080.	6.0
13	214112.	4.0
14	357801.	5.0
15	635788.	7.0
16	621025.	7.0
17	992755.	9.0
18	869011.	4.0
19	1461250.	9.0
20	1932875.	11.0

ble 15.2 Estimate build-up for jobs on offer next period

MPANY NO. 9 ESTIMATE BUILD UP FOR JOBS ON OFFER IN PERIOD 2.3

B NO.	LIKELY COST	RANDOM NO.	ESTIMATED COST
1	149258.	0.96	143638.
2	98093.	1.00	98503.
3	71998.	1.04	74917.
4	123488.	1.04	127955.
5	59731.	0.99	59028.
6	57524.	1.00	57781.
7	89108.	1.01	90162.
8	113161.	0.98	110374.
9	179724.	0.98	176813.
10	387531.	1.04	402836.
11	329509.	1.03	339938.
12	165069.	0.99	163080.
13	218673.	0.98	214112.
14	351302.	1.02	357801.
15	645890.	0.98	635788.
16	622194.	1.00	621025.
17	988661.	1.00	992755.
18	854236.	1.02	869011.
19	1484108.	0.98	1461250.
20	1949741.	0.99	1932875.

Job lists

A list of jobs available each quarter is given to each company. The jobs are described in terms of the particular company's cost estimate and the job duration. The list shown in Table 15.1 is drawn from a predetermined distribution of contracts, based on figures obtained from the *Annual Bulletin of Construction Statistics, 1970* issued by the Department of the Environment.

The estimate is calculated by varying the likely cost by a factor of variation in the range of 0.9 to 1.1. Table 15.2 shows the calculations for the estimates (this information is not available to the participants).

At this stage companies are asked to submit tenders. Two extreme forms of the game have been used, which are:

(a) When all companies know exactly what companies are bidding for which jobs. This represents the fullest information possible, a situation which is unlikely in practice.
(b) When companies are completely in the dark about what jobs interest their competitors. Again this will be a rare situation in real life although slightly more realistic than (a). The real world situation lies somewhere between (a) and (b).

Tender list

When all tenders have been calculated each company receives its own list of jobs for which it tendered (see Table 15.3).

Table 15.3 Company tender report

```
COMPANY TENDER REPORT
COMPANY NUMBER   9
PERIOD 2.2
JOB NO ESTIMATED COST   MARK UP   TENDER
     1        95782.       9.00    104402.
     2        59490.       9.50     65151.
     4        86790.       9.50     95035.
     5       125153.       9.00    136417.
     6        66097.       9.50     72376.
     8        65058.      10.00     71563.
    10       151916.       9.75    166728.
    13       308267.      10.50    340635.
    15       667007.      11.00    740378.
    16       858433.      11.50    957153.
    17       413000.      11.00    458430.
```

A complete list of all jobs and tenders with the winning (lowest) tender starred is placed on public display accessible to all companies (see Table 15.4).

CO. NO. / JOB NO. — report

JOB NO.	1	2	3	4	5	6	7	8	9	10
1	0.	110211.	110975.	0.	0.	8.	0.	0.	1044402.	73573.
2	68188.	0.	67304.	0.	0.	0.	0.	0.	65151.	69114.
3	95015.	0.	92877.	0.	0.	0.	95103.	161577.	95035.	339556.
4	0.	0.	0.	0.	0.	0.	0.	0.	136417.	341551.
5	75877.	0.	76358.	148394.	0.	160568.	0.	84809.	72376.	347602.
6	0.	0.	0.	162192.	0.	80798.	0.	0.	71563.	169714.
7	60675.	163429.	0.	66664.	0.	174266.	208321.	219149.	166728.	69114.
8	346749.	0.	0.	337908.	0.	76588.	0.	249766.	340635.	339556.
9	0.	0.	0.	183685.	0.	339644.	0.	412398.	0.	0.
10	290059.	166863.	0.	205612.	0.	224919.	0.	0.	0.	0.
11	210127.	0.	0.	0.	0.	0.	0.	0.	0.	0.
12	0.	0.	0.	0.	165777.	0.	733359.	0.	0.	0.
13	0.	0.	0.	0.	0.	0.	0.	0.	0.	0.
14	0.	816438.	0.	0.	0.	0.	0.	0.	0.	0.
15	0.	0.	0.	0.	0.	0.	0.	564303.	740378.	719994.
16	473334.	0.	714993.	1071577.	0.	0.	487821.	0.	957153.	0.
17	0.	0.	0.	451021.	0.	0.	0.	0.	458430.	0.
18	0.	0.	0.	0.	0.	0.	0.	0.	0.	0.
19	0.	0.	0.	0.	0.	0.	0.	0.	0.	0.
20	1952324.	0.	0.	0.	0.	1817874.	0.	2167695.	0.	*1663323.

TENDER REPORT PERIOD 2.2

JOB NO.	11	12	13	14	15	16	17	18	19	20
1	64701.	110550.	69465.	70493.	0.	0.	0.	118072.	0.	322988.
2	54955.	52586.	57665.	0.	0.	0.	0.	0.	0.	0.
3	94018.	139315.	92078.	0.	0.	0.	0.	0.	0.	0.
4	0.	0.	75079.	0.	0.	0.	0.	0.	0.	0.
5	0.	161472.	73849.	0.	0.	0.	0.	0.	0.	0.
6	0.	0.	302116.	0.	0.	0.	0.	0.	0.	0.
7	0.	165955.	296341.	0.	0.	0.	0.	193916.	717478.	726552.
8	0.	0.	208459.	0.	0.	0.	0.	0.	0.	0.
9	0.	0.	342029.	0.	0.	0.	0.	0.	0.	0.
10	0.	0.	0.	0.	0.	0.	0.	0.	0.	0.
11	0.	0.	0.	0.	325179.	314459.	0.	0.	0.	0.
12	0.	0.	0.	0.	155971.	163758.	0.	0.	752759.	0.
13	0.	0.	0.	0.	754705.	0.	0.	0.	0.	0.
14	0.	0.	1049464.	0.	1024724.	0.	0.	717478.	0.	0.
15	0.	734071.	487702.	0.	458740.	490447.	0.	0.	0.	0.
16	0.	0.	669248.	0.	672136.	0.	0.	0.	0.	0.
17	0.	0.	1675983.	0.	1706669.	0.	0.	752759.	0.	0.
18	0.	1693337.	1720020.	0.	1796684.	0.	0.	0.	0.	0.
19	0.	0.	0.	0.	0.	0.	0.	0.	0.	0.
20	0.	0.	0.	0.	0.	0.	0.	0.	0.	0.

Jobs won list
Each successful company receives a list of the contracts it has won (see Table 15.5). This list gives the 'actual cost' of these jobs; the 'actual cost' is based on the likely cost and is drawn from a distribution whose mean is likely cost and whose range is 0·95 to 1·05 of likely cost. The purpose

Table 15.5 Details of jobs won

COMPANY NO. 9 DETAILS OF JOBS WON IN PERIOD 2.2

JOB NO.	ACTUAL COST	TENDER	DURATION(QTRS)
1	99668.	104402.	7.0
5	129174.	136417.	6.0
6	64005.	72376.	7.0
16	951450.	957153.	7.0

of introducing this variable is to simulate the variability in performance in executing contracts. The variability represents the ease or dificulty of the contract.

State of company report
This is the main control document and is issued at the start of the game to show the company's initial capacity, workload, overheads, profit and cash position. An updated report, containing any new jobs or costs incurred, is issued every quarter.

The state of company report shows the complete records for six years. Take any point in the game, say period 2.2: everything earlier than 2.2 is historical information, everything later than 2.2 is the effect of existing workload and overheads if no action is taken by the company.

The following description of the entries in this report includes an explanation of any assumptions made. (Reference should be made to Table 15.6; the upper part is the company's profit and loss statement.)

Time period   This gives the year and quarter number.

Workload actual cost   Actual costs are direct contract costs. Each job won is assumed to have a uniform 'spend rate' (i.e. a job whose actual cost is £150 000 and lasts three-quarters will cost £50 000 per quarter). All contracts commence in the quarter immediately succeeding the quarter in which the contract is awarded.

The figures shown are a total of the actual costs in the time period for all the company's contracts.

Contribution   Contribution is the difference between tender value and actual costs. (For example, using the previous example, if the contract with an actual cost of £150 000 was awarded at a sum of £165 000 the contribution would be £15 000. Again, if the duration is three-quarters this would mean a quarterly contribution of £5000.)

Table 15.6 Company report

```
COMPANY NUMBER  9
PERIOD 2.2
COMPANY REPORT ASSUMING NO MORE JOBS TENDERED FOR
```

TIME PERIOD	WORKLOAD ACTUALCOST	CONTRI-BUTION	TENDERING COSTS	WORK SUB-CONTRACTED	SUB-CONT. COSTS	COMPANY OVERHEADS	INTEREST +CHARGE -EARNED	PROFIT/ LOSS	ANNUAL PROF/LOSS
1.1	300000.	30000.	5657.	0.	0.	16000.	-1200.	9543.	0.
1.2	375045.	31916.	7804.	0.	0.	16000.	-696.	8609.	0.
1.3	240303.	18010.	7901.	0.	0.	16000.	293.	-6184.	9535.
2.1	312934.	20726.	6649.	15574.	934.	16000.	510.	-2433.	0.
2.2	415574.	19730.	7487.	24612.	1477.	16000.	-810.	-5602.	0.
2.3	424612.	21361.	7243.	351114.	21067.	16000.	609.	-3967.	0.
2.4	751114.	33224.	0.	323477.	19409.	16000.	492.	-4335.	-19026.
3.1	723477.	31754.	0.	277510.	16651.	16000.	1467.	-5122.	0.
3.2	677510.	30161.	0.	0.	0.	16000.	3741.	-6231.	0.
3.3	349393.	13558.	0.	0.	0.	16000.	5995.	-8436.	0.
3.4	349393.	13558.	0.	0.	0.	16000.	5282.	-7723.	-32063.
4.1	306410.	10222.	0.	0.	0.	16000.	3894.	-9672.	0.
4.2	159303.	2687.	0.	0.	0.	16000.	4834.	-18148.	0.
4.3	0.	0.	0.	0.	0.	16000.	4343.	-20343.	0.
4.4	0.	0.	0.	0.	0.	16000.	2253.	-18253.	-73843.
5.1	0.	0.	0.	0.	0.	16000.	1100.	-17100.	0.
5.2	0.	0.	0.	0.	0.	16000.	1613.	-17613.	0.
5.3	0.	0.	0.	0.	0.	16000.	2141.	-18141.	-73686.
6.1	0.	0.	0.	0.	0.	16000.	2885.	-18685.	0.
6.2	0.	0.	0.	0.	0.	16000.	3246.	-19246.	0.
6.3	0.	0.	0.	0.	0.	16000.	3823.	-19823.	0.
6.4	0.	0.	0.	0.	0.	16000.	4418.	-20418.	-83301.

Table 15.6 – continued

WORK CURRENTLY SUB-CONTRACTED ABOVE £ 400000.
INTEREST CHARGED AT 3% PER QTR FOR THE FIRST £ -160000.BORROWED,4% BETWEEN £ -160000.& -240000.& THEN @5%
COMPANY CASH STATEMENT

TIME PERIOD	CONTRACT PAYMENTS	SUB-CONT PAYMENTS	COMPANY TENDERING COSTS	COMPANY O'HEADS	CONTRACT RECEIPTS	CASH RETENTION RECEIPTS	INTEREST +CHARGE -EARNED	NET CASH FLOW	CUMULATIVE CASH FLOW	CASH FOR DIVS.TAX ETC.
1·1	300000.	0.	5657.	16000.	297000.	0.	-1200.	-23457.	16543.	0.
1·2	300000.	0.	7804.	16000.	366265.	25750.	-496.	-26307.	-9765.	0.
1·3	375045.	0.	7901.	16000.	232481.	25750.	293.	-7224.	-16988.	0.
1·4	240303.	0.	6649.	16000.	300293.	47060.	510.	-5230.	-30323.	8104.
2·1	312934.	0.	7487.	16000.	391773.	52686.	910.	10023.	-26300.	0.
2·2	415574.	934.	7243.	16000.	401375.	8696.	609.	3899.	-16602.	0.
2·3	424612.	1477.	0.	16000.	705904.	10202.	492.	-32509.	-48911.	2260.
2·4	751114.	21067.	0.	16000.	679708.	17764.	1467.	-73543.	-124713.	0.
3·1	723477.	10409.	0.	16000.	636904.	97084.	3741.	-65155.	-189868.	0.
3·2	677510.	16651.	0.	16000.	326656.	86248.	5995.	17829.	-172039.	0.
3·3	749393.	0.	0.	16000.	326656.	11580.	5282.	42230.	-129809.	0.
3·4	749393.	0.	0.	16000.	284968.	58384.	3894.	-31051.	-160860.	0.
4·1	306410.	0.	0.	16000.	145791.	103501.	4834.	16108.	-144752.	0.
4·2	159303.	0.	0.	16000.	0.	56697.	4343.	69646.	-75106.	0.
4·3	0.	0.	0.	16000.	0.	0.	2253.	78443.	-36662.	0.
4·4	0.	0.	0.	16000.	0.	0.	1100.	-17100.	-53762.	0.
5·1	0.	0.	0.	16000.	0.	0.	1613.	-17613.	-71375.	0.
5·2	0.	0.	0.	16000.	0.	0.	2141.	-18141.	-89516.	0.
5·3	0.	0.	0.	16000.	0.	0.	2685.	-18685.	-108202.	0.
5·4	0.	0.	0.	16000.	0.	0.	3246.	-19246.	-127248.	0.
6·1	0.	0.	0.	16000.	0.	0.	3823.	-19823.	-147271.	0.
6·2	0.	0.	0.	16000.	0.	0.	4418.	-20418.	-167690.	0.
6·3	0.	0.	0.	16000.	0.	0.	5108.	-21108.	-188797.	0.
6·4	0.	0.	0.	16000.	0.	0.	5952.	-21952.	-210749.	0.

ANNUAL AVERAGE OF CASH ACCOUNT
YEAR 1 -10133. YEAR 2 -52581." YEAR 3 -163146. YEAR 4 -77571. YEAR 5 -99135. YEAR 6 -178627.

The figures shown are totals of the contributions earned in the time period for all the company's contracts.

Tendering costs   Companies are charged $\frac{1}{4}$% of the estimated cost of each job they tender for. The figure shown in each time period is the total tendering costs incurred in that time period.

Work subcontracted   If companies exceed their capacity (capacity is expressed in terms of actual cost) then it is assumed that the company has reluctantly to subcontract the excess work. The starting capacity of each company is decided at the commencement of the game; as the game proceeds each company can choose to grow or contract (i.e. get smaller). This choice is allowed only every six months and is limited to within ±10% (i.e. if a company has an annual capacity of £4 million, and in a particular quarter had £1·2 million of work in actual cost, then £0·2 million would be subcontracted). Company overheads are linked to capacity (see company overheads).

Subcontracting costs   All excess work subcontracted costs an extra 6% (i.e. using the example of the £0·2 million of subcontracted work the total cost of this would now be £0·2 million + 6% of £0·2 million = £212 000).

Company overheads   This figure represents all costs not directly charged to a contract. Company overheads are directly related to the size of the company (i.e. the company's capacity).

The minimum overheads of any company are £60 000 p.a. (i.e. £15 000 per quarter). The maximum overheads of any company are £800 000 p.a. (i.e. £200 000 per quarter). Otherwise company overheads are 4% of the company's capacity.

If a company decides to increase its capacity, the corresponding increase in company overheads becomes effective immediately. If a company decides to decrease its capacity there is a delay of four quarters (one year) before there is a corresponding decrease in company overheads. This simulates the easy acquisition of overheads (e.g. new staff etc.) and the more difficult process of reducing overheads.

Interest (+ charge, − earned)   This shows in each time period the interest charged or earned and is based on the company's cumulative cash in the preceding quarter. Interest is earned at 3% per quarter if the cumulative cash in the previous quarter is greater than zero. If the cumulative cash is less than zero in the previous quarter then interest is charged at 3% per quarter for the first 10% of the initial company annual capacity, at 4% per quarter for the balance between 10% and 15% of the initial company annual capacity, and at 5% per quarter thereafter.

Profit/loss The profit (+) or loss (−) earned in each quarter. This figure is the contribution less tendering costs, subcontracting costs, overheads and interest (either + or −).

Annual profit/loss The annual profit (+) or annual loss (−) earned in each year.

Between the upper and lower parts of Table 15.6 the current quarterly capacity and the limits for the interest charges are given. The lower table is the company's cash statement. The entries are:

Time period As before.

Contracts payments This shows the cash payments resulting from the contracts. The workload (actual cost) shown in the profit table was a cost liability. The contract payments show the cash flow at the time the payments are made. A delay between cost liability and payment of one quarter is assumed. This delay is regarded as the mean payment delay a contractor might have if he allows, say, a one-week delay for labour, a four-week delay for materials, and a six-week delay for hired plant.

Subcontractor payments This is the payment of the excess subcontracting costs of 6% of work subcontracted. Again a payment delay of one quarter is assumed.

Company overheads These occur quarterly.

Contract receipts Monies received from clients. Payment is received one quarter after the work is executed. The payment is calculated as the tender value of the work done less 10% retention. (If a contract has a tender value of £165 000 and lasts three quarters, the quarterly contract receipts would be £55 000 less 10%, i.e. £49 500).

Retention receipts This is the payment of monies held in retention. Half of the retention for a contract is paid one quarter after the practical completion of the contract. The remaining half is paid two quarters after the practical completion.

Interest charges As before.

Net cash flow The net cash flow in any quarter is the difference between cash in and cash out. Cash in is the sum of contract and retention receipts. Cash out is the sum of contract payments, subcontract payments, tendering costs and company overheads.

Cumulative cash flow   This is a running total of the quarterly cash flows, including any monies taken for tax and dividends.

Cash for dividends, tax etc.   This represents money drawn annually for paying dividends to shareholders and taxation. The company is not given any discretion in this matter, which is a simplification. However, it is necessary to simulate the removal of substantial cash sums from the company for the purposes of dividends and taxation. The money taken for these purposes is calculated as follows:

 (i) If the company shows a profit every year the sum taken is 85% of the annual profit.
 (ii) If the company shows a loss in any year no dividends or tax are paid that year.
(iii) If the company shows a profit following a period of loss the sum taken is 85% of the profit left after having recovered all losses since the last dividend was paid.

If the profit earned after a loss-making period is insufficient to cover losses then no payments are made.

At the foot of the cash statement the annual average of the cash account is given.

Evaluation and Comment

The game was designed to demonstrate the problems of overall control of a contracting company. This control can be thought of at two levels:

1. *Overall plans*:   preparation of targets for turnover and profit. Decisions as to the ideal size of company, target market share and cash requirements.

2. *Quarterly decisions*   which are:

> How many jobs should be tendered for?
> Which jobs?
> At what mark-up?

To take these decisions effectively the participant needs, or needs to develop, some analytical skills and a knowledge of the interdependency of one set of decisions or targets on other decisions or targets.

Used in the context of undergraduate and postgraduate teaching within the Department of Civil Engineering at Loughborough, where subjects include finance, managerial economics, statistics and operational research, the game gives students the opportunity to apply their skills in an integrated and changing situation and it has proved stimulating and useful in illustrating the problems of company control described. Some points that the game has successfully demonstrated both with students and company executives are:

(*a*) The difficulties of recovering overheads with a fluctuating workload
(*b*) The differences between profit and cash
(*c*) The effect of charging for cash at realistic interest rates
(*d*) The concept of breakeven mark-up, which is that mark-ups must contain a positive allowance for profit even if the company only wishes to break even in the long run.

The reasons for (*d*) are that contractors tend to win the contracts in which their estimating errors placed their estimate low in the range of possible estimates – explained as the 'margin lost to competition' in Chapter 11.

The game is capable of being extended in several ways depending on the objectives of the user. At undergraduate level one of the main uses is as an exercise in developing some analytical skills. In other situations the financial aspects may be more important, and extra features such as preparation of twice-yearly reports to shareholders or the maintaining of interfirm comparison ratios can be added.

A difficulty in operating the game has been to decide what should be done with companies in serious cash difficulties. In real life, of course, these companies would be declared bankrupt, would be wound up and their place in the industry would be filled by expansion of other companies and the creation of new companies. In the game situation at least three possibilities exist:

(i) Declare the company bankrupt and have them leave the game.
(ii) Declare the company bankrupt and allow the team to set up a new company.
(iii) Do not have bankruptcy and allow the company to continue struggling.

Part 2 – Contractors' Management Game

The Game Operator's Instructions and Program Listing

Introduction

It is assumed that Part 1, the game description, will have been read. The following information largely describes the game program and gives instructions on how to run it. Some knowledge of the computer language Fortran and of computer systems will be required for the successful setting up and running of this program. The program is written in Fortran for an ICL 1904A computer. All library subroutines are standard ICL routines except for those described separately. Some reprogramming may be necessary for running on other systems.

The program in the form listed runs as a batch program and requires three magnetic tapes for data filing. The input to the program listed is in card form. The program has two functions: (1) to initialise the game for a selected number of companies up to 20; and (2) to process company data each period of the game. This second function has two options: (a) to process company data in a period when no company wishes to change the 'size' of their capacity (known as NO GROWTH); (b) to process company data in a period when one or more companies wish to change the size of their capacity (known as GROWTH).

The program therefore has three types of run:

(i)   Initialisor
(ii) Period processing – NO GROWTH
(iii) Period processing – GROWTH.

Data Files

The data pertaining to each company is stored between runs on magnetic tape. Every run of the program requires two tape files. The use of three tapes in rotation as described below builds some safety into the system should a tape failure result in lost data. The name of the tape files to be used in a run are contained on the first two cards of the data cards required for a run. Card 1 contains the name of the first tape to be used and Card 2 contains the name of the second tape to be used. The format used for these cards is described in 'Card input' below. The tape named in the first card is called 'first tape' and the tape named in the second card is called 'second tape'. Having three tapes named A, B and C the tape rotation works as follows:

First run – the initialising run

First tape	:	A
Second tape	:	B

In this run all input is from cards and the company reports and job estimates for each company are output to lineprinter, to tape A *and* tape B. Thus tapes A and B contain the same data on the initial conditions for each company.

Second run – processing the first period

> First tape   :   A
>
> Second tape :   C

Tape B is retained as security against a failure. In this run input comes from tape file and from cards. The data from tape file is taken from the first tape, in this case tape A. Output of the new company reports and job estimates is to lineprinter, tape A *and* tape C. Thus tapes A and C contain the company reports after period 1.

Third run – processing the second period

> First tape   :   C
>
> Second tape :   B

In this case tape A is retained as a security against failure. In this run, as in all runs processing a period of the game, company data is *read from* first tape and *written to both* tapes.

These three tapes are used in rotation.

Card input data

The initialisation run   is to set up starting conditions in company reports (Table 15.6), to initialise the random number streams and to create the jobs available in the first period (1.1). Two forms are required:

Form 1 – only one is required

Card 1 (Format A8 A4)	Name of first tape file. Up to 12 characters	Cols 1 to 12
Card 2 (Format A8 A4)	Name of second tape file. Up to 12 characters (a different name from the first tape file)	Cols 1 to 12
Card 3 (Format 4I2)	Control card. Number of companies playing game.	Cols 1 and 2
	Run type (1 for period processing NO GROWTH, 2 for initialisation, 3 for period processing with GROWTH). In this run the number would be 2.	Cols 3 and 4
	Number of jobs to be offered next period (range is up to 40)	Cols 5 and 6
	Period number, 0 for initialisation, 1, 2, 3 etc. for subsequent periods up to 20	Cols 7 and 8
Card 4 (Format 3I7)	Three integers of up to seven digits. Each is an initial value for a different random number stream	Cols 1 to 7 8 to 14 15 to 20

Form 2 – one is required for each company

Card 1 (Format 8F 10.0)			
	Workload actual cost	period 1.1	Cols 1 to 10
	Contribution	period 1.1	Cols 11 to 20
	Workload actual cost	period 1.2	Cols 21 to 30
	Contribution	period 1.2	Cols 31 to 40
	Workload actual cost	period 1.3	Cols 41 to 50
	Contribution	period 1.3	Cols 51 to 60
	Workload actual cost	period 1.4	Cols 61 to 70
	Contribution	period 1.4	Cols 71 to 80

Card 2
(Format 8F 10.0)

Card 2 is exactly the same as card 1
except the periods are 2.1 to 2.4

Card 3 (Format 8F 10.0)			
	Contract payments	period 1.1	Cols 1 to 10
	Contract receipts	period 1.1	Cols 11 to 20
	Retention receipts	period 1.1	Cols 21 to 30
	Contract payments	period 1.2	Cols 31 to 40
	Contract receipts	period 1.2	Cols 41 to 50
	Retention receipts	period 1.2	Cols 51 to 60
	Contract payments	period 1.3	Cols 61 to 70
	Contract receipts	period 1.3	Cols 71 to 80

Card 4 (Format 8F 10.0)			
	Retention receipts	period 1.3	Cols 1 to 10
	Contract payments	period 1.4	Cols 11 to 20
	Contract receipts	period 1.4	Cols 21 to 30
	Retention receipts	period 1.4	Cols 31 to 40
	Contract payments	period 2.1	Cols 41 to 50
	Contract receipts	period 2.1	Cols 51 to 60
	Retention receipts	period 2.1	Cols 61 to 70
	Contract payments	period 2.2	Cols 71 to 80

Card 5 (Format 8F 10.0)			
	Contract receipts	period 2.2	Cols 1 to 10
	Retention receipts	period 2.2	Cols 11 to 20
	Contract payments	period 2.3	Cols 21 to 30
	Contract receipts	period 2.3	Cols 31 to 40
	Retention receipts	period 2.3	Cols 41 to 50
	Contract payments	period 2.4	Cols 51 to 60
	Contract receipts	period 2.4	Cols 61 to 70
	Retention receipts	period 2.4	Cols 71 to 80

Card 6 (Format 8F 10.0)			
	Contract payments	period 2.3	Cols 1 to 10
	Contract receipts	period 2.3	Cols 11 to 20
	Retention receipts	period 2.3	Cols 21 to 30
	Contract payments	period 2.4	Cols 31 to 40
	Contract receipts	period 2.4	Cols 41 to 50
	Retention receipts	period 2.4	Cols 51 to 60
	Current cash available to company		Cols 61 to 70

| | Company's initial quarterly capacity, above which work will be automatically subcontracted | Cols 71 to 80 |

At the end of all form 2's ****   Cols 1 to 4

The period processing run   is to process bids submitted by each company. Two types of form:

Form 1 – only one needed
Card 1   As for initialisation run
Card 2   As for initialisation run
Card 3   As for initialisation run (note run type is 1)
               (In a period processing run there is no card 4)

Form 2 – one for each company. The form 2's must be submitted in the order of the company numbers. If one company does not submit any bids then one blank card 1 must be used. Figure 15.2 is the data capture form

Card 1 (Format I2)	The number of jobs being bid for by the company. Even if the company does not bid for any jobs this card must be used	Cols 1 and 2
Card 2 (Format I2, F6.2)	One for each job the company is bidding for. The job number of the job being bid for	Cols 1 and 2
	The percentage mark-up to be applied to the company's estimate for this job	Cols 3 to 8 d.P. col 6

After all form 2's ****   Cols 1 to 4

The period processing run with GROWTH   is to process bids submitted by each company and to adjust companies for changes in capacity and overheads. Three types of form:

Form 1 – only one needed and as for form 1 period processing run. (Note: run type is 3)

Form 2 – one for each company. If a company does not want to change size a blank card 1 must be used

Card 1	One for each company in order of	
(Format F5.1)	company numbers. The percent-	
	age change (+ or −) in company	
	capacity	Cols 1 to 5
		d.P. col 4

Form 3 – as for Form 2 in period processing run

After all form 3's ****   Cols 1 to 4

Additional Output

The output from the program is in two channels thus ensuring that the game controller has a file copy.

In addition to the output described in the game instructions company No. 2 receives an analysis of his competitors' bids. This analysis is presented in tabular form from which cumulative frequency distributions similar to Fig. 11.2 can be drawn. These cumulative frequency distributions are available for competitors Nos. 3 to 20, for all competitors amalgamated and for the lowest bidder only. Reference to Chapter 11 will explain the use of these distributions.

Library subroutines

All subroutines used in the program listed are standard ICL subroutines described in ICL's *Fortran: Compiler Libraries*, except UTR1. UTR1 is Loughborough University of Technology's random number generator, and thus UTR1 will have to be replaced by a random number generator suitable for the particular computer system.

The UTR1 subroutine is used as follows:

$$R = UTR1(I, J, K)$$

where I is an integer variable identifying the stream number, J is an integer which is either zero or non-zero. If zero the random number belongs to a uniform distribution between 0 and 1, the range and mean can be altered algebraically, if non-zero the random number belongs to a normal distribution of mean zero and variance of 1, the mean and variance can be altered algebraically. K is an integer used in the calculation of the random number and is given as a starting value. The variable used as starting values for the three random number streams in the program are called IRAND, JRAND and KRAND and are input by a card in the first run and transferred by tape-file for

The program listing

LOUGHBOROUGH UNIVERSITY COMPUTER CENTRE GEORGE 2L MK4F STREAM A   RUN ON 02/11/81 AT 18:54

```
        JOB R-GAME;CVAD;AW7890
        VOLUME 7000
        JOBCORE 50000
        FORTRAN ,,PDS
        RUN
        GIVEOUTPUT $EV/OUT1
        ***
```

FORTRAN COMPILATION BY #XFAT MK 6C   DATE 02/11/81   TIME 18/54/16

```
0001        SEND TO (ED;SEMICOMPUSER.AXXX)
0002        DUMP ON (ED;PROGRAM USER)
0003        WORK (ED,WORKFILEUSER)
0004        RUN
0005
0006        LIBRARY (ED;SUBGROUPUSUB)
0007        PROGRAM(BIDG).
0008        COMPRESS INTEGER AND LOGICAL
0009        INPUT 1 = CR0
0010        OUTPUT 2 = LP0
0011        OUTPUT 3 = LP1
0012        USE 5 = MT0(DUMMY1(1;999))
0013        USE 6 = MT2(DUMMY2(1;999))
0014        TRACE 2
0015        END
```

The program listing – *continued*

```
0016      MASTER BIDGAMETHREE
0017      REAL NACOST(40),MYCOST(40),LENGTH(40),          ITEND(40,20),MARK
0018     1UP,M(20,33,15),KASH(20)
0019      DIMENSION SP(40,20),P(25),JOBMIN(40),WLOAD(20,26),GROW(20),CAPTA(2
0020     10),EST(40,20),TOTEST(20)
0021      DIMENSION            RIDLOW(40),BID(20,50),ALLJOB(20),FOOL(50),ALL
0022     1BIDS(50),NBID(50),TID(20,50),BEFOOL(50)
0023      DIMENSION FILEA(2),FILER(2)
0024      DATA BIDLOW/40*0.0/
0025      DATA BID/1000*0.0/
0026      DATA ALLJOB/20*0.0/
0027      DATA FOOL/50*0.0/
0028      DATA ALLBIDS/50*0.0/
0029      DATA TID/1000*0.0/
0030      DATA BEFOOL/50*0.0/
0031      DATA ITEND/800*0.0/
0032      DATA M/9900*0.0/
0033      DATA P(1),P(2),P(3),P(4),P(5),P(6),P(7),P(8),P(9),P(10),P(11),P(12
0034     1),P(13),P(14),P(15),P(16),P(17),P(18),P(19),P(20),P(21),P(22),P(23
0035     2),P(24),P(25)/3H1.1,3H1.2,3H1.3,3H1.4,3H2.1,3H2.2,3H2.3,3H2.4,3H3.
0036     31,3H3.2,3H3.3,3H3.4,3H4.1,3H4.2,3H4.3,3H4.4,3H5.1,3H5.2,3H5.3,3H5.
0037     44,3H6.1,3H6.2,3H6.3,3H6.4,3H0.0/
0038      DATA SPACE/8H     /
0039      DATA AST/1H*/
0040      DO 1 J=1,40
0041      DO 1 K=1,20
```

The program listing – *continued*

```
0042        CALL COPY(1,SP(J,K),1,SPACE,1)
0043      1 CONTINUE
0044        READ(1,2)FILEA(1),FILEA(2),IGENA
0045        READ(1,2)FILER(1),FILEB(2),IGENR
0046        CALL FILE(5,FILEA(1),IGENA,999)
0047        CALL FILE(6,FILEB(1),IGENB,999)
0048        READ(1,3)NUMCO,IRUN,NJOBS,NTIME
0049        IF(IRUN.NE.2)GO TO 4
0050   C    READ START CONDITIONS
0051        NTIME=25
0052        READ(1,5)IRAND,JRAND,KRAND
0053        DO 6 KO=1,NUMCO
0054        READ(1,7)((M(KO,KL,L),L=1,2),KL=1,8),((M(KO,KN,N),N=9,11),KN=1,10)
0055       1,KASH(KO),WLOAD(KO,1)
0056        DO 8 KL=2,25
0057        WLOAD(KO,KL)=WLOAD(KO,1)
0058      8 CONTINUE
0059        CAPTA(KO)=WLOAD(KO,1)
0060        OHEAD=0.04*WLOAD(KO,1)
0061        IF(OHEAD.LT.15000.0)OHEAD=15000.0
0062        IF(OHEAD.GT.200000.0)OHEAD=200000.0
0063        DO 9 KL=1,24
0064        M(KO,KL,6)=OHEAD
0065      9 CONTINUE
0066      6 CONTINUE
0067        GO TO 10
0068   C    READ EXISTING CONDITIONS FROM TAPE
0069      4 DO 11 KO=1,NUMCO
0070        DO 11 KH=1,24
0071        READ(5)(M(KO,KH,L),L=1,14),WLOAD(KO,KH),KASH(KO),CAPTA(KO),IALL
0072     11 CONTINUE
```

The program listing – *continued*

```
0073        DO 100 L=1,IALL
0074        DO 100 KO=1,NUMCO
0075        READ(5)EST(L,KO),NACOST(L),LENGTH(L)
0076   100  CONTINUE
0077        DO 12 K2=3,NUMCO
0078        DO 12 K3=1,50
0079        READ(5)BID(K2,K3),FOOL(K3)
0080    12  CONTINUE
0081        READ(5)IRAND,JRAND,KRAND
0082        REWIND 5
0083        IF(IRUN.NE.3)GO TO 13
0084   C    COMPANIES CHANGE
0085        DO 14 I=1,NUMCO
0086        READ(1,15)GROW(I)
0087        IF(GROW(I))16,14,18
0088    18  OHEAD=0.04*(WLOAD(I,NTIME)+(WLOAD(I,NTIME)*(GROW(I)/100.0)))
0089        IF(OHEAD.GT.200000.0)OHEAD=200000.0
0090        IF(OHEAD.LT.15000.0)OHEAD=15000.0
0091        DO 19 KL=NTIMF,24
0092        M(I,KL,6)=OHEAD
0093    19  CONTINUE
0094        GO TO 3000
0095    16  OTIME=NTIME+4
0096        OHEAD=0.04*(WLOAD(I,NTIME)+(WLOAD(I,NTIME)*(GROW(I)/100.0)))
0097        IF(OHEAD.GT.200000.0)OHEAD=200000.0
0098        IF(OHEAD.LT.15000.0)OHEAD=15000.0
0099        DO 20 KL=OTIMF,24
0100        IF ( OTIME - 25 ) 0,0,3000
0101        M(I,KL,6)=OHEAD
0102    20  CONTINUE
0103  3000  DO 21 KL=NTIMF,24
```

The program listing – *continued*

```
0104        WLOAD(I,KL)=WLOAD(I,KL)+WLOAD(I,KL)*(GROW(I)/100.0)
0105     21 CONTINUE
0106     16 CONTINUE
0107   C    CALCULATE TENDERS
0108     13 DO 22 I=1,NUMCO
0109        TOTEST(I)=0.0
0110        WRITE(2,23)
0111        WRITE(3,23)
0112        WRITE(2,24)I,P(NTIME)
0113        WRITE(3,24)I,P(NTIME)
0114        READ(1,25)NJBTND
0115        IF(NJBTND.EQ.0)GO TO 22
0116        DO 26 J=1,NJBTND
0117        READ(1,27)IJOB,MARKUP
0118        Z=EST(IJOB,I)
0119        TOTEST(I)=TOTEST(I)+Z
0120        ITEND(IJOB,I)=EST(IJOB,I)*(MARKUP/100.0+1.0)
0121        WRITE(2,28)IJOB,EST(IJOB,I),MARKUP,ITEND(IJOB,I)
0122        WRITE(3,28)IJOB,EST(IJOB,I),MARKUP,ITEND(IJOB,I)
0123     26 CONTINUE
0124     22 CONTINUE
0125   C    SELECT LOWEST TENDER FOR EACH JOB
0126        DO 29 K=1,IALL
0127        NOCO=0
0128        DO 30 J=1,NUMCO
0129        IF(J.EQ.1)AMIN=999999.0
0130        IF(ITEND(K,J).GT.0.0.AND.ITEND(K,J).LT.AMIN)GO TO 31
0131        GO TO 30
0132     31 AMIN=ITEND(K,J)
0133        NOCO=J
0134     30 CONTINUE
```

The program listing – *continued*

```
0135        IF(NOCO.EQ.0)GO TO 29
0136        JOBMIN(K)=NOCO
0137        CALL COPY(1,SP(K,NOCO),1,AST,1)
0138        BIDLOW(K)=AMIN
0139   29   CONTINUE
0140        WRITE(2,32)P(NTIME)
0141        WRITE(3,32)P(NTIME)
0142        DO 33 I=1,IALL
0143        WRITE(2,34)I,(SP(I,L),ITEND(I,L),L=1,10)
0144        WRITE(3,34)I,(SP(I,L),ITEND(I,L),L=1,10)
0145   33   CONTINUE
0146        WRITE(2,35)P(NTIME)
0147        WRITE(3,35)P(NTIME)
0148        DO 36 I=1,IALL
0149        WRITE(2,34)I,(SP(I,L),ITEND(I,L),L=11,20)
0150        WRITE(3,34)I,(SP(I,L),ITEND(I,L),L=11,20)
0151   36   CONTINUE
0152        WRITE(2,101)P(NTIME)
0153        DO 102 K=1,IALL
0154        WRITE(2,103)K,NACOST(K),LENGTH(K)
0155        WRITE(3,103)K,NACOST(K),LENGTH(K)
0156  102   CONTINUE
0157   C   ADD NEW JOBS TO COMPANY RECORDS
0158        DO 37 J=1,NUMCO
0159        M(J,NTIME,3)=TQTEST(J)*0.0025
0160        MTS=NTIME+1
0161        WRITE(2,104)J,P(NTIME)
0162        WRITE(3,104)J,P(NTIME)
0163        DO 38 MJOB=1,IALL
0164        IF(JOBMIN(MJOB).NE.J)GO TO 38
0165        WRITE(2,105)MJOB,NACOST(MJOB),ITEND(MJOB,J),LENGTH(MJOB)
```

The program listing – *continued*

```
0166        WRITE(3,105)MJOB,NACOST(MJOB),ITEND(MJOB,J),LENGTH(MJOB)
0167        PERCST=NACOST(MJOB)/LENGTH(MJOB)
0168        MTF=NTIME+LENGTH(MJOB)
0169        DO 39 MT=MTS,MTF
0170        IF ( MT - 25 ) 0, 0, 2591
0171        M(J,MT,1)=M(J,MT,1)+PERCST
0172   39   M(J,MT,2)=M(J,MT,2)+(ITEND(MJOB,J)-NACOST(MJOB))/LENGTH(MJOB)
0173  2591  JTS=MTS+1
0174        JTF=MTF+1
0175        LTF=MTF+2
0176        VALUE=ITEND(MJOB,J)/LENGTH(MJOB)
0177        DO 40 M1=JTS,JTF
0178        IF ( M1 - 25 ) 0, 0, 2592
0179        M(J,M1,10)=M(J,M1,10)+0.9*VALUE
0180        M(J,M1,9)=M(J,M1,9)+PERCST
0181   40   CONTINUE
0182  2592  IF ( JTF - 25 ) 0, 0, 38
0183        M(J,JTF,11)=M(J,JTF,11)+0.05*ITEND(MJOB,J)
0184        IF ( LTF - 25 ) 0, 0, 38
0185        M(J,LTF,11)=M(J,LTF,11)+0.05*ITEND(MJOB,J)
0186   38   CONTINUE
0187   37   CONTINUE
0188  C     RECALCULATE STATE OF COMPANY REPORT
0189   10   DO 41 J=1,NUMCO
0190        DO 42 MT=1,24
0191        W=M(J,MT,1)=WLOAD(J,MT)
0192        IF ( W ) 342, 342, 44
0193   44   M(J,MT,4)=W
0194        M(J,MT,5)=0.06*W
0195        GO TO 42
0196  342   M ( J,MT,4 ) = 0.0
```

The program listing – *continued*

```
0197        M ( J, MT, 5 ) = 0.0
0198   42   CONTINUE
0199        DO 43 MOUT=1,24
0200        MSUB=MOUT-1
0201        M2=MOUT-2
0202        M3=MOUT-3
0203        IF(MOUT.NE.1)GO TO 110
0204        M(J,MOUT,15)==(0.03*KASH(J))
0205        M(J,MOUT,7)=M(J,MOUT,2)=M(J,MOUT,3)-M(J,MOUT,5)-M(J,MOUT,6)+M(J,MO
           1UT,15)
0206        M(J,MOUT,12)=M(J,MOUT,11)+M(J,MOUT,10)+M(J,MOUT,9)+M(J,MOUT,3)-M(J
           1,MOUT,6)-M(J,MOUT,15)
0207        M(J,MOUT,6)=M(J,MOUT,15)
0208        M(J,MOUT,13)=M(J,MOUT,12)+KASH(J)
0209        GO TO 43
0210   110  FIFTH=-(CAPTA(J)/2.5)
0211        THIRD=-(CAPTA(J)*3/5)
0212        IF(M(J,MSUB,13).GT.FIFTH)M(J,MOUT,15)==(0.03*M(J,MSUB,13))
0213        IF(M(J,MSUB,13).LT.FIFTH.AND.M(J,MSUB,13).GT.THIRD)M(J,MOUT,15)==(
0214       10.03*FIFTH+0.04*(M(J,MSUB,13)-FIFTH))
0215        IF(M(J,MSUB,13).LT.THIRD)M(J,MOUT,15)==(0.03*FIFTH+0.04*(THIRD-FIFT
0216       1H)+0.05*(M(J,MSUB,13)-THIRD))*(-1)
0217        M(J,MOUT,7)=M(J,MOUT,2)-M(J,MOUT,3)-M(J,MOUT,5)-M(J,MOUT,6)-M(J,MO
0218       1UT,15)
0219        MDIV=(MOUT/4)*4
0220        IF(MDIV.NE.MOUT)GO TO 45
0221        M(J,MOUT,8)=M(J,MOUT,7)+M(J,MSUB,7)+M(J,M2,7)+M(J,M3,7)
0222   45   CUM=0.0
0223        DO 46 KL=4,20,4
0224        CUM=CUM+M(J,KL,8)
0225        IF(CUM.LT.0.0)GO TO 46
0226        M(J,KL,14)=0.85*CUM
```

The program listing – *continued*

```
0228        CUM=0.0
0229    46  CONTINUE
0230        M(J,MOUT,12)=M(J,MOUT,11)+M(J,MOUT,10)-M(J,MOUT,9)-M(J,MOUT,3)-M(J
0231       1,MOUT,6)-M(J,MSUB,5)-M(J,MOUT,15)
0232        M(J,MOUT,13)=M(J,MSUB,13)+M(J,MOUT,12)=M(J,MOUT,14)
0233    45  CONTINUE
0234        CASHA=(M(J,1,13)+M(J,2,13)+M(J,3,13)+M(J,4,13))/4.0
0235        CASHB=(M(J,5,13)+M(J,6,13)+M(J,7,13)+M(J,8,13))/4.0
0236        CASHC=(M(J,9,13)+M(J,10,13)+M(J,11,13)+M(J,12,13))/4.0
0237        CASHD=(M(J,13,13)+M(J,14,13)+M(J,15,13)+M(J,16,13))/4.0
0238        CASHE=(M(J,17,13)+M(J,18,13)+M(J,19,13)+M(J,20,13))/4.0
0239        CASHF=(M(J,21,13)+M(J,22,13)+M(J,23,13)+M(J,24,13))/4.0
0240        WRITE(2,47)J,P(NTIME)
0241        WRITE(3,47)J,P(NTIME)
0242        WRITE(2,48)
0243        WRITE(3,48)
0244        DO 49 MT=1,24
0245        WRITE(2,50)P(MT),(M(J,MT,N),N=1,6),M(J,MT,15),(M(J,MT,L),L=7,8)
0246        WRITE(3,50)P(MT),(M(J,MT,N),N=1,6),M(J,MT,15),(M(J,MT,L),L=7,8)
0247    49  CONTINUE
0248        WRITE(2,51)WLOAD(J,NTIME)
0249        WRITE(3,51)WLOAD(J,NTIME)
0250        WRITE(2,52)FIFTH,FIFTH,THIRD
0251        WRITE(3,52)FIFTH,FIFTH,THIRD
0252        WRITE(2,53)
0253        WRITE(3,53)
0254        DO 54 MT=1,24
0255        MSUB=MT+1
0256        IF(MT.NE.1)GO TO 55
0257        MSUB=25
0258        M(J,MSUB,5)=0.0
```

The program listing – *continued*

```
0259   59  WRITE(2,56)P(MT),M(J,MT,9),M(J,MT,15),M(J,MT,3),M(J,MT,6),M(J,MT,
0260      110),M(J,MT,11),M(J,MT,15),(M(J,MT,N),N=12,14)
0261       WRITE(3,56)P(MT),M(J,MT,9),M(J,MT,15),M(J,MT,3),M(J,MT,6),M(J,MT,
0262      110),M(J,MT,11),(M(J,MT,N),N=12,14)
0263   54  CONTINUE
0264       WRITE(2,57)CASHA,CASHB,CASHC,CASHD,CASHE,CASHF
0265       WRITE(3,57)CASHA,CASHB,CASHC,CASHD,CASHE,CASHF
0266   41  CONTINUE
0267    C  CALCULATE THE BIDDING RECORDS OF COMPANY NO.2'S COMPETITORS
0268       DO 58 K1=1,IALL
0269       IF(ITEND(K1,2).EQ.0.0)GO TO 58
0270       LOWBID=NINT((BIDLOW(K1)/EST(K1,2))*100.0)
0271       LOWBID=LOWBID-85
0272       DO 59 K3=1,50
0273       IF(K3.EQ.LOWBID)FOOL(K3)=FOOL(K3)+1
0274   59  CONTINUE
0275       DO 60 K2=3,NUMCO
0276       IF(ITEND(K1,K2).EQ.0.0)GO TO 60
0277       IBID=NINT((ITEND(K1,K2)/EST(K1,2))*100.0)
0278       IBID=IBID-85
0279       DO 61 K3=1,50
0280       IF(K3.EQ.IBID)BID(K2,K3)=BID(K2,K3)+1
0281   61  CONTINUE
0282   60  CONTINUE
0283   58  CONTINUE
0284       DO 62 K2=3,NUMCO
0285       DO 63 K3=1,50
0286       ALLJOB(K2)=ALLJOB(K2)+BID(K2,K3)
0287   63  CONTINUE
0288   62  CONTINUE
0289       DO 64 K3=1,50
```

The program listing – *continued*

```
0290            DO 65 K2=3,NUMCO
0291            ALLBIDS(K3)=ALLBIDS(K3)+BID(K2,K3)
0292      65    CONTINUE
0293      64    CONTINUE
0294            DO 66 K2=3,NUMCO
0295            TOTBID=ALLJOB(K2)
0296            DO 67 K3=1,50
0297            IF(BID(K2,K3).EQ.0.0)GO TO 67
0298            TID(K2,K3)=(TOTBID/ALLJOB(K2))*100.0
0299            TOTBID=TOTBID-BID(K2,K3)
0300      67    CONTINUE
0301      66    CONTINUE
0302            SUMBID=0.0
0303            DO 68 K3=1,50
0304            SUMBID=SUMBID+ALLBIDS(K3)
0305      68    CONTINUE
0306            BIDSUM=SUMBID
0307            DO 69 K3=1,50
0308            IF(ALLBIDS(K3).EQ.0.0)GO TO 69
0309            DUMMY=ALLBIDS(K3)
0310            ALLBIDS(K3)=(BIDSUM/SUMBID)*100.0
0311            BIDSUM=BIDSUM-DUMMY
0312      69    CONTINUE
0313            SUMLOW=0.0
0314            DO 70 K3=1,50
0315            SUMLOW=SUMLOW+FOOL(K3)
0316      70    CONTINUE
0317            TOTLOW=SUMLOW
0318            DO 71 K3=1,50
0319            IF(FOOL(K3).EQ.0.0)GO TO 71
0320            DUMMY=FOOL(K3)
```

The program listing – *continued*

```
0321            BEFOOL(K3)=(TOTLOW/SUMLOW)*100.0
0322            TOTLOW=TOTLOW-DUMMY
0323    71   CONTINUE
0324            DO 72  K3=1,50
0325            NBID(K3)=K3+85
0326    72   CONTINUE
0327            WRITE(2,73)P(NTIME)
0328            WRITE(3,73)P(NTIME)
0329            DO 74  K3=1,50
0330            WRITE(2,75)NBID(K3),(TID(K2,K3),K2=3,20),ALLBIDS(K3),BEFOOL(K3)    2C
0331            WRITE(3,75)NBID(K3),(TID(K2,K3),K2=3,20),ALLBIDS(K3),BEFOOL(K3)    2C
0332    74   CONTINUE
0333    C   CSELECT JOBS FOR NEXT PERIOD
0334            IA=NINT(NJOBS*0.4)
0335            IB=NINT(NJOBS*0.3)
0336            IC=NINT(NJOBS*0.2)
0337            ID=NINT(NJOBS*0.1)
0338            IALL=IA+IB+IC+ID
0339            DO 111 K=1,IA
0340            MYCOST(K)=ANINT((50.0+100.0*UTR1(1,0,KRAND))*1000.0)
0341            LENGTH(K)=ANINT(3.0+4.0*UTR1(1,0,KRAND))
0342    111  CONTINUE
0343            KKK=IA+1
0344            KK=IA+IB
0345            DO 76  K=KKK,KK
0346            MYCOST(K)=ANINT((150.0+250.0*UTR1(1,0,KRAND))*1000.0)
0347            LENGTH(K)=ANINT(4.0+3.0*UTR1(1,0,KRAND))
0348    76   CONTINUE
0349            KKK=KK+1
0350            KK=KK+IC
0351            DO 77  K=KKK,KK
```

The program listing – *continued*

```
0352        MYCOST(K)=ANINT((400.0+600.0*UTR1(1,0,KRAND))*1000.0)
0353        LENGTH(K)=ANINT(4.0+5.0*UTR1(1,0,KRAND))
0354    77  CONTINUE
0355        KKK=KK+1
0356        KK=KK+ID
0357        DO 78 K=KKK,KK
0358        MYCOST(K)=ANINT((1000.0+1000.0*UTR1(1,0,KRAND))*1000.0)
0359        LENGTH(K)=ANINT(5.0+6.0*UTR1(1,0,KRAND))
0360    78  CONTINUE
0361    C   CALCULATE EACH COMPANIES' ESTIMATE FOR EVERY JOB
0362        LTIME=NTIME+1
0363        IF(LTIME.GT.24)LTIME=1
0364        DO 79 J=1,NUMCO
0365        WRITE(2,80)J,P(LTIME)
0366        DO 112 K1=1,IALL
0367    81  RA=1.0+0.0333*UTR1(2,1,JRAND)
0368        IF(RA.LT.0.90)GO TO 81
0369        IF(RA.GT.1.10)GO TO 81
0370        EST(K1,J)=MYCOST(K1)*RA
0371        WRITE(2,82)K1,MYCOST(K1),RA,EST(K1,J)
0372    112 CONTINUE
0373    79  CONTINUE
0374        DO 200 J=1,NUMCO
0375        WRITE(2,203)J,P(LTIME)
0376        WRITE(3,203)J,P(LTIME)
0377        DO 201 K1=1,IALL
0378        WRITE(2,202)K1,EST(K1,J),LENGTH(K1)
0379        WRITE(3,202)K1,EST(K1,J),LENGTH(K1)
0380    201 CONTINUE
0381    200 CONTINUE
0382    203 FORMAT(1H1,11HCOMPANY NO.,I2,38HESTIMATES FOR JOBS ON OFFER IN PER
```

The program listing – *continued*

```
0383       1IOB ,'A3//1H ,27HJOB NO. ESTIMATE  DURATION)
0384   202 FORMAT(1H ,2X,I2,4X,F10.0,4X,F4.1)
0385   c   CALCULATE ACTUAL COSTS
0386       DO 83 K1=1,IALL
0387    84 PERF=1.0+0.0166*UTR1(2,1,IRAND)
0388       IF(PERF.LT.0.05)GO TO 84
0389       IF(PERF.GT.1.05)GO TO 84
0390       NACOST(K1)=MYCOST(K1)*PERF
0391    83 CONTINUE
0392       WRITE(2,85)IRAND,JRAND,KRAND
0393   c   UPDATE TAPE RECORDS
0394       DO 86 KO=1,NUMCO
0395       DO 86 KH=1,24
0396       WRITE(6)(M(KO,KH,L),L=1,14),WLOAD(KO,KH),KASH(KO),CAPTA(KO),IALL
0397    86 CONTINUE
0398       DO 87 L=1,IALL
0399       DO 87 KO=1,NUMCO
0400       WRITE(6)EST(L,KO),NACOST(L),LENGTH(L)
0401    87 CONTINUE
0402       DO 88 K2=3,NUMCO
0403       DO 88 K3=1,50
0404       WRITE(6)BID(K2,K3),FOOL(K3)
0405    88 CONTINUE
0406       WRITE(6)IRAND,JRAND,KRAND
0407       REWIND 6
0408       DO 89 KO=1,NUMCO
0409       DO 89 KH=1,24
0410       WRITE(5)(M(KO,KH,L),L=1,14),WLOAD(KO,KH),KASH(KO),CAPTA(KO),IALL
0411    89 CONTINUE
0412       DO 90 L=1,IALL
0413       DO 90 KO=1,NUMCO
```

The program listing – *continued*

```
0414    90  WRITE(5)EST(L,KO),NACOST(L),LENGTH(L)
0415        CONTINUE
0416        DO 91 K2=3,NUMCO
0417        DO 91 K3=1,50
0418        WRITE(5)BID(K2,K3),FOOL(K3)
0419    91  CONTINUE
0420        WRITE(5)IRAND,JRAND,KRAND
0421        REWIND 5
0422    2   FORMAT(A8,A4,66X,I2)
0423    3   FORMAT(4I2)
0424    5   FORMAT(3I7)
0425    7   FORMAT(8F10.0)
0426    19  FORMAT(F5.1)
0427    23  FORMAT(1H1,21HCOMPANY TENDER REPORT)
0428    24  FORMAT(1H ,15HCOMPANY NUMBER ,I2/1H ,7HPERIOD ,A3/1H ,38HJOB NO ES
0429       1TIMATED COST MARK UP TENDER)
0430    25  FORMAT(I2)
0431    27  FORMAT(I2,F6.2)
0432    28  FORMAT(1H ,2X,I2,5X,F10.0,5X,F6.2,2X,F10.0)
0433    32  FORMAT(1H1,13HTENDER REPORT/1H ,7HPERIOD ,A3//1H ,107H CO. NO.
0434          1         2       3      4      5       6        7
0435    10/1H ,8H JOB NO.)
0436    34  FORMAT(1H ,2X,I3,4X,10(A1,F8.0,2X))
0437    35  FORMAT(1H1,13HTENDER REPORT/1H ,7HPERIOD ,A3//1H ,107H CO. NO.
0438          1         2       3      4      5       6        7
0439    20/1H ,8H JOB NO.)
0440    47  FORMAT(1H1,17H  COMPANY NUMBER ,I2/1H ,9H PERIOD ,A3/1H ,51H COM
0441       1PANY REPORT ASSUMING NO MORE JOBS TENDERED FOR)
0442    48  FORMAT(1H ,99H TIME  WORKLOAD  CONTRI- TENDERING  WORK SUB-
0443       1SUB-CONT.  COMPANY  INTEREST  PROFIT/  ANNUAL /1H ;101H PERIOD
0444       2 ACTUALCOST  BUTION    COSTS   CONTRACTED COSTS  OVERHEADS  +C
```

The program listing – *continued*

```
0445        3HARGE    LOSS    PROF/LOSS/1H ,72X,7H=EARNED)
0446   50 FORMAT(1H ,3X,A3,3X,9(F10.0))
0447   51 FORMAT(1H ,37HWORK CURRENTLY SUB-CONTRACTED ABOVE £,F10.0)
0448   52 FORMAT(1H ,46HINTEREST CHARGED AT 3% PER QTR FOR THE FIRST £,F10.0
0449      1,21HBORROWED,4% BETWEEN £,F10.0,3H&£,F10.0,10H& THEN @5%)
0450   53 FORMAT(1H ,22HCOMPANY CASH STATEMENT/1H ,11OH TIME '----------
0451      1----=CASH OUT-----------=CASH IN-----=  INTEREST NET
0452      2  CUMULATIVE CASH FOR/1H ,1O9H PERIOD  CONTRACT SUB-CONT TEN
0453      3DERING COMPANY CONTRACT RETENTION +CHARGE CASH  CASH
0454      4 DIVS.TAX/1H ,11X,94HPAYMENTS PAYMENTS  COSTS  OTHEADS RECEI
0455      5PTS  RECEIPTS  -EARNED FLOW  FLOW  ETC.)
0456   56 FORMAT(1H ,3X,A3,4X,10(F10.0))
0457   57 FORMAT(1H ,3OHANNUAL AVERAGE OF CASH ACCOUNT/1H ,6HYEAR 1,F10.0,2X
0458      1,6HYEAR 2,F10.0,2X,6HYEAR 3,F10.0,2X,6HYEAR 4,F10.0,2X,6HYEAR 5,F1
0459      2O.0,2X,6HYEAR 6,F10.0)
0460   73 FORMAT(1H1,5OHCOMPANY NO.2 BIDDING RECORD OF COMPETITORS PERIOD,A
0461      13//1H ,7HBID/EST,2OX,9HCOMPANIES/1H ,10X,96H3   4   5   6   7
0462      2 8   9   10  11  12  13  14  15  16  17  18  19  20
0463      3 ALL LOW)
0464   75 FORMAT(1H ,3X,I3,2X,2OF5.1)
0465  101 FORMAT(1H1,7HPERIOD ,A3,11HJOB DETAILS/1H ,36HJOB NO.  ACTUAL COST
0466      1 DURATION(QTRS))
0467  103 FORMAT(1H ,2X,I2,5X,F10.0,6X,F4.1)
0468   80 FORMAT(1H1,11HCOMPANY NO.,I2,48H ESTIMATE BUILD UP FOR JOBS ON OF
0469      1FER IN PERIOD ,A3//1H ,47HJOB NO. LIKELY COST RANDOM NO. ESTIMAT
0470      2ED COST)
0471   82 FORMAT(1H ,2X,I2,5X,F10.0,4X,F4.2,7X,F10.0)
0472   85 FORMAT(1H1,6HIRAND=,I7,6HJRAND=,I7,6HKRAND=,I7)
0473  106 FORMAT(1H1,12HCOMPANY NO. ,I2,31H DETAILS OF JOBS WON IN PERIOD ,A
0474      13//1H ,45HJOB NO. ACTUAL COST TENDER DURATION(QTRS))
0475  105 FORMAT(1H ,2X,I2,6X,F10.0,1X,F10.0,5X,F4.1)
```

The program listing – *continued*

```
0476        STOP
0477        END

END OF SEGMENT, LENGTH 4345, NAME  BIDGAMETHREE

0478        FINISH

END OF COMPILATION -  NO ERRORS

S/C SUBFILE:       363 BUCKETS USED

CONSOLIDATED BY XPCK 12K    DATE    02/11/81    TIME 18/55/23
```

subsequent runs. UTR 1 is used in the program to select random numbers from:

1. A uniform distribution of range 50 000 to 150 000 representing the true cost of small jobs (program statement 340)
2. A uniform distribution of range 3 to 7 representing the duration, in quarters, of small jobs (program statement 341)
3. A uniform distribution of range 150 000 to 400 000 representing the true cost of medium–small jobs (program statement 346)
4. A uniform distribution of range 4 to 7 representing duration of medium–small jobs (program statement 347)
5. A uniform distribution of range 400 000 to 1 000 000 representing the true cost of medium–large jobs (program statement 352)
6. A uniform distribution of range 4 to 9 representing duration of medium–large jobs (program statement 353)
7. A uniform distribution of range 1 000 000 to 2 000 000 representing the true cost of large jobs (program statement 358)
8. A uniform distribution of range 5 to 11 representing duration of large jobs (program statement 359)
9. A normal distribution of mean 1·0 and standard deviation 0·033 representing the factor of inaccuracy in estimating (program statement 367)
10. A normal distribution of mean 1·0 and standard deviation 0·0166 representing the factor of variability of on-site performance (program statement 387).

Part 3 – Bidding game

Introduction

This is a simplified manual game which demonstrates the effect of variability in an estimate, the margin lost to competition and the difficulties of recovering overheads from an uncertain turnover.

The description given is in the form of instructions to the participants. It is envisaged that the participating group will be divided into teams of four to six, each team representing a company.

General Notes on Bidding Game

Tender = estimated direct cost + mark-up
Mark-up = contribution, the amount added to estimated direct cost for profit and overheads
True cost = direct cost to the company undertaking the project

In estimating the direct cost the company is trying to estimate *true cost*. To simulate estimating variability

Estimated direct cost = true cost × a factor of variation

In this game the assumption is

$$\text{Estimated direct cost} = \text{true cost} \pm 10\%$$

The factor of variation within the range $\pm 10\%$ will be obtained by random selection (see Note 1). Thus a project whose *true cost* is given as £1000 may be estimated as having a direct cost of between £900 and £1100.

For a company

Turnover = sum of successful tenders
         (winning tenders being defined as the lowest)
Company total contribution = turnover − sum of true costs for all contracts won
Company profit = contribution − overheads

Specific game notes
(These notes may have to be adjusted to suit numbers playing and time available.)

Table 15.7 supplies a list of jobs available over the next year; the overheads cost charges on each company. The jobs listed will be offered to the companies in groups of three.

Each company will enter their mark-up for each job. The game controller will supply the factor of variation to produce the estimated cost. The job will be awarded to the lowest tender. All tenders will be displayed on a central control board. At the end of the game companies will supply their turnover, contribution and profit for comparison. The average of the ratio (estimated cost/true cost) for all winning tenders will be calculated.

Note 1: The generation of random numbers in the range 0·90 to 1·10 can be by desk-top computer, tables or by selecting ping-pong balls from a drum. Some pocket calculators also provide a random number generator.

Table 15.7 List of jobs available in one year   381

Contract no.	True cost (£)	Est. cost (£)	Mark-up (%)	Tender (£)
1	1 000			
2	1 000			
3	1 000			
4	1 000			
5	1 000			
6	1 000			
7	1 000			
8	1 000			
9	1 000			
10	10 000			
11	10 000			
12	10 000			
13	20 000			
14	20 000			
14	20 000			
15	20 000			
16	50 000			
17	50 000			
18	50 000			
19	100 000			
20	100 000			
21	100 000			
22	200 000			
23	200 000			
24	200 000			
25	5 000 000			
26	1 000 000			
27	2 000 000			
28	50 000			
29	200 000			
30	100 000			
31	500 000			
32	50 000			
33	1 000 000			
34	200 000			
35	10 000			
36	500 000			
37	200 000			
38	100 000			
39	10 000			
40	20 000			
41	300 000			
42	20 000			
43	500 000			
44	600 000			
45	700 000			
46	1 000 000			
47	500 000			
48	1 000 000			

Company overheads
£23 000

CHAPTER 16

INVESTMENT APPRAISAL EXERCISE

Summary

The chapter is in two parts. Part 1 is an exercise designed to demonstrat
why DCF yield is the most appropriate measure when selecting from
different projects in order to promote the fastest rate of growth. Part
is a computer program for calculating DCF yield.

The background theory of investment appraisal is explained in
Chapter 13.

What Method of Selecting Projects for Investment Produces the Fastest Rate of Growth?

The exercise given in Part 1 is designed to compare the effects on com
pany growth of different methods of selecting investment projects. Th
computer program given in Part 2 produces the information required t
repeat the above exercise for a different set of projects.

Part 1 – Exercise

Instructions

1. Table 16.1 gives the projected cash flows for 50 different project
(If you wish to repeat this exercise using other projects, create your ow
list similar to Table 16.1.) For each project the items given in Table 16.
have been calculated using the computer program listed in this chapte

Table 16.1 Projected cash flows for 50 projects. Also given: total investment, total cash return, undiscounted profit, payback period, average
annual return, average annual rate of return, DCF yield

```
PROGRAM DCFY
COMPACT DATA (15AH)
COMPACT PROGRAM (DBM)
CORE              3328


            SEG    DCF
            CLV    SPFIL

LAST BUCKET USED OF PROGRAM USE2(1)      IS      27


PROJECT    1
   YEAR     CASH FLOW
    0        -200.00
    1         100.00
    2         100.00
    3         100.00
    4         100.00
    5          50.00
TOTAL INVESTMENT IS      -200.00
TOTAL RETURN IS           450.00
UNDISCOUNTED PROFIT IS          250.0
PAYBACK PERIOD IS 2.000YEARS
AVERAGE ANNUAL RETURN IS         90.00

AVERAGE ANNUAL RATE OF RETURN IS        45.00%
THE D.C.F. YIELD IS    38.2%


PROJECT    2
   YEAR     CASH FLOW
    0        -200.00
    1          50.00
    2          50.00
    3         100.00
    4         300.00
TOTAL INVESTMENT IS      -200.00
TOTAL RETURN IS           500.00
UNDISCOUNTED PROFIT IS          300.0
PAYBACK PERIOD IS 3.000YEARS
AVERAGE ANNUAL RETURN IS        125.00

AVERAGE ANNUAL RATE OF RETURN IS        62.50%
THE D.C.F. YIELD IS    33.9%


PROJECT    3
   YEAR     CASH FLOW
    0        -300.00
    1         100.00
    2         100.00
    3         700.00
    4         200.00
    5          50.00
    6          50.00
TOTAL INVESTMENT IS      -300.00
TOTAL RETURN IS          1200.00
UNDISCOUNTED PROFIT IS          900.0
PAYBACK PERIOD IS 2.143YEARS
AVERAGE ANNUAL RETURN IS        200.00
```

Table 16.1 – *continued*

```
AVERAGE ANNUAL RATE OF RETURN IS        66.67%
THE D.C.F. YIELD IS    62.1%


PROJECT    4
    YEAR     CASH FLOW
      0        -300.00
      1         100.00
      2         100.00
      3         200.00
TOTAL INVESTMENT IS       -300.00
TOTAL RETURN IS            400.00
UNDISCOUNTED PROFIT IS          100.0
PAYBACK PERIOD IS   2.500YEARS
AVERAGE ANNUAL RETURN IS        133.33

AVERAGE ANNUAL RATE OF RETURN IS        44.44%
THE D.C.F. YIELD IS    13.9%


PROJECT    5
    YEAR     CASH FLOW
      0        -300.00
      1         200.00
      2         100.00
      3         100.00
TOTAL INVESTMENT IS       -300.00
TOTAL RETURN IS            400.00
UNDISCOUNTED PROFIT IS          100.0
PAYBACK PERIOD IS   2.000YEARS
AVERAGE ANNUAL RETURN IS        133.33

AVERAGE ANNUAL RATE OF RETURN IS        44.44%
THE D.C.F. YIELD IS    18.5%


PROJECT    6
    YEAR     CASH FLOW
      0        -300.00
      1         200.00
      2           5.00
      3         200.00
TOTAL INVESTMENT IS       -300.00
TOTAL RETURN IS            405.00
UNDISCOUNTED PROFIT IS          105.0
PAYBACK PERIOD IS   2.475YEARS
AVERAGE ANNUAL RETURN IS        135.00

AVERAGE ANNUAL RATE OF RETURN IS        45.00%
THE D.C.F. YIELD IS    16.9%


PROJECT    7
    YEAR     CASH FLOW
      0        -300.00
      1         100.00
      2          50.00
      3         400.00
TOTAL INVESTMENT IS       -300.00
TOTAL RETURN IS            550.00
UNDISCOUNTED PROFIT IS          250.0
```

Table 16.1 – *continued*

```
PAYBACK PERIOD IS   2.375YEARS
AVERAGE ANNUAL RETURN IS          183.33

AVERAGE ANNUAL RATE OF RETURN IS          61.11%
THE D.C.F. YIELD IS    27.9%


PROJECT    8
   YEAR    CASH FLOW
      0      -800.00
      1       300.00
      2       300.00
      3       400.00
      4       100.00
TOTAL INVESTMENT IS      -800.00
TOTAL RETURN IS          1100.00
UNDISCOUNTED PROFIT IS      300.0
PAYBACK PERIOD IS   2.500YEARS
AVERAGE ANNUAL RETURN IS      275.00

AVERAGE ANNUAL RATE OF RETURN IS          34.37%
THE D.C.F. YIELD IS    15.5%


PROJECT    9
   YEAR    CASH FLOW
      0      -500.00
      1        20.00
      2        30.00
      3        20.00
      4        30.00


PROJECT   10
   YEAR    CASH FLOW
      0      -400.00
      1       100.00
      2       200.00
      3       300.00
      4       400.00
TOTAL INVESTMENT IS      -400.00
TOTAL RETURN IS          1000.00
UNDISCOUNTED PROFIT IS      600.0
PAYBACK PERIOD IS   2.333YEARS
AVERAGE ANNUAL RETURN IS      250.00

AVERAGE ANNUAL RATE OF RETURN IS          62.50%
THE D.C.F. YIELD IS    38.2%


PROJECT   11
   YEAR    CASH FLOW
      0      -700.00
      1       200.00
      2       300.00
      3       100.00
      4       500.00
TOTAL INVESTMENT IS      -700.00
TOTAL RETURN IS          1100.00
UNDISCOUNTED PROFIT IS      400.0
PAYBACK PERIOD IS   3.200YEARS
AVERAGE ANNUAL RETURN IS      275.00
```

Table 16.1 – *continued*

AVERAGE ANNUAL RATE OF RETURN IS   39.20%
THE D.C.F. YIELD IS   18.2%

PROJECT 12
   YEAR   CASH FLOW
     0   -1000.00
     1   500.00
     2   300.00
     3   200.00
     4   200.00
     5   200.00
TOTAL INVESTMENT IS   -1000.00
TOTAL RETURN IS   1400.00
UNDISCOUNTED PROFIT IS   400.0
PAYBACK PERIOD IS 3.000YEARS
AVERAGE ANNUAL RETURN IS   280.00

AVERAGE ANNUAL RATE OF RETURN IS   28.00%
THE D.C.F. YIELD IS   15.4%

PROJECT 13
   YEAR   CASH FLOW
     0   -900.00
     1   200.00
     2   300.00
     3   400.00
     4   500.00
     5   600.00
TOTAL INVESTMENT IS   -900.00
TOTAL RETURN IS   2000.00
UNDISCOUNTED PROFIT IS   1100.0
PAYBACK PERIOD IS 3.000YEARS
AVERAGE ANNUAL RETURN IS   400.00

AVERAGE ANNUAL RATE OF RETURN IS   44.44%
THE D.C.F. YIELD IS   27.5%

PROJECT 14
   YEAR   CASH FLOW
     0   -800.00
     1   400.00
     2   500.00
     3   600.00
     4   700.00
     5   100.00
TOTAL INVESTMENT IS   -800.00
TOTAL RETURN IS   2300.00
UNDISCOUNTED PROFIT IS   1500.0
PAYBACK PERIOD IS 1.300YEARS
AVERAGE ANNUAL RETURN IS   460.00

AVERAGE ANNUAL RATE OF RETURN IS   57.50%
THE D.C.F. YIELD IS   51.5%

PROJECT 15
   YEAR   CASH FLOW
     0   -800.00

Table 16.1 – *continued*

```
      1         100.00
      2         100.00
      3         100.00
      4         500.00
      5        1000.00
TOTAL INVESTMENT IS      -800.00
TOTAL RETURN IS          1800.00
UNDISCOUNTED PROFIT IS       1000.0
PAYBACK PERIOD IS  4.000YEARS
AVERAGE ANNUAL RETURN IS         360.00

AVERAGE ANNUAL RATE OF RETURN IS          45.00%
THE D.C.F. YIELD IS    22.0%


PROJECT  16
   YEAR     CASH FLOW
      0       -600.00
      1        300.00
      2        300.00
      3        100.00
      4        100.00
      5         50.00
TOTAL INVESTMENT IS      -600.00
TOTAL RETURN IS           850.00
UNDISCOUNTED PROFIT IS        250.0
PAYBACK PERIOD IS  2.000YEARS
AVERAGE ANNUAL RETURN IS         170.00

AVERAGE ANNUAL RATE OF RETURN IS          28.33%
THE D.C.F. YIELD IS    18.4%


PROJECT  17
   YEAR     CASH FLOW
      0       -500.00
      1         50.00
      2        100.00
      3        100.00
      4        300.00
      5        300.00
TOTAL INVESTMENT IS      -500.00
TOTAL RETURN IS           850.00
UNDISCOUNTED PROFIT IS        350.0
PAYBACK PERIOD IS  3.833YEARS
AVERAGE ANNUAL RETURN IS         170.00

AVERAGE ANNUAL RATE OF RETURN IS          34.00%
THE D.C.F. YIELD IS    15.4%


PROJECT  18
   YEAR     CASH FLOW
      0       -500.00
      1          1.00
      2          1.00
      3          1.00
      4          1.00
      5       2000.00
TOTAL INVESTMENT IS      -500.00
TOTAL RETURN IS          2004.00
UNDISCOUNTED PROFIT IS       1504.0
```

Table 16.1 – *continued*

```
PAYBACK PERIOD IS  4.248YEARS
AVERAGE ANNUAL RETURN IS        400.80

AVERAGE ANNUAL RATE OF RETURN IS        80.16%
THE D.C.F. YIELD IS   32.1%


PROJECT  19
    YEAR     CASH FLOW
     0       -500.00
     1        500.00
     2          1.00
     3          1.00
     4          1.00
     5          1.00
TOTAL INVESTMENT IS      -500.00
TOTAL RETURN IS           504.00
UNDISCOUNTED PROFIT IS         4.0
PAYBACK PERIOD IS  1.000YEARS
AVERAGE ANNUAL RETURN IS        100.80

AVERAGE ANNUAL RATE OF RETURN IS        20.16%
THE D.C.F. YIELD IS    0.8%


PROJECT  20
    YEAR     CASH FLOW
     0       -500.00
     1        100.00
     2        100.00
     3        100.00
     4        100.00
     5        200.00
TOTAL INVESTMENT IS      -500.00
TOTAL RETURN IS           600.00
UNDISCOUNTED PROFIT IS        100.0
PAYBACK PERIOD IS  4.500YEARS
AVERAGE ANNUAL RETURN IS        120.00

AVERAGE ANNUAL RATE OF RETURN IS        24.00%
THE D.C.F. YIELD IS    5.7%


PROJECT  21
    YEAR     CASH FLOW
     0       -500.00
     1        100.00
     2        100.00
     3        200.00
     4        100.00
     5        100.00
TOTAL INVESTMENT IS      -500.00
TOTAL RETURN IS           600.00
UNDISCOUNTED PROFIT IS        100.0
PAYBACK PERIOD IS  4.000YEARS
AVERAGE ANNUAL RETURN IS        120.00

AVERAGE ANNUAL RATE OF RETURN IS        24.00%
THE D.C.F. YIELD IS    6.3%


PROJECT  22
```

Table 16.1 – *continued*

```
YEAR      CASH FLOW
  0        -500.00
  1         200.00
  2         100.00
  3         100.00
  4         100.00
  5         100.00
TOTAL INVESTMENT IS       -500.00
TOTAL RETURN IS            600.00
UNDISCOUNTED PROFIT IS      100.0
PAYBACK PERIOD IS  4.000YEARS
AVERAGE ANNUAL RETURN IS        120.00

AVERAGE ANNUAL RATE OF RETURN IS        24.00%
THE D.C.F. YIELD IS      7.2%


PROJECT   23
  YEAR      CASH FLOW
    0       -2000.00
    1         500.00
    2         500.00
    3         500.00
    4         500.00
    5         500.00
    6         500.00
TOTAL INVESTMENT IS       -2000.00
TOTAL RETURN IS            3000.00
UNDISCOUNTED PROFIT IS      1000.0
PAYBACK PERIOD IS  4.000YEARS
AVERAGE ANNUAL RETURN IS        500.00

AVERAGE ANNUAL RATE OF RETURN IS        25.00%
THE D.C.F. YIELD IS     13.0%


PROJECT   24
  YEAR      CASH FLOW
    0       -1500.00
    1         400.00
    2         400.00
    3         400.00
    4         400.00
    5         400.00
    6         400.00
TOTAL INVESTMENT IS       -1500.00
TOTAL RETURN IS            2400.00
UNDISCOUNTED PROFIT IS       900.0
PAYBACK PERIOD IS  3.750YEARS
AVERAGE ANNUAL RETURN IS        400.00

AVERAGE ANNUAL RATE OF RETURN IS        26.67%
THE D.C.F. YIELD IS     15.3%


PROJECT   25
  YEAR      CASH FLOW
    0       -1400.00
    1         800.00
    2         400.00
    3         300.00
    4         300.00
```

Table 16.1 – *continued*

```
    5        300.00
    6        300.00
TOTAL INVESTMENT IS    =1400.00
TOTAL RETURN IS         2400.00
UNDISCOUNTED PROFIT IS      1000.0
PAYBACK PERIOD IS  2.667YEARS
AVERAGE ANNUAL RETURN IS        400.00

AVERAGE ANNUAL RATE OF RETURN IS        28.57%
THE D.C.F. YIELD IS   23.0%


PROJECT  26
    YEAR    CASH FLOW
    0      -1200.00
    1        600.00
    2        600.00
    3        600.00
    4        300.00
    5        300.00
    6        300.00
TOTAL INVESTMENT IS    =1200.00
TOTAL RETURN IS         2700.00
UNDISCOUNTED PROFIT IS      1500.0
PAYBACK PERIOD IS  2.000YEARS
AVERAGE ANNUAL RETURN IS        450.00

AVERAGE ANNUAL RATE OF RETURN IS        37.50%
THE D.C.F. YIELD IS   36.1%


PROJECT  27
    YEAR    CASH FLOW
    0      -1000.00
    1        600.00
    2        600.00
    3        300.00
    4        200.00
    5        200.00
    6        200.00
TOTAL INVESTMENT IS    =1000.00
TOTAL RETURN IS         2100.00
UNDISCOUNTED PROFIT IS      1100.0
PAYBACK PERIOD IS  1.667YEARS
AVERAGE ANNUAL RETURN IS        350.00

AVERAGE ANNUAL RATE OF RETURN IS        35.00%
THE D.C.F. YIELD IS   37.1%


PROJECT  28
    YEAR    CASH FLOW
    0      -1000.00
    1        200.00
    2        200.00
    3        200.00
    4        300.00
    5        600.00
    6        600.00
TOTAL INVESTMENT IS    =1000.00
TOTAL RETURN IS         2100.00
UNDISCOUNTED PROFIT IS      1100.0
```

Table 16.1 – *continued*

```
PAYBACK PERIOD IS   4.167YEARS
AVERAGE ANNUAL RETURN IS       350.00

AVERAGE ANNUAL RATE OF RETURN IS        35.00%
THE D.C.F. YIELD IS   20.3%


PROJECT  29
   YEAR    CASH FLOW
      0      -800.00
      1       700.00
      2       100.00
      3       100.00
      4       100.00
      5       100.00
      6       100.00
TOTAL INVESTMENT IS     -800.00
TOTAL RETURN IS         1200.00
UNDISCOUNTED PROFIT IS        400.0
PAYBACK PERIOD IS  2.000YEARS
AVERAGE ANNUAL RETURN IS       200.00

AVERAGE ANNUAL RATE OF RETURN IS        25.00%
THE D.C.F. YIELD IS   22.7%


PROJECT  30
   YEAR    CASH FLOW
      0      -600.00
      1       100.00
      2       100.00
      3       100.00
      4       100.00
      5       100.00
      6       400.00
TOTAL INVESTMENT IS     -600.00
TOTAL RETURN IS          900.00
UNDISCOUNTED PROFIT IS        300.0
PAYBACK PERIOD IS  5.250YEARS
AVERAGE ANNUAL RETURN IS       150.00

AVERAGE ANNUAL RATE OF RETURN IS        25.00%
THE D.C.F. YIELD IS   10.2%


PROJECT  31
   YEAR    CASH FLOW
      0      -500.00
      1       400.00
      2       100.00
      3        50.00
      4        50.00
      5        50.00
      6        50.00
TOTAL INVESTMENT IS     -500.00
TOTAL RETURN IS          700.00
UNDISCOUNTED PROFIT IS        200.0
PAYBACK PERIOD IS  2.000YEARS
AVERAGE ANNUAL RETURN IS       116.67

AVERAGE ANNUAL RATE OF RETURN IS        23.33%
THE D.C.F. YIELD IS   19.0%
```

Table 16.1 – *continued*

```
PROJECT   32
    YEAR    CASH FLOW
     0        -400.00
     1          50.00
     2          50.00
     3          50.00
     4          50.00
     5         100.00
     6         400.00
TOTAL INVESTMENT IS      -400.00
TOTAL RETURN IS           700.00
UNDISCOUNTED PROFIT IS        300.0
PAYBACK PERIOD IS  5.250YEARS
AVERAGE ANNUAL RETURN IS         116.67

AVERAGE ANNUAL RATE OF RETURN IS          29.17%
THE D.C.F. YIELD IS   12.7%


PROJECT   33
    YEAR    CASH FLOW
     0        -100.00
     1          20.00
     2          20.00
     3          20.00
     4          20.00
     5          20.00
     6          20.00
TOTAL INVESTMENT IS      -100.00
TOTAL RETURN IS           120.00
UNDISCOUNTED PROFIT IS         20.0
PAYBACK PERIOD IS  5.000YEARS
AVERAGE ANNUAL RETURN IS          20.00

AVERAGE ANNUAL RATE OF RETURN IS          20.00%
THE D.C.F. YIELD IS    5.4%


PROJECT   34
    YEAR    CASH FLOW
     0       -1600.00
     1         500.00
     2         500.00
     3         500.00
     4         300.00
     5         600.00
     6         200.00
     7         200.00
TOTAL INVESTMENT IS     -1600.00
TOTAL RETURN IS          2800.00
UNDISCOUNTED PROFIT IS       1200.0
PAYBACK PERIOD IS  3.333YEARS
AVERAGE ANNUAL RETURN IS         400.00

AVERAGE ANNUAL RATE OF RETURN IS          25.00%
THE D.C.F. YIELD IS   19.0%


PROJECT   35
    YEAR    CASH FLOW
```

Table 16.1 – *continued*

```
    0        -1600.00
    1          200.00
    2          200.00
    3          300.00
    4          300.00
    5          500.00
    6          500.00
    7          500.00
TOTAL INVESTMENT IS    -1600.00
TOTAL RETURN IS         2500.00
UNDISCOUNTED PROFIT IS       900.0
PAYBACK PERIOD IS  5.200YEARS
AVERAGE ANNUAL RETURN IS        357.14

AVERAGE ANNUAL RATE OF RETURN IS       22.32%
THE D.C.F. YIELD IS    10.4%



PROJECT  36
   YEAR      CASH FLOW
    0        -1300.00
    1          100.00
    2          100.00
    3         1000.00
    4          100.00
    5          200.00
    6          100.00
    7          200.00
TOTAL INVESTMENT IS    -1300.00
TOTAL RETURN IS         1800.00
UNDISCOUNTED PROFIT IS       500.0
PAYBACK PERIOD IS  4.000YEARS
AVERAGE ANNUAL RETURN IS        257.14

AVERAGE ANNUAL RATE OF RETURN IS       19.78%
THE D.C.F. YIELD IS     9.4%



PROJECT  37
   YEAR      CASH FLOW
    0        -1001.00
    1          320.00
    2          480.00
    3          630.00
    4          840.00
    5          950.00
    6           10.00
    7           11.00
TOTAL INVESTMENT IS    -1001.00
TOTAL RETURN IS         3241.00
UNDISCOUNTED PROFIT IS      2240.0
PAYBACK PERIOD IS  2.319YEARS
AVERAGE ANNUAL RETURN IS        463.00

AVERAGE ANNUAL RATE OF RETURN IS       46.25%
THE D.C.F. YIELD IS    44.7%



PROJECT  38
   YEAR      CASH FLOW
    0         -900.00
    1          500.00
```

Table 16.1 – *continued*

```
    2          320.00
    3          408.00
    4          105.00
    5          500.00
    6          800.00
    7           90.00
TOTAL INVESTMENT IS      -900.00
TOTAL RETURN IS         2723.00
UNDISCOUNTED PROFIT IS        1823.0
PAYBACK PERIOD IS  2.196YEARS
AVERAGE ANNUAL RETURN IS        389.00

AVERAGE ANNUAL RATE OF RETURN IS        43.22%
THE D.C.F. YIELD IS    40.2%


PROJECT   39
   YEAR      CASH FLOW
    0         -605.00
    1          150.00
    2          150.00
    3          150.00
    4          150.00
    5          150.00
    6          150.00
    7          150.00
TOTAL INVESTMENT IS      -605.00
TOTAL RETURN IS         1050.00
UNDISCOUNTED PROFIT IS        445.0
PAYBACK PERIOD IS  4.033YEARS
AVERAGE ANNUAL RETURN IS        150.00

AVERAGE ANNUAL RATE OF RETURN IS        24.79%
THE D.C.F. YIELD IS    16.0%


PROJECT   40
   YEAR      CASH FLOW
    0         -505.00
    1          400.00
    2          300.00
    3          200.00
    4          100.00
    5           50.00
    6           50.00
    7           50.00
TOTAL INVESTMENT IS      -505.00
TOTAL RETURN IS         1150.00
UNDISCOUNTED PROFIT IS        645.0
PAYBACK PERIOD IS  1.350YEARS
AVERAGE ANNUAL RETURN IS        164.29

AVERAGE ANNUAL RATE OF RETURN IS        32.53%
THE D.C.F. YIELD IS    47.9%


PROJECT   41
   YEAR      CASH FLOW
    0         -405.00
    1           50.00
    2           50.00
    3           50.00
```

Table 16.1 – *continued*

```
        4           300.00
        5           330.00
        6           200.00
        7           100.00
TOTAL INVESTMENT IS      -405.00
TOTAL RETURN IS          1080.00
UNDISCOUNTED PROFIT IS          675.0
PAYBACK PERIOD IS  3.850YEARS
AVERAGE ANNUAL RETURN IS         154.20

AVERAGE ANNUAL RATE OF RETURN IS         38.10%
THE D.C.F. YIELD IS    24.7%


PROJECT  42
   YEAR      CASH FLOW
      0        -305.00
      1         100.00
      2          50.00
      3         100.00
      4          50.00
      5         100.00
      6          50.00
      7         100.00
TOTAL INVESTMENT IS      -305.00
TOTAL RETURN IS           550.00
UNDISCOUNTED PROFIT IS          245.0
PAYBACK PERIOD IS  4.050YEARS
AVERAGE ANNUAL RETURN IS          78.57

AVERAGE ANNUAL RATE OF RETURN IS         25.76%
THE D.C.F. YIELD IS    17.5%


PROJECT  43
   YEAR   CASH FLOW
      0        -301.00
      1         201.00
      2         100.00
      3         500.00
      4        1000.00
      5         500.00
      6        1000.00
      7         500.00
TOTAL INVESTMENT IS      -301.00
TOTAL RETURN IS          3801.00
UNDISCOUNTED PROFIT IS         3500.0
PAYBACK PERIOD IS  2.000YEARS
AVERAGE ANNUAL RETURN IS         543.00

AVERAGE ANNUAL RATE OF RETURN IS        180.40%
THE D.C.F. YIELD IS    96.2%


PROJECT  44
   YEAR   CASH FLOW
      0        -302.00
      1          50.00
      2          50.00
      3          50.00
      4         100.00
      5         100.00
```

Table 16.1 – *continued*

```
     6           100.00
     7            50.00
TOTAL INVESTMENT IS       -302.00
TOTAL RETURN IS            500.00
UNDISCOUNTED PROFIT IS          198.0
PAYBACK PERIOD IS  4.520YEARS
AVERAGE ANNUAL RETURN IS          71.43

AVERAGE ANNUAL RATE OF RETURN IS          23.65%
THE D.C.F. YIELD IS   13.1%


PROJECT  45
    YEAR      CASH FLOW
     0         -2000.00
     1           300.00
     2           300.00
     3           300.00
     4           300.00
     5           300.00
     6           300.00
     7           300.00
     8           300.00
     9           300.00
    10           300.00
TOTAL INVESTMENT IS     -2000.00
TOTAL RETURN IS          3000.00
UNDISCOUNTED PROFIT IS          1000.0
PAYBACK PERIOD IS  6.667YEARS
AVERAGE ANNUAL RETURN IS          300.00

AVERAGE ANNUAL RATE OF RETURN IS          15.00%
THE D.C.F. YIELD IS    8.1%


PROJECT  46
    YEAR      CASH FLOW
     0         -1900.00
     1           300.00
     2           300.00
     3           300.00
     4           400.00
     5           400.00
     6           400.00
     7           400.00
     8           400.00
     9           400.00
    10           400.00
TOTAL INVESTMENT IS     -1900.00
TOTAL RETURN IS          3700.00
UNDISCOUNTED PROFIT IS          1800.0
PAYBACK PERIOD IS  5.500YEARS
AVERAGE ANNUAL RETURN IS          370.00

AVERAGE ANNUAL RATE OF RETURN IS          19.47%
THE D.C.F. YIELD IS   13.4%


PROJECT  47
    YEAR      CASH FLOW
     0         -2001.00
     1           600.00
```

Table 16.1 – continued

```
   2        600.00
   3        600.00
   4        600.00
   5        600.00
TOTAL INVESTMENT IS    -2001.00
TOTAL RETURN IS         3000.00
UNDISCOUNTED PROFIT IS      999.0
PAYBACK PERIOD IS  3.335YEARS
AVERAGE ANNUAL RETURN IS      600.00

AVERAGE ANNUAL RATE OF RETURN IS       29.99%
THE D.C.F. YIELD IS   15.2%


PROJECT  48
   YEAR    CASH FLOW
   0       -2050.00
   1        1000.00
   2         600.00
   3         600.00
   4         600.00
TOTAL INVESTMENT IS    -2050.00
TOTAL RETURN IS         2800.00
UNDISCOUNTED PROFIT IS      750.0
PAYBACK PERIOD IS  2.750YEARS
AVERAGE ANNUAL RETURN IS      700.00

AVERAGE ANNUAL RATE OF RETURN IS       34.15%
THE D.C.F. YIELD IS   15.2%


PROJECT  49
   YEAR    CASH FLOW
   0       -1500.00
   1         500.00
   2         500.00
   3         300.00


PROJECT  50
   YEAR    CASH FLOW
   0       -3000.00
   1         300.00
   2         300.00
   3         300.00
   4         800.00
   5         300.00
   6         300.00
   7         300.00
   8         800.00
   9         300.00
  10         300.00
TOTAL INVESTMENT IS    -3000.00
TOTAL RETURN IS         4000.00
UNDISCOUNTED PROFIT IS      1000.0
PAYBACK PERIOD IS  7.500YEARS
AVERAGE ANNUAL RETURN IS      400.00

AVERAGE ANNUAL RATE OF RETURN IS       13.33%
THE D.C.F. YIELD IS    5.4%
```

The computer program operating instructions attached will allow you to calculate these items for your projects.

2. Determine a number of rules for selecting projects for investment. For example, one selection rule is that projects with the largest average annual rate of return and projects up to the maximum cash amount available could be selected on this basis. Other selection rules are:

> Largest investment
> Smallest investment
> Shortest duration
> Shortest payback period
> Largest undiscounted profit
> Largest DCF yield
> or
> Random selection

With each of these selection rules there will be the difficulty of the maximum available cash, and the project that best satisfies the selection rule may have to be put aside until the cash becomes available. The project selected will be the one that falls in with the cash limit and meets the criterion of the selection rule.

3. For each chosen selection rule complete Table 16.2 (an example is given below). Table 16.2 should be completed by considering the investments you can make each year, starting at year 0 and progressing through each year in turn. Each time an investment is made the amount will appear as a negative sum in the year in which the investment is made. The returns derived from that investment will be shown as positive sums in the year in which they occur. A project can only be invested in once and should then be struck off the list. After completing the investments for one year total the amounts available each year for further investment. Assume that all monies being returned from projects are available for investment.

When you have completed Table 16.2 for up to say, 10 years or for all projects, find the total investment and total return for each year and also the cumulative investment and the cumulative return. Draw graphs of the above against time and compare the graphs for different selection rules. Alternatively, complete the investment programme for all projects and plot the present worth of future cash flows for each year.

Observe which selection rule produces the fastest rate of growth in investment and return.

Example

An example of how to complete Table 16.2 is given in Table 16.3. The selection rule is: smallest investment, smallest duration. The starting capital is £500.

Table 16.2 Possible investment programme 399

Selection rule	YEAR								
Starting capital	0	1	2	3	4	5	6	7	8
PROJECT(S)									
Available for investment									
PROJECT(S)									
Available for investment									
PROJECT(S)									
Available for investment									
PROJECT(S)									
Available for investment									
PROJECT(S)									
Available for investment									
PROJECT(S)									
Available for investment									
PROJECT(S)									
Available for investment									
PROJECT(S)									
Available for investment									
PROJECT(S)									
Available for investment									
PROJECT(S)									
Available for investment									
Total investment									
Cumulative investment									
Total return									
Cumulative return									

Year 0 First selection is project 33 – reason: smallest investment. The project number is entered in the project box, the £100 investment is entered in Year 0 as −100, the £20 returns for six years are entered as +20 in years 1 to 6. Project 33 is struck off the list of available projects.

Second selection is project 2 – reason: smallest investment, smallest duration. The project number 2, the investment −200 and the returns of 50, 50, 100 and 300 are entered as shown. Project 2 is struck off.

Third selection is project 1 – reason: smallest investment. The project number, the investment and the returns are entered as shown. Project 1 is struck off.

This completes the possible investments for year 0 since all the starting capital of £500 is invested. The amounts available for investment in each of the following years are calculated and entered as shown.

Year 1 No investment is possible since only £170 is available and the remaining smallest project is £300. The £170 is carried forward into year 2.

Year 2 First selections can be from projects 3 to 7 because all have investments of £300 and durations of three years. Project 5 is chosen randomly, entered as shown and struck off the list of available projects. The amounts available for investment are calculated.

Year 3 The above process is continued.

When the whole investment programme is complete, calculate at the foot of the table the total investment and return and the cumulative investment and return for each year. Draw graphs of total investment *v.* years, cumulative investment *v.* years, total return *v.* years, cumulative return *v.* years. Compare these graphs with other selection rules. Alternatively complete the investment programme for all projects and plot the present worth of future cash flows for each year.

A modification to the exercise

The exercise as stated is unrealistic in that it is assumed that all projects are available from year 0 and remain available until investment in the project takes place.

The exercise can be modified by listing the projects that are available in each year. For example, Table 16.4 gives a suggested availability list for projects.

The exercise can be repeated using the restricted availability list.

Table 16.3 Example of an investment programme

Selection rule	Smallest investment	YEAR								
Starting capital	£500	0	1	2	3	4	5	6	7	8
						(£)				
Year 0	33	−100	20	20	20	20	20	20		
PROJECT(S)	2	−200	50	50	100	300				
	1	−200	100	100	100	100	50			
Available for investment		0	170	170	220	420	70	20		
Year 1 PROJECT(S)			None							
Available for investment		0	0	340	220	420	70	20		
Year 2 PROJECT(S)	5			−300	200	100	100			
Available for investment				40	460	520	170	20		
Year 3 PROJECT(S)				etc.						
Available for investment										
Year 4 PROJECT(S)										
Available for investment										
Year 5 PROJECT(S)										
Available for investment										
Year 6 PROJECT(S)										
Available for investment										
Year 7 PROJECT(S)										
Available for investment										

Table 16.3 – *continued*

Selection rule	Smallest investment	YEAR								
Starting capital	£500	0	1	2	3	4	5	6	7	8
Year 8 PROJECT(S)											
Available for investment											
Year 9 PROJECT(S)											
Available for investment											
Total investment		−500	−0	−300	etc.						
Cumulative investment		−500	−500	−800	etc.						
Total return		0	170	170	460	etc.					
Cumulative return		0	170	340	800	etc.					

Table 16.4 Availability of projects

Year	Projects available
0	1, 5, 8, 28, 43
1	2, 7, 14, 29, 41
2	3, 9, 16, 30, 40
3	4, 10, 20, 31, 44
4	6, 21, 32, 45
5	11, 19, 33, 39, 46
6	17, 30, 36, 47
7	12, 23, 37, 49
8	18, 24, 35, 48, 49
9	26, 34, 38, 50
10	13, 22, 27, 42

Part 2 – A Computer Program to calculate DCF yield and other measures of profitability

Introduction

This computer program is written in Fortran for an ICL 1904A. The input data required is:

Card 1	Only one card of this type required	
(Format 13)	The total number of projects to be processed	Cols 1 to 3

One set of cards 2 and 3 are required for each project.

Card 2	Only one per project	
(Format 13)	The number of years in the project (excluding year zero)	Cols 1 to 3
Card 3	As many as required per project	
(Format 8F10.0)	The cash flows for each year of the project as follows:	

Year 0	Cols 1 to 10
Year 1	Cols 11 to 20
Year 2	Cols 21 to 30
Year 3	Cols 31 to 40
etc.	
Year 8 would be on a second card 3	

After all projects   ******** in cols 1 to 4

Program listing

```
LOUGHBOROUGH UNIVERSITY COMPUTER CENTRE GEORGE 2L MK4F STREAM B     RUN ON 02/11/81 AT 21:33

     JOB R-DCF,CVAD,AW7890
     FORTRAN ,,PDS
     RUN
     GIVEOUTPUT $CV/OUT2
     ****

FORTRAN COMPILATION BY #XFAT MK 6C     DATE  02/11/81   TIME  21/33/21

0001          SEND TO (ED=SEMICOMPUSER,AXXX)
0002          DUMP ON (ED=PROGRAM USER)
0003          WORK (ED,WORKFILEUSER)
0004          RUN
0005
0006          PROGRAM (DCFY)
0007          COMPACT
0008          COMPRESS INTEGER AND LOGICAL
0009          INPUT 1=CR0
0010          OUTPUT 2=LP0
0011          TRACE 1
0012          END
```

Program listing – *continued*

```
0013          MASTER DCF
0014          DIMENSION CASH(20)
0015    C     READ NUMBER PROJECTS TO BE PROCESSED
0016          READ(1,20)NPROJ
0017    20    FORMAT(I3)
0018          DO 21 M=1,NPROJ
0019    C     READ NUMBER OF YEARS IN PROJECT
0020          READ(1,1)N
0021    1     FORMAT(I3)
0022    C     READ CASH FLOW FOR EACH YEAR STARTING IN YEAR ZERO
0023          READ(1,17)(CASH(J),J=1,N+1)
0024    17    FORMAT(8F10.0)
0025    C     WRITES CASH FLOWS FOR PROJECT
0026          WRITE(2,16)M
0027    16    FORMAT(1H ,//1H ,8HPROJECT ,I3,/1H ,3X,4HYEAR,4X,9HCASH FLOW)
0028          DO 18 J=1,N+1
0029          NYEAR=J-1
0030          WRITE(2,19)NYEAR,CASH(J)
0031    19    FORMAT(1H ,4X,I3,4X,F10.2)
0032    18    CONTINUE
0033    C     CALCULATE TOTAL INVESTMENT
0034          SUMNEG=0.0
0035          DO 2 J=1,N+1
0036          IF(CASH(J))3,2,4
0037    3     SUMNEG=SUMNEG+CASH(J)
0038          NN=J
0039          GO TO 2
0040    4     GO TO 6
0041    2     CONTINUE
0042    C     CALCULATE TOTAL RETURN AND PAYBACK
0043    6     SUMPOS=0.0
```

Program listing – *continued*

```
0044        ISK=1
0045        DO 8 J=NN+1,N+1
0046        SUMPOS=SUMPOS+CASH(J)
0047        P=SUMPOS+SUMNEG
0048        IF(P.GE.0.0)ISK=ISK+1
0049        IF(ISK.NE.2)GO TO 8
0050        PAYBAC=J-2+((CASH(J)-P)/CASH(J))
0051      8 CONTINUE
0052        PROFIT=SUMPOS+SUMNEG
0053        IF(PROFIT.LE.0.0)GO TO 21
0054 C      CALCULATE AVERAGE ANNUAL RATE OF RETURN
0055        AVERTN=SUMPOS/((N+1)-NN)
0056        AVERAT=(AVERTN/SUMNEG)*(-100.0)
0057        WRITE(2,7)SUMNEG,SUMPOS,PROFIT,PAYBAC,AVERTN
0058      7 FORMAT(1H ,19HTOTAL INVESTMENT IS,2X,F10.2/
0059        11H ,19HTOTAL RETURN IS ,2X,F10.2/
0060        51H ,22HDISCOUNTED PROFIT IS,2X,F10.1/
0061        21H ,17HPAYBACK PERIOD IS,2X,F5.3,5HYEARS,/
0062        31H ,24HAVERAGE ANNUAL RETURN IS,2X,F10.2/)
0063        WRITE(2,22)AVERAT
0064     22 FORMAT(1H ,32HAVERAGE ANNUAL RATE OF RETURN IS,2X,F10.2,1H%)
0065 C      CALCULATE D.C.F. YIELD
0066        YI=AVERAT/100.0
0067     13 PW=0.0
0068        DO 9 J=1,N+1
0069        NYEAR=J-1
0070        PW=PW+(CASH(J)*1.0/((1.0+YI)**NYEAR))
0071      9 CONTINUE
0072        IF(PW)12,11,10
0073     12 YI=YI-0.01
0074        GO TO 13
```

Program listing – *continued*

```
0075        10 YI=YI+0.0005
0076           PW=0.0
0077           DO 14 J=1,N+1
0078           NYEAR=J-1
0079           PW=PW+(CASH(J)*1.0/((1.0+YI)**NYEAR))
0080        14 CONTINUE
0081           IF(PW)11,11,10
0082        11 YI=YI-0.0005
0083           YI=YI*100.0
0084           WRITE(2,15)YI
0085        15 FORMAT(1H ,19HTHE D.C.F. YIELD IS,2X,F5.1,1HX)
0086        21 CONTINUE
0087           STOP
0088           END


END OF SEGMENT, LENGTH  297, NAME DCF


0089           FINISH

END OF COMPILATION - NO ERRORS


S/C SUBFILE:      11 BUCKETS USED


CONSOLIDATED BY XPCK 12K    DATE    02/11/81    TIME 21/33/29
```

CHAPTER 17

A LABOUR-SCHEDULING GAME FOR CONSTRUCTION WORK

Summary

A civil engineering project is expressed in the form of a network diagram with predetermined labour resources allocated to each of the activities. Random changes in productivity are then introduced. The player counteracts these changes by adjusting the resources of labour and the extent to which overtime is used.

Introduction

The successful completion of a construction project on time and at the estimated cost is dependent upon many interacting and complex human and administrative factors. However, in the final analysis the efficient use of labour, plant and materials provides the foundation on which sound project management is based. This game simulates experience in understanding the interrelationships between network plans, bar charts and associated resources.

Before attempting to play this game the player is recommended to read the fundamentals of planning as described in Chapter 2.

Structure of the Game

The gaming model simulates a civil engineering project as shown on drawings No. 51910 and No. 51911. The work involves the construction of a sewage works. The logic of the construction plan is expressed in network form, as shown in Fig. 17.1, and this is the basis on which all calculations are subsequently made. A listing of the network data, (to enable the player to include the project details in a computer program)

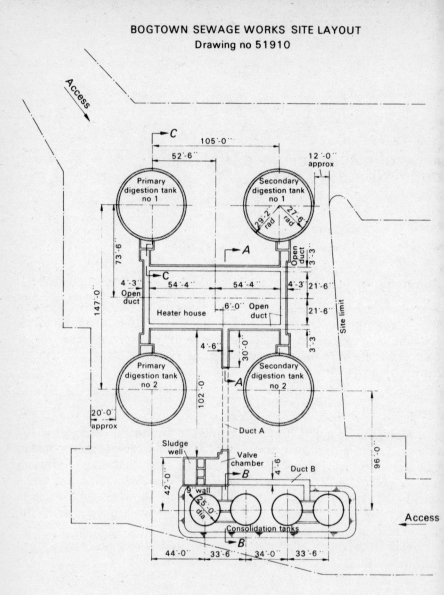

BOGTOWN SEWAGE WORKS SITE LAYOUT
Drawing no 51910

BOGTOWN SEWAGE WORKS SITE LAYOUT
Drawing no 51911

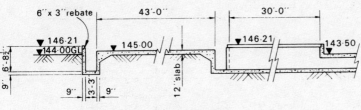

SECTION A-A

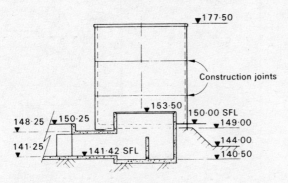

Construction joints

SECTION B-B

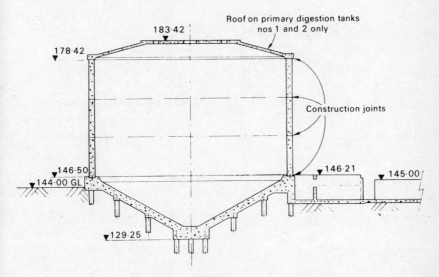

Roof on primary digestion tanks
nos 1 and 2 only

Construction joints

SECTION C-C

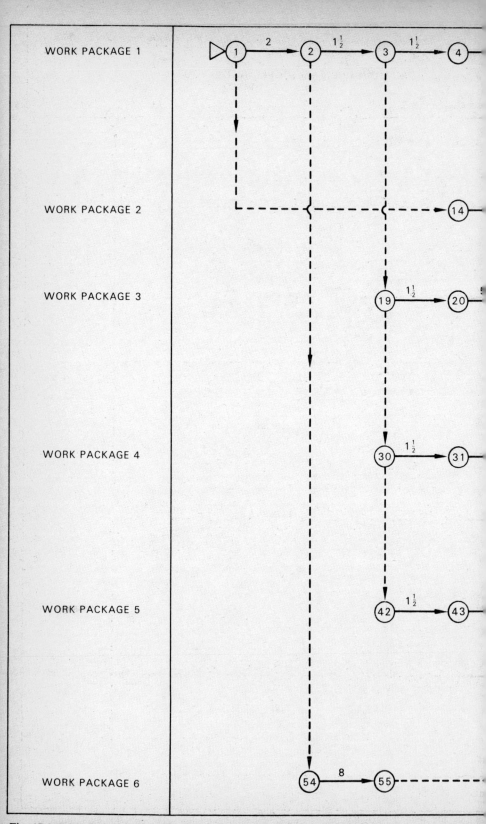

Fig. 17.1 Critical path diagram for the sewage works game.

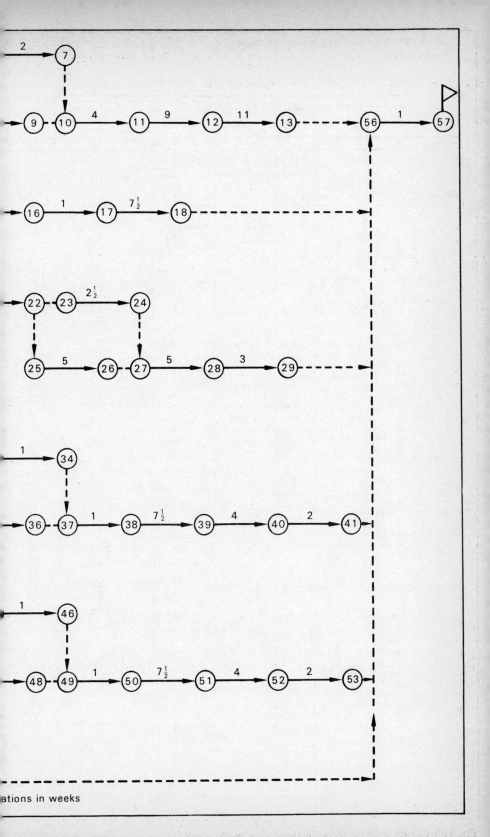

ations in weeks

Table 17.1 Network data for the sewage works game

```
                    PROGRAM DATA CARDS
                    ------------------

1        10        20        30        40        50        60        70

                    PRODUCTIVITY FACTOR CARD(FIRST CARD)
                    -----------------------------------

0801100901 00075120 -EXAMPLE

                              NETWORK DATA CARDS
                              ------------------

   0   1 0                                                    0.00.
   1   2 1 START ON SITE AND CLEAR                            2.00.
   2   3 1 PILE TESTING                                       1.50.
   3   4 1 PILE HEATER HOUSE                                  0.50.
   4   5 1 START EXCAVATING HEATER HOUSE FOUNDATIONS          2.00.
   5   6 0 DUMMY                                              0.01.
   6   7 1 COMPLETE EXCAVATION HEATER HOUSE FOUNDATIONS       2.00.C
   1  14 0 DUMMY                                              0.01.
   5   8 0 DUMMY                                              0.01.C
   8   9 1 CONSTRUCT HEATER HOUSE FOUNDATIONS-START           8.00.C
  10  11 1 COMPLETE HEATER HOUSE FOUNDATIONS                  4.00.
   7  10 0 DUMMY                                              0.01.C
  11  12 1 CONSTRUCT HEATER HOUSE SUPERSTRUCTURE              9.00.C
  12  13 1 INSTALL PLANT,TEST AND COMMISSION                 11.02.C
  13  56 0 DUMMY                                              0.01.C
  14  15 2 SHEET PILE SLUDGE WELL                             1.50.C
  15  16 2 EXCAVATE AND CONSTRUCT SLUDGE WELL                10.00.C
  16  17 2 REMOVE SHEET PILING                                1.00.0
  17  18 2 CONSTRUCT VALVE CHAMBER                            7.52.C
  18  56 0 DUMMY                                              0.01.C
   3  19 0 DUMMY                                              0.01.C
  19  20 5 PILE CONSOL TANKS                                  0.50.C
  20  21 5 CONSTRUCT CONSOL CHAMBERS AND DUCT b               5.50.C
  21  22 5 START CONSOL TANK BASES                            1.50.C
   9  10 0 DUMMY                                              0.01.0
  22  23 0 DUMMY                                              0.01.C
  23  24 5 COMPLETE CONSOL TANK BASES                         2.50.0
  22  25 0 DUMMY                                              0.01.0
  25  26 5 START CONSOL TANK WALLS                            5.00.C
  26  27 0 DUMMY                                              0.01.0
  24  27 0 DUMMY                                              0.01.0
  27  28 5 COMPLETE CONSOL TANK WALLS                         5.00.C
  28  29 5 TEST AND COMMISSION CONSOL TANKS                   3.02.0
  29  56 0 DUMMY                                              0.01.0
   3  30 0 DUMMY                                              0.01.0
  30  31 4 PILE TANKS P1 AND S1                               1.50.0
  31  32 4 EXCAVATE AND BLINDING TANKS P1 AND S1-START        1.00.0
  32  33 0 DUMMY                                              0.01.0
  33  34 4 COMPLETE EXCAVATION AND BLINDING TANKS P1 AND S1   1.00.0
  33  35 0 DUMMY                                              0.01.0
  35  36 4 CONSTRUCT BASES P1 AND S1-START                    2.00.0
  34  37 0 DUMMY                                              0.01.0
  36  37 0 DUMMY                                              0.01.0
  37  38 4 COMPLETE BASES P1 AND S1                           1.00.0
  38  39 4 CONSTRUCT WALLS P1 AND S1                          7.50.0
  39  40 4 CONSTRUCT ROOF P1                                  4.00.0
  40  41 4 INSTALL PLANT TEST AND COMMISSION TANKS P1 AND S1  2.02.0
  41  56 0 DUMMY                                              0.01.0
   3  42 0 DUMMY                                              0.01.0
  42  43 5 PILE TANKS P2 AND S2                               1.50.0
```

Table 17.1 – *continued*

```
                    PROGRAM DATA CARDS
                    ------------------
```

	10	20	30	40	50	60	70	80

```
44 5EXCAVATE AND BLINDING TANKS P2 AND S2-START           1.00.0
45 0DUMMY                                                 0.01.0
46 5COMPLETE EXCAVATION AND BLINDING TANKS P2 AND S2      1.00.0
47 0DUMMY                                                 0.01.0
48 5CONSTRUCT BASES P2 AND S2                             2.00.0
49 0DUMMY                                                 0.01.0
50 5COMPLETE BASES P2 AND S2                              1.00.0
49 0DUMMY                                                 0.01.0
51 5CONSTRUCT WALLS P2 AND S2                             7.50.0
52 5CONSTRUCT ROOF P2                                     4.00.0
53 5INSTALL PLANT TEST AND COMMISSION TANKS P2 AND S2     2.02.0
56 0DUMMY                                                 0.01.0
54 0DUMMY                                                 0.01.0
55 0CONSTRUCT DUCT A                                      8.02.0
56 0DUMMY                                                 0.01.0
57 0CLEAR SITE                                            1.01.0
 0 0                                                      0.00.0
```

```
               CONTROL CARD(FINAL CARD)
               ------------------------
```

```
682791  -EXAMPLE
```

is given in Table 17.1. Because many managers generally prefer to use bar charts rather than networks for programming purposes, the plan has been converted into a linked bar chart as shown in Fig. 17.2.

The plan is expressed in terms of fairly broad activities, e.g. 'Construct foundations'. Such an activity involves several trades, but in order to keep the resource of labour in simple terms the game does not differentiate between the trades and skills needed to carry out an operation.

The plan divides the project into six clearly defined work packages, each to be constructed by a separate work gang

1	Construction of the heater house	Gang 1
2	Construction of the valve chamber	Gang 2
3	Construction of the consolidation tanks	Gang 3
4	Construction of the first two digestion tanks	Gang 4
5	Construction of the second two digestion tanks	Gang 5
6	Construction of duct A.	Gang 6

ACTIVITY No.	ACTIVITY DESCRIPTION	DURATION (wks)			
			1	2	3
1.	START ON SITE	0			
2.	CLEAR SI	2			
3.	PILE TESTING	$1\frac{1}{2}$			
4.	PILE HEATER HOUSE	$\frac{1}{2}$			
5.	EXC HEATER HOUSE FOUNDS	4		START COMPLETE	
6.	CONSTRUCT H. HOUSE FOUNDS	12		START	
7.	HEATER HOUSE SUPERSTRUCTURE	9			
8.	INSTALL PLANT, TEST & COMMISSION	11			
9.	SHEET PILE SLUDGE WELL	$1\frac{1}{2}$		SCHEDULE START	
10.	EXC & CONSTRUCT SLUDGE WELL	10			
11.	WITHDRAW SHEET PILING	1			
12.	CONSTRUCT VALVE CHAMBER	$7\frac{1}{2}$			
13.	PILE CONSOL TANKS	$\frac{1}{2}$			
14.	CONSOL CHAMBERS & DUCT B	$5\frac{1}{2}$			STARTCOMPLETE
15.	CONSOL TANK BASES	4			START
16.	CONSOL TANK WALLS	10			
17.	TEST & COMMISSION CONSOL TANKS	3			
18.	PILE TANKS P_1 & S_1	$1\frac{1}{2}$		START COMPLETE	
19.	EXC & BLIND P_1 & S_1	2		START COMPLETE	
20.	CONSTRUCT BASES P_1 & S_1	3			
21.	CONSTRUCT WALLS P_1 & S_1	$7\frac{1}{2}$			
22.	CONSTRUCT ROOF P_1	4			
23.	INSTALL PLANT, TEST & COMMISSION	2			
24.	PILE TANKS P_2 & S_2	$1\frac{1}{2}$		START—COMPLETE	
25.	EXC & BLIND P_2 & S_2	2		START—COMPLETE	
26.	CONSTRUCT BASES P_2 & S_2	3			
27.	CONSTRUCT WALLS P_2 & S_2	$7\frac{1}{2}$			
28.	CONSTRUCT ROOF P_2	4			
29.	INSTALL PLANT, TEST & COMMISSION	2			
30.	CONSTRUCT DUCT A	8			
31.	CLEAR SITE	1			

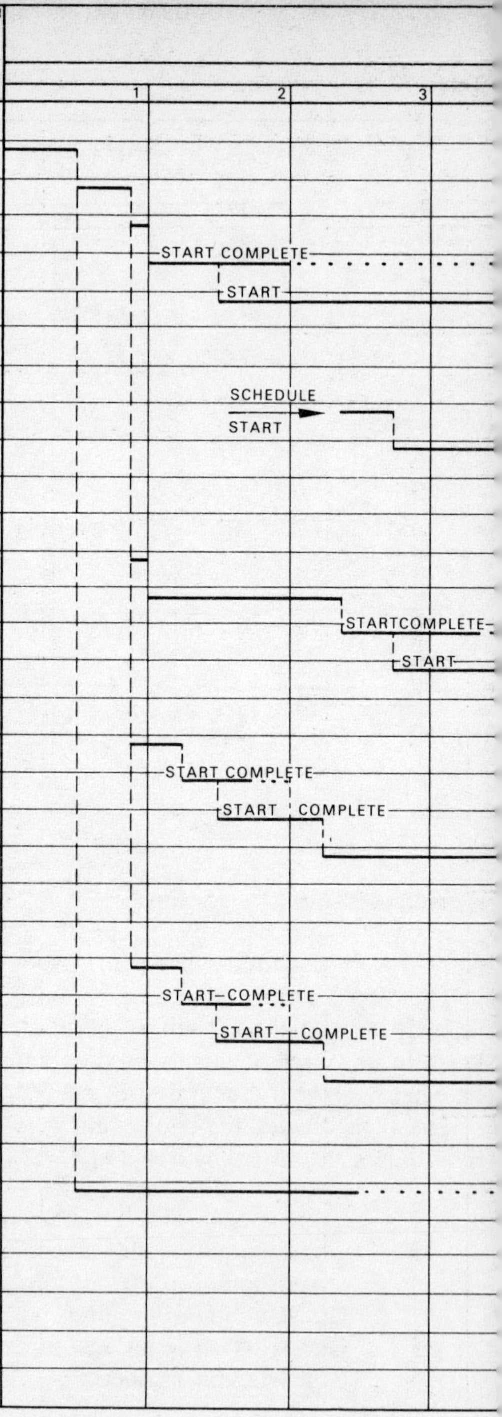

Fig. 17.2 Linked bar chart.

5	6	7	8	9		NOTES

ACTIVITY No.	ACTIVITY DESCRIPTION	DURATION (wks)	1	2	3
1.	START ON SITE	0			
2.	CLEAR SITE	2			
3.	PILE TESTING	$1\frac{1}{2}$			
4.	PILE HEATER HOUSE	$\frac{1}{2}$			
5.	EXC HEATER HOUSE FOUNDS	4		START–COMPLETE	
6.	CONSTRUCT H. HOUSE FOUNDS	12		START	
7.	HEATER HOUSE SUPERSTRUCTURE	9			
8.	INSTALL PLANT, TEST & COMMISSION	11			
9.	SHEET PILE SLUDGE WELL	$1\frac{1}{2}$		SCHEDULE / START	
10.	EXC & CONSTRUCT SLUDGE WELL	10			
11.	WITHDRAW SHEET PILING	1			
12.	CONSTRUCT VALVE CHAMBER	$7\frac{1}{2}$			
13.	PILE CONSOL TANKS	$\frac{1}{2}$			
14.	CONSOL CHAMBERS & DUCT B	$5\frac{1}{2}$			
15.	CONSOL TANK BASES	4			START-COMPLE
16.	CONSOL TANK WALLS	10			START
17.	TEST & COMMISSION CONSOL TANKS	3			
18.	PILE TANKS P_1 & S_1	$1\frac{1}{2}$		START COMPLETE	
19.	EXC & BLIND P_1 & S_1	2		START—COMPLETE	
20.	CONSTRUCT BASES P_1 & S_1	3			
21.	CONSTRUCT WALLS P_1 & S_1	$7\frac{1}{2}$			
22.	CONSTRUCT ROOF P_1	4			
23.	INSTALL PLANT, TEST & COMMISSION	2			
24.	PILE TANKS P_2 & S_2	$1\frac{1}{2}$		START —COMPLETE	
25.	EXC & BLIND P_2 & S_2	2		START—COMPLETE	
26.	CONSTRUCT BASES P_2 & S_2	3			
27.	CONSTRUCT WALLS P_2 & S_2	$7\frac{1}{2}$			
28.	CONSTRUCT ROOF P_2	4			
29.	INSTALL PLANT, TEST & COMMISSION	2			
30.	CONSTRUCT DUCT A	8			
31.	CLEAR SITE	1			

Fig. 17.3 Updated bar chart after three months of play.

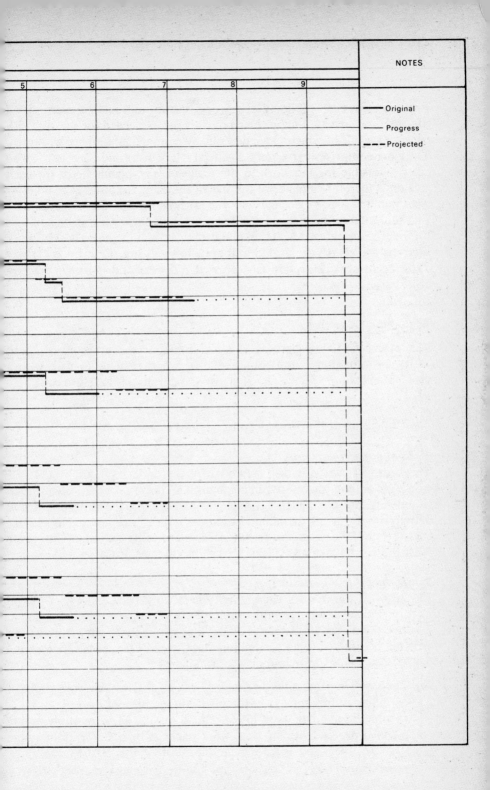

NOTES

Original

Progress

Projected

The Tender Plan

The planned cost of doing the work shown in the later section on 'Information' is based upon the labour resources needed for the six work packages, each of which is carried out by a single gang of six workmen. The gang comprises carpenters, steelfixers, labourers and concretors, who are responsible for the work in the package. The planned cost for each section is therefore a factor of the size of the gang, the number of 40-hour weeks in the work package and the weekly direct cost of each man. The sum total of the planned cost for each work package, with an addition for overheads, gives the total planned cost of the job. The six work sections are clearly separated and are shown in Fig. 17.2. Each activity duration in a work section is expressed in weeks and is shown starting at its earliest time.

The Game Objective

The objective of the game is to allocate labour resources each month to the project after consideration of the progress made to date with a view to achieving both the planned cost and duration for the project.

The Principles of the Game

1 *Sequence constraints*
The order of the activities is limited by the logic imposed by the network. No activity therefore can begin until all those activities, upon which it depends, are complete. But a player can control the progress of any activity by means of the labour resources which it requires. No activity can start until the necessary resources have been allocated to it. The player must therefore make allocations to the activities he decides should start.

2 *Productivity variations*
The planned duration of each activity in a work package is based upon historical data combined with the author's planning experience, but in practice the output of the gangs of workmen is likely to vary from day to day and it is this varying production that the game player has to counteract. The variations in output are determined by:

(*a*) The average productivity achieved by the gang in each work package as influenced by the age of the plant, the number of men in the gang, the conditions they work in etc. This is simulated by multiplying the planned productivity for each work package by a factor in the range 0·75 to 1·25 and is chosen at the start of the play by the game supervisor. Thus each package has a different average productivity.

(b) Uncontrollable factors caused by random variations in productivity – bad weather, industrial unrest, machine breakdowns, untimely supply of materials, are examples. This influence is simulated by multiplying the average productivity determined in stage (a) above, by a random number selected in the range 0·75 to 1·25.

3 Labour availability

Before any progress can be made on a work section, some labour must be assigned to it. The player thus has complete control over the start time and some control over the future progression of each activity in the work packages. However, it is desirable in practice to build up labour gradually and then keep the number of men steady, finally reducing labour again gradually as the project nears completion. No hard and fast rules are incorporated into the game to ensure that this feature is achieved, but the following limitations are included to encourage the situation:

(a) The maximum number of men allowed in each gang is nine men.

(b) The maximum number of men that can be hired or fired at the start of a game period is three in each gang.

(c) Any workman hired will incur costs from the date of hire but his output will be 75% of the output per man for the rest of the gang for the first period of his employment. After that he works normally.

(d) Any workman fired must be given one game period of notice. This implies that the player must indicate a reduction in the gang size one period before sacking occurs. The workman then under notice will produce an output 50% of the output per man for the rest of the gang during the game period under notice.

(e) To avoid high initial costs when hiring the workforce at the beginning of the contract limitations, b, c and d do not apply during the first game period.

4 Materials

The smooth flow of materials on a construction project is initiated from sensible purchasing policies based on a well conceived precontract plan, followed up by constant checking and the monitoring of deliveries. To simulate this process in detail will not be meaningful since in most types of construction work slight changes in the sequence of the operation is often sufficient to overcome all but the worst problems associated with the timing of materials deliveries. The gaming model described will, therefore, deal only with labour. The player may then progress on to more complex situations in the game described in Chapter 18, when construction plant and equipment is introduced.

Information

Planned duration	=	9·75 months
Planned total cost	=	£72 210
Planned cost		
Gang 1	=	£18 240
Gang 2	=	£9 600
Gang 3	=	£9 840
Gang 4	=	£9 120
Gang 5	=	£9 120
Gang 6	=	£3 840
Planned overhead	=	£12 450

Planned manhour cost based on a 40-hour week   = £2

Manhour cost of time worked over 40 hours per week = £3

Overheads

Overheads are included and spread in proportion over each work package. The overheads represent the cost of head office services, site staff and other administrative costs. The total planned overhead for the contract is £12 450 spread over 9·75 months. This is equivalent to £1280 each month. In order to keep the effect of overhead allocation fairly uncomplicated, actual overhead is incurred at a similar rate. However, because the value of overhead in receipts for work done is related to the progress in each work package, there is likely to be some imbalance between the money received for overhead and that actually incurred until the project is complete. Provided that the project is completed in the planned time, then the game will enable the planned overhead cost and the actual overhead cost to be the same value finally, but if the project period overruns the planned 9·75 months, then actual overhead is continuously incurred each extra month. Therefore there is every incentive to try to finish on time.

Using the Game

The game is to be played by an individual using the facilities of a computer. Although by minor modification the player and the computer can operate interactively, the form of the game provides a semi-interactive process using a batch processing facility. By the use of computer file storage, the decisions made by the player in each game period are recorded and can be used to make decisions for the subsequent period. In this way the player has time to make considered judgements on the project's progress and on the resources to be used. A listing of the

Fortran statements is given in Fig. 17.4 at the end of the chapter.

The supervisor is responsible for setting the average productivity factors for the gangs for each player. This is done at the beginning of the game. The supervisor is also responsible for issuing each player with a job number, file name and program and data cards.

The player makes decisions each game period about the gang sizes and hours to be worked on the project. A game period represents one month of construction time. The number of players is not limited, but between 8 and 16 participants should bring an element of competition to bear.

Instructions

Game supervisor
1. The *productivity factor card*, as shown in Table 17.1, assigns to each gang the *actual* average productivity to be achieved during the course of the project. Any number between 0·75 and 1·25 is punched for each gang.

Punch columns	1,	2,	3	for	Gang No. 1
Punch columns	4,	5,	6	for	Gang No. 2
Punch columns	7,	8,	9	for	Gang No. 3
Punch columns	10,	11,	12	for	Gang No. 4
Punch columns	13,	14,	15	for	Gang No. 5
Punch columns	16,	17,	18	for	Gang No. 6

This is the first data card and should be included in each round of play with the network data cards.

Game player
2. The game is to be played in monthly periods. As a result most participants will probably complete the contract in 10–15 plays. At the beginning of each monthly period the player needs to insert the *control card* as shown in Table 17.1. This card contains information indicating the month, the hours to be worked each week during the month and the gang sizes. The effect of allocating more than 40 hours per week of worktime will be that all gangs work the overtime.

Punch in columns 1 and 2	Month number, e.g. 02
Punch in columns 3 and 4	Hours to be worked each week during the month, e.g. 45
Punch in columns 5	Number of men in gang No. 1
Punch in columns 6	Number of men in gang No. 2
Punch in columns 7	Number of men in gang No. 3
Punch in columns 8	Number of men in gang No. 4
Punch in columns 9	Number of men in gang No. 5
Punch in columns 10	Number of men in gang No. 6

Table 17.2 Example of computer output progress data

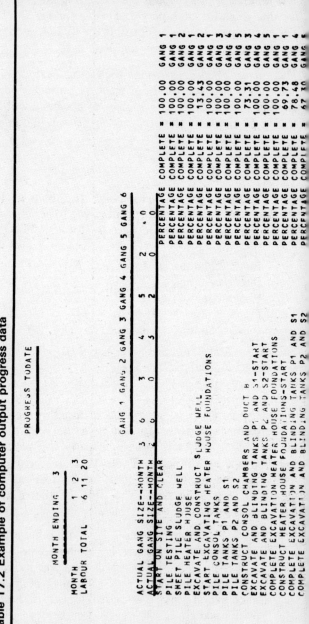

```
PROGRESS TODATE


MONTH ENDING    3

MONTH            1   2   3
LABOUR TOTAL     6  11  20


                       GANG 1   GANG 2   GANG 3   GANG 4   GANG 5   GANG 6

ACTUAL GANG SIZE--MONTH 1    3        6        3        4        2        0
ACTUAL GANG SIZE--MONTH 2    6        0        0        5        2        0
START ON SITE AND CLEAR                                              PERCENTAGE COMPLETE = 100.00   GANG 1
PILE TESTING                                                        PERCENTAGE COMPLETE = 100.00   GANG 1
SHEET PILE SLUDGE WELL                                              PERCENTAGE COMPLETE = 100.00   GANG 2
PILE HEATER HOUSE                                                   PERCENTAGE COMPLETE = 100.00   GANG 2
EXCAVATE AND CONSTRUCT SLUDGE WELL                                  PERCENTAGE COMPLETE =  13.43   GANG 1
START EXCAVATING HEATER HOUSE FOUNDATIONS                           PERCENTAGE COMPLETE = 100.00   GANG 1
PILE CONSOL TANKS                                                   PERCENTAGE COMPLETE = 100.00   GANG 3
PILE TANKS P1 AND S1                                                PERCENTAGE COMPLETE = 100.00   GANG 4
PILE TANKS P2 AND S2                                                PERCENTAGE COMPLETE = 100.00   GANG 5
CONSTRUCT CONSOL CHAMBERS AND DUCT H                                PERCENTAGE COMPLETE =  73.31   GANG 3
EXCAVATE AND BLINDING TANKS P1 AND S1-START                        PERCENTAGE COMPLETE = 100.00   GANG 4
EXCAVATE AND BLINDING TANKS P2 AND S2-START                        PERCENTAGE COMPLETE = 100.00   GANG 5
COMPLETE EXCAVATION HEATER HOUSE FOUNDATIONS                        PERCENTAGE COMPLETE = 100.00   GANG 1
CONSTRUCT HEATER HOUSE FOUNDATIONS-START                            PERCENTAGE COMPLETE =  69.73   GANG 1
COMPLETE EXCAVATION AND BLINDING TANKS P1 AND S1                    PERCENTAGE COMPLETE =  78.48   GANG 4
COMPLETE EXCAVATION AND BLINDING TANKS P2 AND S2                    PERCENTAGE COMPLETE =  67.50   GANG 5
```

```
ACTUAL  COST GANG 1 =  5760.00UNITS
PLANNED COST GANG 2 =  1564.47UNITS
ACTUAL  COST GANG 2 =   960.00UNITS
PLANNED COST GANG 3 =  2175.51UNITS
ACTUAL  COST GANG 3 =  2240.00UNITS
PLANNED COST GANG 4 =  1576.69UNITS
ACTUAL  COST GANG 4 =  2240.00UNITS
PLANNED COST GANG 5 =  1523.02UNITS
ACTUAL  COST GANG 5 =   640.00UNITS
PLANNED COST GANG 6 =     0.00UNITS
ACTUAL  COST GANG 6 =     0.00UNITS
ACTUAL  OVERHEAD COST =  3923.04UNITS
PLANNED OVERHEAD COST =  2541.13UNITS


TOTAL ACTUAL COST = 15763.04UNITS
TOTAL PLANNED COST = 14738.59UNITS

PROJECTED COMPLETION TIME 10.02MONTHS
```

Sequence of decisions for each player

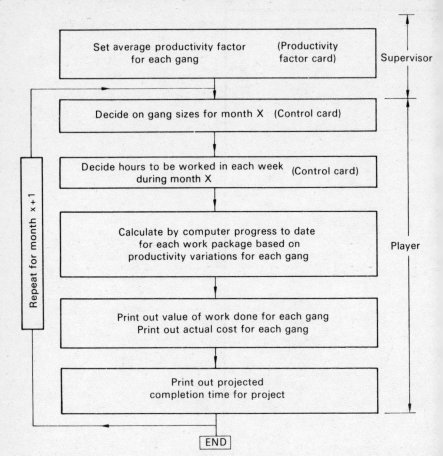

Progressing

Typical computer printout results for the progress on each activity are shown in Table 17.2 for month ending No. 3.

  (i) Colour in under each activity bar on Fig. 17.2 the percentage complete to the end of the month being played. (Figure 17.3 shows this done after three play periods.)

 (ii) Draw a thick line down the bar chart at the end of the month to show up the progress to date.

(iii) Predict the completion time for each uncompleted activity to give the predicted project completion time for each work package.

(iv) Review the resources needed for each activity to produce the required progress.

 (v) Consider the costs incurred to date.

(vi) Adjust resources for the next month and play the next game period until the project is complete.

```
JOB FCHOO1,C,FCH1008
UP 5
LET ED(PREVWEEK),SCV/FCHPREVWEEK
JOBTIME 250
VOLUME 1000
LUFORTRAN
RUN ,,250
****
```

```
FORTRAN COMPILATION BY #XFAT MK 5A     DATE  10/02/76   TIME  18/36/11
```

```
0001        LIST
0002        SEND TO (ED,SEMICOMPUSER,AXXX)
0003        DUMP ON (ED,PROGRAM USER)
0004        WORK (ED,WORKFILEUSER)
0005        RUN
0006        LIBRARY(ED,SUBGROUPNAGF)
0007        PROGRAM (FCHOO1)
0008        INPUT 1 = CRO
0009        OUTPUT 2 = LPO
0010        USE 3 = ED1(PREVWEEK)
0011        TRACE 2
0012        COMPRESS INTEGER AND LOGICAL
0013        END
```

```
0014        MASTER GAME
0015        DIMENSION I(3,100),RI(9,100),IN(100),IO(100),KX(10,100),JK(100),ES
0016       1(100),TE(100),JM(100),AES(100),AEF(100),KK(10,100),COST(6),
0017       2PMH(100),PERC(100),IGANG(9),ACTR(9),AMH(99),ZES(100),MC(6),PCOST(6
0018       3),MZ(10),ACOST(10),NGANG(9),JGANG(9,100),MR(100),NTOT(100),POVHD(1
0019       100),ZGANG(9)
0021        READ(1,166)(ACTR(J),J=1,6)
0022   166  FORMAT(6F3.0)
0023        IB=1
0024        IE=57
0025        NA=0
0026        DO 400 K=1,100
            READ(1,103)(I(J,K),J=1,3),(RI(N,K),N=1,9)
```

Fig. 17.4 Listing of game Fortran statements.

```
0027  103 FORMAT(I4,I4,I2,7A8,F6.1,F3.1)
0028      IF(I(1,K).GT.999B)GO TO 251
0029      NA=NA+1
0030  400 CONTINUE
0031  251 DO 5 L=1,NA
0032      IF(I(2,L).EQ.0)GO TO 6
0033      IN(I(2,L))=IN(I(2,L))+1
0034  6   IF(I(1,L).EQ.0)GO TO 5
0035      IO(I(1,L))=IO(I(1,L))+1
0036      IF(IO(I(1,L)).EQ.0)GO TO 5
0037      KX(IO(I(1,L)),I(1,L))=L
0038  5   CONTINUE
0039      COST(1)=6.0*80.0
0040      COST(2)=6.0*80.0
0041      COST(3)=6.0*80.0

0042      COST(4)=6.0*80.0
0043      COST(5)=6.0*80.0
0044      COST(6)=6.0*80.0
0045      MZ(1)=1
0046      MZ(2)=14
0047      MZ(3)=19
0048      MZ(4)=30
0049      MZ(5)=42
0050      MZ(6)=54
0051      MCF=1
0052  222 WRITE(2,222)
0053  357 FORMAT(1H ,//1H ,27X,15HPROGRESS TODATE/1H ,27X,15(1H-))
0054      JK(1)=IB
0055      DO 361 NX=1,6
0056      MC(NX)=0
0057  361 CONTINUE
0058      LA=1
0059      ES(1)=0.0
0060      TE(1)=0.0
0061      DO 10 JQ=1,NA
0062      N=JK(JQ)
0063      IF(N.NE.0)GO TO 11
0064  40  WRITE(2,12)
0065  12  FORMAT(1H ,26HERROR CARDS IN WRONG ORDER)
0066      GO TO 359
0067  11  DO 14 IM=1,IO(I(2,N))
0068      M=KX(IM,I(2,N))
0069      IF(I(2,M).EQ.0)GO TO 40
0070      JM(I(2,M))=JM(I(2,M))+1
0071      IF(MCF.EQ.1)GO TO 335
0072      GO TO 309
```

```
0074        IF(JMI(2,M)).EQ.INI(2,M))GO TO 336
0075        GO TO 620
0076   336  ZAX=AES(M)
0077        DO 338 KE=1,JMC I(2,M))
0078        NB=KKKE,I(2,M))
0079        IF(ZAX.GE.AES(NB))GO TO 338
0080        ZAX=AES(NB)
0081   338  CONTINUE
0082        LA=LA+1
0083        JK(LA)=M
0084        TB(I(2,M))=ZAX
0085        GO TO 620
0086   309  IF(PERC(M).GT.0.0.AND.PERC(M).LT.100.0)GO TO 332
0087        IF(PERC(M).EQ.100.0)GO TO 848
0088        IF(ES(I(1,M)).GE.FLOAT(NR))GO TO 331
0089        IF(RI(9,M).EQ.1.0)GO TO 331
0090        IF(ZGANG(I(3,M)).EQ.0)GO TO 151
0091        GO TO 150
0092   151  AMH(M)=0.0
0093        EB(I(1,M))=FLOAT(NR)
0094        GO TO 331
0095   150  IF(I(3,M).EQ.1)GO TO 301
0096        IF(I(3,M).EQ.2)GO TO 302
0097        IF(I(3,M).EQ.3)GO TO 303
0098        IF(I(3,M).EQ.4)GO TO 304
0099        IF(I(3,M).EQ.5)GO TO 305
0100        IF(I(3,M).EQ.6)GO TO 306
0101        GO TO 331
0102   301  RM=RI(8,M)*ACTR(1)*6.0/100.0
0103        GO TO 320
0104   302  RM=RI(8,M)*ACTR(2)*6.0/100.0
0105        GO TO 320
0106   303  RM=RI(8,M)*ACTR(3)*6.0/100.0
0107        GO TO 320
0108   306  RM=RI(8,M)*ACTR(4)*6.0/100.0
0109        GO TO 320
0110   305  RM=RI(8,M)*ACTR(5)*6.0/100.0
0111        GO TO 320
0112   306  RM=RI(8,M)*ACTR(6)*6.0/100.0
0113   320  X=GOSABF(75.0,125.0)
0114        PMH(M)=RM*40.0*X/100.0
0115   321  DUR=FLOAT(NR)=ES(I(1,M))
0116        WORKCON=ZGANG(I(3,M))*FLOAT(IOT)
0117        SMH=DUR*WORKCON*4.0
0118        AMH(M)=SMH
0119        GO TO 324
0120
```

Fig. 17.4 – *continued*

```
0121   332 IF(ZGANG(I(3,M)).EQ.0)GO TO 326
0122       X=GQ5ABF(25.,175.0)
0123       PMH(M)=PMH(M)+PERC(M)/100.0+(PMH(M)-(PMH(M)*PERC(M)/100.0))*X/100.
0124    10
0125       WORK=ZGANG(I(3,M))*FLOAT(IOT)
0126       AMH(M)=AMH(M)*WORK*4.0
0127   326 IF(AMH(M).GT.PMH(M))GO TO 322
0128       PERC(M)=(AMH(M)/PMH(M))*100.00
0129       IF(PERC(M).EQ.0.0)GO TO 733
0130       GO TO 326
0131   322 EDUR=AMH(M)-PMH(M)
0132       TIME=EDUR/(ZGANG(I(3,M))*FLOAT(IOT))
0133       PERC(M)=100.0
0134       ZES(M)=FLOAT(NR)-TIME/4.0
0135   848 WRITE(2,328)RI(1,M),RI(2,M),RI(3,M),RI(4,M),RI(5,M),RI(6,M),RI(7,M
0136      1),PERC(M),I(3,M)
0137   328 FORMAT(1H ,7A8,3X,22HPERCENTAGE COMPLETE = ,F6.2,2X,4HGANG,I2)
0138       CO=0.0
0139       GO TO 330
0140   331 ZES(M)=ES(I(1,M))+RI(8,M)/4.0
0141       GO TO 329
0142   326 WRITE(2,328)RI(1,M),RI(2,M),RI(3,M),RI(4,M),RI(5,M),RI(6,M),RI(7,M
0143      1)/PERC(M),I(3,M)
0144   733 CO=(1.0-PERC(M)/100.0)*RI(8,M)/4.0
0145       ZES(M)=FLOAT(NR)+CO
0146   330 IF(ZES(M).LT.FLOAT(NR))GO TO 713
0147       GO TO 714
0148   713 IF(RI(9,M).EQ.2.0)GO TO 714
0149       GO TO 329
0150   716 MC(I(3,M))=MC(I(3,M))+1
0151       NG=I(3,M)
0152   362 IF(MC(I(3,M)).EQ.1)GO TO 351
0153       GO TO 329
0154   351 PCOST(I(3,M))=(AES(M)-TE(MZ(NG))*4.0*COST(NG)*((100.0-PERC(M)))*RI
0155      1(8,M)/1.0*COST(NG))/100.0
0156       POVHD(I(3,M))=(AES(M)-TE(MZ(NG))*4.0*100.0000*((100.0-PERC(M))*RI
0157      1(8,M)/1.0*100.0)/100.0
0158       PLCOST=PLCOST+PCOST(NG)
0159       PHD=PHD+POVHD(NG)
0160       ACOST(NG)=ACOST(NG)*FLOAT(NGANG(NG))*((FLOAT(IOT)-40.0)*8.0*1.25)*
0161      1FLOAT(NGANG(NG))*40.0*2.0*4.0
0162       TCOST=TCOST+ACOST(NG)
0163   329 KK(JH(I(2,M)),I(2,M))=M
0164       IF(JH(I(2,M)).EQ.IN(I(2,M)))GO TO 16
0165       GO TO 620
```

```
0167        DO 18 K=1,JM(I(2,M))
0168        NB=KKK,I(2,M))
0169        IF(ZMAX.GE.ZES(NB))GO TO 18
0170        ZMAX=ZES(NB)
0171     18 CONTINUE
0172        LA=LA+1
0173        JK(LA)=M
0174        ES(I(2,M))=ZMAX
0175    620 IF(JM(I(2,M)).EQ.IN(I(2,M)))GO TO 610
0176        GO TO 14
0177    610 JM(I(2,M))=0
0178        IF(I(2,M).EQ.IE)GO TO 7
0179     14 CONTINUE
0180     10 CONTINUE
0181      7 IF(MCF.EQ.0)GO TO 453
0182        WRITE(2,700)TE(57)
0183    700 FORMAT(1H ,F7.2)
0184        MCF=0
0185        GO TO 355
0186    453 WRITE(2,639)
0187    639 FORMAT(1H ,//1H ,12HCOST SUMMARY/1H ,12(1H-))
0188        DO 501 ND=1,6
0189        WRITE(2,352)ND,PCOST(ND)
0190    353 FORMAT(1H ,18HPLANNED COST GANG ,I2,2H =,F9.2,5HUNITS)
0191    352 WRITE(2,356)ND,ACOST(ND)
0192    356 FORMAT(1H ,18HACTUAL COST GANG ,I2,2H =,F9.2,5HUNITS)
0193    501 CONTINUE
0194        ACTO=326.92*4.0
0195        TVD=TVD+ACTO
0196        TCOST=TCOST+TVD
0197        PLCOST=PLCOST+PHD
0198        WRITE(2,744)TVD,PHD
0199    746 FORMAT(1H ,22HACTUAL OVERHEAD COST =,F9.2,5HUNITS/1H ,23HPLANNED O
0200       1VERHEAD COST =,F9.2,5HUNITS)
0201        WRITE(2,358)TCOST,PLCOST
0202    358 FORMAT(1H ,//1H ,10(1H-)/1H ,19HTOTAL ACTUAL COST =,F9.2,5HUNITS/1
0203       1H ,20HTOTAL PLANNED COST =,F9.2,5HUNITS)
0204        WRITE(2,649)ES(IE)
0205    649 FORMAT(1H ,//1H ,25HPROJECTED COMPLETION TIME,F6.2,6HMONTHS/////)
0206        IF(ES(IE).LE.FLOAT(NR))GO TO 716
0207        GO TO 715
0208    716 WRITE(2,717)
0209    717 FORMAT(1H ,22HGAME NOW COMPLETE-STOP)
0210    715 REWIND 3
0211        WRITE(3)AMH,PMH,PERC,ES,TVD,ACOST,JGANG,MR,NTOT
0212    355 READ(1,354,END=359)NR,IOT,(IGANG(J),J=1,6)
```

Fig. 17.4 – *continued*

```
0213   354 FORMAT(I2,I2,6I1)
0214       IF(NR.EQ.1)GO TO 511
0215       READ(3)AMH,PMH,PERC,ES,TVD,ACOST,JGANG,MR,NTOT
0216   511 ITOTG=0
0217       PLCOST=0.0
0218       PHD=0.0
0219       TCOST=0.0
0220       MR(NR)=NR
0221       WRITE(2,500)NR
0222   500 FORMAT(1H ,5X,12HMONTH ENDING,I4/1H ,5X,16(1H--))
0223       DO 730 NF=1,6
0224       JGANG(NF,NR)=IGANG(NF)
0225       ITOTG=ITOTG+IGANG(NF)
0226       NTOT(NR)=ITOTG
0227       IF(NR.EQ.1)GO TO 881
0228       XGANG=IABS(JGANG(NF,NR)-JGANG(NF,NR-1))
0229       IF(JGANG(NF,NR).GT.JGANG(NF,NR-1))GO TO 878
0230       GO TO 879
0231   878 ZGANG(NF)=FLOAT(JGANG(NF,NR-1))+XGANG*0.75
0232       NGANG(NF)=JGANG(NF,NR)
0233       GO TO 730
0234   879 IF(JGANG(NF,NR).LT.JGANG(NF,NR-1))GO TO 880
0235       GO TO 881
0236   880 NGANG(NF)=JGANG(NF,NR-1)
0237       ZGANG(NF)=FLOAT(JGANG(NF,NR))+XGANG*0.5
0238       GO TO 730
0239   881 ZGANG(NF)=JGANG(NF,NR)
0240       NGANG(NF)=JGANG(NF,NR)
0241   730 CONTINUE
0242       WRITE(2,740)(MR(JT),JT=1,NR)
0243   740 FORMAT(1H ,12HMONTH ,2X,35I3/1H ,14X,105(1H--))
0244       WRITE(2,741)(NTOT(JU),JU=1,NR)
0245   741 FORMAT(1H ,12HLABOUR TOTAL,2X,35I3)
0246       WRITE(2,750)
0247   750 FORMAT(1H ,//1H ,27X,6HGANG 1,1X,6HGANG 2,1X,6HGANG 3,1X,6HGANG 4
0248      1,1X,6HGANG 5,1X,6HGANG 6/1H ,27X,39(1H--))
0249       WRITE(2,751)NR,(JGANG(NF,NR),NF=1,6)
0250   751 FORMAT(1H ,23HACTUAL GANG SIZE--MONTH,I3,I4,3X,I4,3X,I4,3X,I4,3X,I
0251      16,3X,I4)
0252       NY=NR-1
0253       IF(NY.EQ.0)GO TO 357
0254       WRITE(2,751)NY,(JGANG(NF,NY),NF=1,6)
0255       GO TO 357
0256   359 STOP
0257       END
```

Fig. 17.4 *continued*

```
END OF SEGMENT, LENGTH 2513, NAME  GAME

   0258        FINISH

END OF COMPILATION - NO ERRORS

S/C SUBFILE:         48 BUCKETS USED


CONSOLIDATED BY XPCK 12F    DATE    10/02/76    TIME 18/36/32

PROGRAM FCMO
EXTENDED DATA (22AM)
COMPACT PROGRAM (DBM)
CORE   14976

         SEG    GAME
         SEG    FLOAT
         SEG    GO5ABF
         SEG    IABS
         SEG    GO5AAF


LAST BUCKET USED OF PROGRAM USEP(1)    IS    61
```

Fig. 17.4 – *continued*

CHAPTER 18

ROADWAY CONSTRUCTION GAME

Summary

The game simulates the construction of a length of road pavement. The road is represented by a sequence of activities from subgrade trim to finishes, which are carried out by gangs of subcontract workmen and machines. The progress of each process is influenced by factors causing variations in weekly production, interference between gangs and resources used, to which each player must react in order to control construction time and cost.

Introduction

A. A. Lilley (ref. 1) describes an operations research technique for examining the influence on productivity of the interaction between the different operations in the construction of a road pavement from subgrade trim to the final finishings. Using the method it is possible to simulate the effect on production rates and progress of changes in labour and plant resources for each of the processes in pavement construction. The technique lends itself well to the idea of a management game in which the player makes the decisions about the resources to be used.

Game Objectives

It is fairly easy to schedule repetition construction using line of balance planning techniques; however, it is seldom possible to execute the project in strict accordance with the schedule. In practice, productivity will vary substantially from day to day, even if the assumed average figures are correct. The project manager will therefore have to take corrective action to control the operation and to minimise the interference that can occur when some activities are delayed by more than the buffer time allowed. The objective of this game is to simulate the important effects of varying production and thus provide simulated experience of the problems of trying to control repetitive work by means of a pre-prepared schedule.

Description of the Simulation Model

The simulation models the construction of 10 km of road pavement. The work involves the following sequence of activities.

Process *No.*

1	↓	Subgrade surface trim
2	↓	Lay sub-base
3	↓	Road drains
4	↓	Kerbing
5	↓	Lean mix concrete road base
6	↓	Wearing surface
7	↓	Road finishes and markings

Each process is performed by a separate gang of workers or machines. The order of the processes is fixed as shown above, e.g. it is impossible

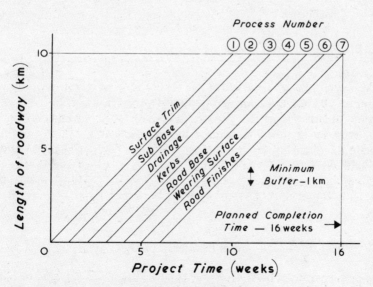

Fig. 18.1 Programme for roadway construction.

for the sub-base to be ahead of the surface trim. In addition each process requires a minimum length of motorway in which to move resources, store equipment and handle materials (called the minimum buffer).

The construction of the carriageway has a planned cost based on a target completion of 200 m of carriageway per day (Fig. 18.1). The planned labour and equipment resources for each operation are shown in Tables 18.1 and 18.2.

Table 18.1 Planned resources for the road construction game

		Types of Resource			
		Fixed	Variable		
Process No.	Process Description			No. reqd	Resource Code
1	Surface trim	—	Bulldozer and scraper	3	M
2	Sub-base	Bulldozer	Lorries	20	C
3	Drainage	—	Excavator and gang	10	G
4	Kerbs	—	Men	10	L
5	Road base	Concrete paver	Lorries	10	C
6	Wearing surface	Bitumen paver	Lorries	5	C
7	Road finishes	—	Men	10	L

Table 18.2 Planned costs for the game

Rate of pay for a worker	£2·00 per hour
Overtime pay after 40 hours	£3·00 per hour
Delivery charge for bringing any machine (except lorries) on to site	£250·00
Hire charge for a machine (except lorries) excluding driver	£500·00 per week
Hire charge for lorry excluding driver	£150·00 per week
Overheads	0·2 × direct costs

Resources

Fixed　These resources cannot be altered by the player.

Variable　These are the resources which control the rate of production and may be varied by the player. For example, only one concrete paver is to be used but its speed can be varied by increasing the supply of materials to it, e.g. by increasing the number of trucks used.

The Principles of the Game

The game attempts to simulate the actual progress of the road construction. To achieve this the player controls the actual progress of each process by making decisions at the start of each week about the size of the labour gangs, the rate of supply of materials, numbers of machines and hours to be worked. In practice, the progress of each operation is likely to fluctuate due to a whole series of factors; in order to prevent the game becoming too complex, these factors are grouped under the following four headings:

(a) The average productivity achieved as determined by the nature of the operation, the age of the equipment, the temperament of the workers, etc.

(b) Uncontrollable factors which cause random variations in productivity, such as machine breakdowns, bad weather, etc.

(c) Interference between operations.

(d) Controllable factors such as the number of men and/or machines on each operation or the overtime worked.

Item (a) is simulated by multiplying the estimated production by a number fixed by the game supervisor. This is done for each operation at the beginning of the game and is within the range 0·75 to 1·25.

Item (b) is simulated by multiplying the resulting output rates in item (a) for each week by a random number lying in the range 0·75 to 1·25.

Item (c) depends upon the minimum buffer between processes and is fixed at 1 km. Interference between processes is likely to occur when rates of progress differ between the processes. This is simulated by allowing players to make decisions about the number of men and machines to be used and the hours to be worked each week on each process.

Through item (d), by changing the resources for each process, progress is speeded up or slowed down. However, in order to discourage the player from making unrealistic decisions the following rules apply:

(i) *Drainage, kerbing and road finishes* are controlled by the numbers of men or gangs working. The player may not increase the resources on these processes by more than three men or three gangs of men, at any one time. In addition, during the first week of employment the production of the new resources is only half that of the existing resources. Men or gangs of men may be sacked at the beginning of each week's play to take effect immediately. But not more than three men or three gangs may be removed at any one time in each process.

(ii) *Lay sub-base* is carried out by supplying materials to be spread by a bulldozer. Similarly the lean mix concrete road base and tarmac wearing surface are formed by a paving machine supplied with materials by trucks. The production for these processes is assumed to be governed by the rate of supply of materials. The player therefore changes production rates by altering the numbers of trucks supplying materials. However, since the trucks can only be hired for one week at a time, a penalty is automatically incurred if production levels are not achieved during the week they are on hire. Trucks may only be hired or taken off hire at the beginning of each week.

(iii) *Subgrade trim* is carried out by bulldozer and scraper acting as one unit. Each unit may be hired or taken off hire at the beginning of each week. But a penalty cost in the form of a transport charge discourages the player from making too many changes in this resource.

Costs

Direct planned costs are based on the program shown in Fig. 18.1 and the charges shown in Tables 18.1 and 18.2. A forty-hour working week is assumed to be the norm. The total costs for a typical process therefore are simply a summation of the weekly charges for labour and plant multiplied by the number of men or machines involved, plus the cost of bringing on to site the machines to be used. The weekly direct planned cost is assumed to be a straight proportion of the total planned cost, related to the length of pavement completed on each process.

Direct actual costs depend upon the skill of the player in using resources economically. The cost is once again built up by multiplying the resources used by the weekly cost of employing them. However, labour required over and above forty hours during the week must be paid for at the premium rate of £3 per hour. While machinery will be charged the extra hours pro-rata on weekly hire cost, the driver will be paid at the premium rate of £3 per hour.

Furthermore any additional machinery brought on to site incurs a £250 transport charge.

Overheads are included to cover site administration costs and head office services. These are based on 20% of the direct planned cost. Thus the total planned cost of the project consists of the direct planned cost plus overheads. These overheads are assumed to be spread uniformly at £2156·87 per week throughout the planned duration of the project. Therefore, as an incentive to complete the job on time, this sum is added each week to the direct actual costs. Clearly the player who takes longer than the planned 16 weeks will incur this same weekly sum as a penalty.

Using the Game

The game is designed to be played by about twenty players. Each player is required to produce decisions regarding the level of resources to be used and hours to be worked on each of the construction processes in each round of play (a round of play represents one week of actual construction time). This information is punched on to computer cards and used as data by the simulation model stored on computer file. Someone familiar with the computer is required to act as the game supervisor.

The Supervisor (First stage of the game)

It is the responsibility of the supervisor to set up the game on the computer as follows.

A computer disk file called INIT is created to store the game program. At this stage it is necessary to include as data all the standard information upon which the game is dependent. The data is that described in Tables 18.1 and 18.2 plus the allocation of the average productivity factors for each process, and remains constant throughout the duration of the game. A second disk file called PLAY is also created; this stores data pertaining to the current level of progress for each player. PLAY uses information both from INIT and from the data input by the player at the beginning of each week of play. Thus the program reads the data held in INIT and fills up PLAY with suitable starting values. As the game is arranged to use the batch processing facility of the computer, the weekly decisions of each player are also required to be input on cards. However, with a minor modification of the program the computer can be used interactively and can thus produce immediate progress results for the player. The computer program statements for INIT and PLAY are shown in Fig. 18.2 at the end of the chapter.

The data for INIT is entered as follows:

Card 1

Pay rate (£)	– hourly rate of pay for labour
Standard week (hours)	– number of hours in the normal working week
Overtime rate	– a multiplying factor related to the pay rate

Transportation cost for a machine (£)– cost in pounds to bring an item of
equipment on to site

Hire cost of a machine (£/week) – weekly cost in pounds to hire an
item of equipment

Maximum working rate (m/hour) – maximum rate of progress which
can be made on a road process,
expressed in terms of metres per
hour of pavement construction

Hire cost of a lorry (£/week) – weekly cost in pounds to hire a
lorry

Target rate of work (m/day) – planned daily rate of pavement
completion expressed in metres
per day

Projected length of carriageway (km) – length of road to be constructed
during the game in kilometres

Number of players in the game

Overhead proportion – expressed as a proportion of the
direct costs of the works

Minimum buffer (m) – minimum length of carriageway
required between construction
processes in metres

Format of the above is F6.2, F6.0, F6.4, 4F6.0, 2F6.0, I6, F6.2, F6.0.

Cards 2–8 inclusive
For each process:

Process name (up to 16 characters).
Process type (L,G,M, or C).
Number of production units (variable).
Average productivity factor.
Format – 4A4, A1, I6, F6.3

An example of typical data as input by the supervisor is shown in
Fig. 18.3 at the end of the chapter.

The Player (Second stage of the game)

Once the game is set up by the supervisor, each player is in a position
to make decisions about which of the project processes to go ahead with.
To do this, the resources must be allocated and time made available to
each of the processes for each week under consideration. This is achieved
by each player punching data cards containing the following information:

Card 1
Column 1 – $
Column 2 – space

Columns 3 and 4 – the player's number, e.g. 07
Columns 5 and 6 – the week of play, e.g. 18

Cards 2 to 8 inclusive (one card for each process)
Columns 1 and 2 – the process number, e.g. 04
Columns 3 and 4 – production units required, e.g. 13
Columns 5 and 6 – hours to be worked in the week, e.g. 48

Card 9
Column 1 – $

It is not necessary for each player to put in cards every round of play
or to be playing the same week number. If a player, however, does include
information for a week of play, then card No. 1 must be included followed
by the decisions for each process on separate cards, in strict process
order. Processes not in operation, whether they have not started or have
been completed, should not be included in the data.

The last card for each player must be the $ card.

The cards are then handed to the supervisor, who will use the information as data for the program PLAY held on the computer file storage. An
example of a typical week as input by a player is shown in Fig. 18.4.

Sequence of decisions

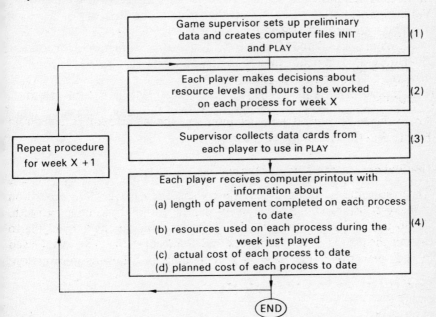

Game supervisor sets up preliminary
data and creates computer files INIT
and PLAY   (1)

Each player makes decisions about
resource levels and hours to be worked
on each process for week X   (2)

Supervisor collects data cards from
each player to use in PLAY   (3)

Repeat procedure
for week X +1

Each player receives computer printout with
information about
(a) length of pavement completed on each process
    to date
(b) resources used on each process during the
    week just played   (4)
(c) actual cost of each process to date
(d) planned cost of each process to date

END

Progressing

After each week of play, each player should plot graphically his progress made to date on each process. Typical computer progress information is shown in Fig. 18.5. By this plotting, the player is able to observe which processes are moving ahead too quickly and may therefore interfere with less efficient processes. Conversely, those processes which are lagging behind can be considered and additional resources allocated with a view to improving the production rate. Figure 16.6 shows the progress made to completion on a typical game by a single player. When all the processes are complete the player can then compare the achieved project cost with the planned cost and the achieved project duration with the planned duration.

When sufficient players have tried the game, it will be possible to view the effects of different lengths of buffer and resource usage.

The game winner is the player who achieves the lowest project cost in the shortest construction time.

References

1. Lilley, A. A. An application of operation research to concrete road construction, Technical Report, Cement and Concrete Association, 1969.

2. Harris, F. C. and Evans, J. B. Road construction game for site managers. American Society of Civil Engineers, *Journal of the Construction Division.* September, 1977.

3. Woods, D. G. and Harris, F. C. Truck allocation model for concrete distribution. American Society of Civil Engineers, *Journal of the Construction Division.* June, 1980.

4. Speed, T. J. and Harris, F. C. Management games for use in the construction industry. Chartered Institute of Building. Occasional paper No. 15, 1977.

```
0001   LIST
0002   SEND TO (ED,SEMICOMPUSER,AXXX)
0003   DUMP ON (ED,PROGRAM USER)
0004   WORK (ED,WORKFILEUSER)
0005   RUN
0006   LIBRARY (ED,SUBGROUPNAGF)
0007   PROGRAM (MWAY)
0008   INPUT 1 = CRO
0009   OUTPUT2 = LPO
0010   OUTPUT3 = MTO/FORMATTED(FCHMWAY-INIT)
0011   OUTPUT4 = MT1/FORMATTED(PLAY)
0012   COMPRESS INTEGER AND LOGICAL
0013   TRACE 2
0014   END
```

```
0015        MASTER INITIAL MWAY
0016  C       THIS PROGRAM IS RUN BY THE GAME SUPERVISOR BEFORE PLAYING
0017  C       COMMENCES. INITIALISATION DATA IS READ FROM CARDS, CHECKED ,
0018  C       AND FINALLY WRITTEN TO THE DISK FILE FCHMWAY-INIT . THE
0019  C       TRANSIENT FILE 'PLAY' IS ALSO INITIALISED
0020          DIMENSION PRNAM (4,7) , IPRTYP (7) ; IUNITP (7) , STDPRD (7)
0021          DIMENSION PLCOST (7) ,IALPPR (7)
0022          DIMENSION START (7,20) , IUNIPQ (7,20) , IWKPLR (20) , EXPEND (20)
0023          DIMENSION PRCOST (7,20)
0024          DATA START,EXPEND,PRCOST,IUNIPQ,IWKPLR /300*0.0,160*0/
0025          WRITE (2,6)
0026  6       FORMAT('1     ROAD WAY CONSTRUCTION GAME - INITIALISATION DATA',
0027        &   '  INCLUDING STANDARD PROCESS PRODUCTIVITIES',
0028        &   /,90('-')
0029        &   /'0     PAYRAT  STDHRS  OVRRAT  COSTIN  HIRECO  RATWRK',
0030        &   '0   WAGHIR  TARGET  PROJLN  NPLAYR  OHRATE  OPRWID'
0031        &   /11X,'E',23X,'E',5X,'E/WK',4X,'M/HR',4X,'E/WK',6X,'M/DAY',
0032        &   4X,'KM',22X,'M')
0033  C       READ BASIC GAME PARAMETERS ...
0034          READ (1,7) PAYRAT,STDHRS,OVRRAT,COSTIN,HIRECO,RATWRK,WAGHIR,
0035        &   TARGET,PROJLN,NPLAYR,OHRATE,OPRWID
0036  7       FORMAT(F6.2,F6.0,F6.4,6F6.0,16,F6.2,F6.0)
0037  C       ... AND WRITE THEM OUT UNDER THE HEADINGS
0038          WRITE (2,8) PAYRAT,STDHRS,OVRRAT,COSTIN,HIRECO,RATWRK,WAGHIR,
0039        &   TARGET,PROJLN,NPLAYR,OHRATE,OPRWID
0040  8       FORMAT(' ',F6.2,2X,F6.0,2X,F6.4,2X,
0041        &   6(F6.0,2X),16,2X,F6.2,2X,F6.0 )
```

Fig. 18.2 Listing of game Fortran statements.

Fig. 18.2 – *continued*

```
0043  C        HEADING FOR NEXT PART
0044           WRITE(2,9)
0045     9 FORMAT('0        PROCESS NO. AND NAME IPRTYP IUNITP',
0046          ,'  STDPRD PLCOST'/8X;20('-'),/4(2X,6('-')) )
0047  C        NOW READ PROCESS PARAMETERS
0048           DO 25 I=1,7
0049           READ (1,10) (IPRNAM(J,I),J=1,4) , IALFPR(I) , IUNITP(I) ,
0050          STDPRD (I)
0051    10 FORMAT(4A4,A1,I6,F6.3)
0052  C        FOR FUTURE USE,CONVERT PROCESS TYPE TO A NUMERIC CODE :
0053  C
0054           DO 20 K=1,4
0055           J=1
0056           CALL COMP ( J,IALFPR(I),1,ITYPE,K )
0057           IF (J.NE.1) GO TO 20
0058  C        MATCH FOUND
0059           IPRTYP(I) = K
0060           GO TO 59
0061    20 CONTINUE
0062  C        MATCH NOT FOUND
0063           WRITE (2,21) I,(IPRNAM(J,I),J=1,4),IPRTYP(I)
0064    21 FORMAT(1X,20('*'),'PROCESS NO.',I2,' ',4A4,' HAS AN UNKNOWN',
0065          'PROCESS TYPE ',A1,/' THIS MUST BE CORRECTED AND',
0066          ' THE JOB RERUN BEFORE PLAY CAN COMMENCE !')
0067           STOP
0068    59 CONTINUE
0069  C        IF PRODUCTIVITY IS GIVEN AS ZERO, USE A RANDOM NUMBER 75%-125%
0070           IF ( ABS(STDPRD(I)) .LE. 1E04 ) STDPRD (I) = GO5ABF ( 0.75,1.25)
0071  C        ALL THIS INFORMATION IS WRITTEN LATER
0072  C        NEXT PROCESS
0073    25 CONTINUE
0074  C        CALCULATE PLANNED DURATION OF PROJECT (WEEKS)
0075  C        ( PROCESS ELAPSED TIME PLUS 6 BUFFERS )
0076           PLNDUR = (6 * OPRWID + PROJLN + 1000 ) / ( TARGET * 5 )
0077  C        PLANNED DIRECT COST, PLDICO
0078           PLDICO = 0.0
0079  C        PLANNED DURATION OF A PROCESS (WKS)
0080           PRTIME = PROJLN *1000 /( TARGET * 5 )
0081  C        ADD THE CONTRIBUTIONS FROM EACH PROCESS
0082           DO 60 I=1,7
0083           JUMPPR = IPRTYP (I)
0084           GO TO ( 41,42,43,44 ), JUMPPR
0085  C        TYPE L ( LABOURERS )
0086    41 PLCOST(I) = IUNITP(I) * PRTIME = PAYRAT * STDHRS
0087           PLDICO = PLDICO + PLCOST (I)
0088           GO TO 50
0089  C        TYPE G  ( GANG SIZE IS 3 )
```

```
C          TYPE M   ( 2 DRIVERS AND 2 MACHINES PER UNIT )
43    PLCOST(I) = IUNITP(I) * 2 * ( COSTIN + PRTIME * HIRECO
     &          + PRTIME + PAYRAT + STDHRS )
      PLDICO = PLDICO + PLCOST (I)
      GO TO 50
C          TYPE C   ( COST OF MACHINE PLUS LORRY DRIVERS )
46    PLCOST(I) = PRTIME + ( IUNITP(I) + WAGHIR + HIRECO ) + COSTIN
     &          + IUNITP (I) + PRTIME + PAYRAT + STDHRS
      PLDICO = PLDICO + PLCOST (I)
C
C      ALSO ,FOR TYPE C, SET IUNIPQ TO =1 TO SIGNIFY THAT NO
C          MACHINES ARE ON SITE AT START OF GAME
      DO 440 K=1,NPLAYR
      IUNIPQ (I,K) = =1
440   CONTINUE
C      WRITE OUT PROCESS PARAMETERS
50    WRITE (2,11) I,(IPRNAM(J,I),J=1,4) , IALFPR(I) , IUNITP(I) ,
     &          STDPRD (I) , PLCOST (I)
11    FORMAT(10 ',I3,')',4A4,4X,A1,4X,I5,4X,F6,3,2X,F8,2)
C      NEXT PROCESS
60    CONTINUE
C      OVERHEAD COST IS PLANNED WEEKLY COST * OHRATE
      OHCOST = PLDICO * OHRATE / PLNDUR
C      ADD OVERHEADS TO TOTAL COST
      TOCOST = PLDICO * ( 1.0 + OHRATE)
C      PRINT RESULTS OF THESE CALCULATIONS
      WRITE (2,51) PLNDUR,OHCOST,PLDICO,TOCOST
51    FORMAT (          PLANNED DURATION IS 1',F6,1,' WEEKS'/
     &                  OVERHEAD COST IS: £',F9,2,' PER WEEK'/
     &                  PLANNED DIRECT COST IS 1 £',F10,2/
     &                  PLANNED TOTAL COST IS 1 £',F10,2,
     &              ( INCLUDING OVERHEADS ) 1 )
C      NOW WRITE EVERYTHING TO DISK
      WRITE (3,37) PAYRAT,STDHRS,OVRRAT,COSTIN,HIRECO,RATWRK,WAGHIR,
     &      TARGET,PROJLN,NPLAYR,OHCOST,OPRWID,PNDUR,TOCOST
37    FORMAT(F6,2,F6,0,F6,4,6F6,0,I6,F9,2,F6,0,F6,1,F10,2)
      DO 30 I=1,7
      WRITE (3,27) (IPRNAM(J,I),J=1,4) , IPRTYP(I) , IUNITP(I) ,
     &      STDPRD (I) , PLCOST (I)
27    FORMAT(4A4,I1,I6,F6,3,F8,2)
30    CONTINUE
C      WRITE OUT INITIAL VERSION OF 'PLAY!
C          ( ALL ZERO EXCEPT IUNIPQ FOR "C" PROCESSES )
      DO 40 I=1,NPLAYR
      WRITE ( 4,29 )  ( START(J,I),J=1,7 ), (IUNIPQ(J,I),J=1,7),
     &      ( PRCOST(J,I),J=1,7 ), IWKPLR(I) , EXPEND (I)
29    FORMAT (7F10,2,7I6,(F10,2,F10,2)
40    CONTINUE
```

Fig. 18.2 – *continued*

```
0141      C              INITIALISATION COMPLETE
0142             WRITE (2,31)
0143          31 FORMAT(/// INITIALISATION COMPLETE!)
0144             STOP
0145             END
```

END OF SEGMENT, LENGTH   657, NAME INITIALWAY

```
0146          FINISH
```

END OF COMPILATION = NO ERRORS

FORTRAN COMPILATION BY #XFAT 11K 5A   DATE 14/07/76   TIME 09/58/03

```
0001       LIST
0002       SEND TO (ED,SEMICOMPUSER,AXXX)
0003       DUMP ON (ED,PROGRAM USER)
0004       WORK (ED,WORKFILEUSER)
0005       RUN
0006       LIBRARY (ED,SUBGROUPNAGF)
0007       PROGRAM (PLAY)
0008       INPUT 1 = CRO
0009       OUTPUT2 = LPO
0010       INPUT 3 = MTO/FORMATTED(FCHMWAY=INIT)
0011       INPUT 4 = MT1/FORMATTED(FCHMWAY=PLAY)
0012       OUTPUT5 = MT2/FORMATTED(PLAY)
0013       INPUT 6 =        /ARRAY
0014       TRACE 2
0015       COMPRESS INTEGER AND LOGICAL
0016       END
0017       MASTER PLAY
0018       LOGICAL MSEEN(20) , EQUAL , TO WORK (7,20)
0019       INTEGER HOURS
0020       DIMENSION ACLENG (7)
0021       DIMENSION START (7,20),IWKPLR (20),IUNIPQ (7,20),EXPEND (20)
0022       DIMENSION IWEEK (20)
```

```
0026      DIMENSION PRCOST, ( 7,50/
0027      DATA TPROC,NPROD,HOURS/230*0./140*0.0/
0028      DATA MSEEN,TO WORK /160*.FALSE./
0029      CALL DEFBUF ( 6,80,BUFFER )
0030   C
0031          READ FIXED DATA FROM INITR
0032      READ (3,7) PAYRAT,STDHRS,OVRRAT,COSTIN,AIRECO,RATWRK,WAGHIR,
0033     8          TARGET,PROJLN,NPLAYR,OHCOST,OPRWID,PLNDUR,TOCOST
0034    7 FORMAT(F6.2,F6.0,F6.4,6F6.0,I6,F9.2,F6.0,F6.1,F10.2)
0035      DO 10 I=1,7
0036          READ (3,9) (IPRNAM(J,I),J=1,4) , IPRTYP(I) , IUNITP(I) ,
0037     8                STDPRD(I), PLCOST (I)
0038    9 FORMAT(4A4,I1,I6,F6.3,F8.2)
0039   10 CONTINUE
0040   C
0041          READ DATA REFERRING TO PREVIOUS OPERATIONS FROM "PLAY"
0042      DO 20 I=1,NPLAYR
0043          READ (4,17) (START (J,I),J=1,7), (IUNIPQ (J,I),J=1,7) ,
0044     8              ( PRCOST (J,I),J=1,7)    IWKPLR (I) , EXPEND (I)
0045   17 FORMAT (7F10.2,716,/F10.2,216,F10.2 )
0046
0047   20 CONTINUE
0048   C
0049   C       THE INPUT DECK CONSISTS OF ANY NUMBER OF PLIES , BUT NOT MORE
0050   C       THAN ONE FROM EACH PLAYER. WEEK NUMBER IS SPECIFIED SEPARATELY
0051   C       ON EACH PLY
0052   C
0053          READ INPUT DECK - TERMINATED BY END-OF-FILE
0054      NPLIES = 0
0055   30 READ (1,31,END=99) BUFFER
0056   31 FORMAT(10A8)
0057   C          REREAD PREVIOUS CARD FROM BUFFER
0058      READ (6,32) DOLLAR,I,J
0059   32 FORMAT (A1,1X,2I2 )
0060   C          EACH PLY SHOULD START WITH A HEADER CARD , CONSISTING OF
0061   C          $ , VALID PLAYER NO., VALID WEEK NO.
0062      IF ( EQUAL ( DOLLAR,1,1,'$1' )
0063     8         .AND. I .GT. 0
0064     8         .AND. I .LE. NPLAYR
0065     8         .AND. J .GT. 0 ) GO TO 40
0066      WRITE (2,3) I,J,NPLAYR
0067    3 FORMAT ('PLAYER',I10/' WEEK NO',I10/' TOTAL PLAYERS',I10)
0068   35 WRITE (2,33) BUFFER
0069   33 FORMAT(1X,20(1>),'THE FOLLOWING CARD IS IGNORED - HEADER EXP',
0070     8          'ECTED' /1X,10A8)
0071   C          KEEP ON LOOKING FOR A HEADER
          GO TO 30
```

Fig. 18.2 – continued

```
0072  C     IS WEEK NO. CORRECT ? & IS THIS THE PLAYERS ONLY PLY ?
0073  40    IF ( J=1 .EQ. IWKPLR (I) .AND. .NOT. MSEEN (I) ) GO TO 45
0074        WRITE (2,61) I , IWKPLR (I)
0075  41    FORMAT (1X,20(1>),'LAST WEEK RECORDED FOR PLAYER',I3,' WAS ',I3 )
0076        GO TO 35
0077  C     HEADER CARD OK
0078  45    IPLAYR = I
0079        IWEEK (IPLAYR) = J
0080        IPRPRV = 0
0081  C     COUNT NUMBER OF PLIES
0082        NPLIES = NPLIES + 1
0083  C     REMEMBER THIS PLAYER
0084        MSEEN (IPLAYR) = .TRUE.
0085  C     READ A PLY CARD FOR EACH PROCESS ( MAX 7 )
0086        DO 60 K=1,7
0087        READ (1,31) BUFFER
0088  C     IT MAY BE A PLY TERMINATOR ...
0089        READ (6,32) DOLLAR
0090  C     ....  IF IT IS, GET NEXT HEADER
0091        IF ( EQUAL ( DOLLAR(1,1,ISI ) ) GO TO 30
0092  C     OTHERWISE READ PROCESS NO.,? NO. UNITS , NO. HRS
0093        READ (6,51) I,J,IHRS
0094  51    FORMAT (3I2)
0095  C     CHECK FOR NONSENSE INPUT
0096        IF ( I .GE. 1
0097      &     .AND. I .LE. 7
0098      &     .AND. J .GE. 0
0099      &     .AND. IHRS .GE. 0
0100      &     .AND. IHRS .LE. 60 ) GO TO 55
0101        WRITE ( 2,53) IPLAYR,I,J,IHRS
0102  53    FORMAT ( 1X,20(1>),'PLAYER NO',I3,' INPUT PLY IGNORED'/
0103      &     25X,'NONSENSE PROCESS INFORMATION'/
0104      &     25X,'PROCESS NO',I5/
0105      &     25X,'PROD. UNITS',I5,
0106      &     25X,'HOURS TO WORK',I5 )
0107  C     CHECK PROCESSES ARE IN ASCENDING NUMERIC ORDER & NO GAPS
0108        GO TO 30
0109  55    IF ( IPRPRV.EQ.0
0110      &.OR. IPRPRV+1 .EQ. I ) GO TO 59
0111  C     IGNORE WHOLE PLY IF ORDER IS WRONG
0112        MSEEN (IPLAYR) = .FALSE.
0113        WRITE (2,52) IPLAYR
0114  52    FORMAT(' PROCESSES IN WRONG ORDER - PLY IGNORED,PLAYER NO.', I3)
0115  C     GET NEXT HEADER
0116        GO TO 30
0117  C     REMEMBER THIS PROCESS NO.
0118  59    IPRPRV = I
0119  C     PROCESS INPUT OK - SO STORE PROCESS INFORMATION
0120        TO WORK (I,IPLAYR) = .TRUE.
```

```
0125        DU CONTINUE
0126  C        IF THE SEVENTH PROCESS IS WORKING ...
0127  C        SKIP PLAYER'S END DOLLAR CARD
0128
0129        READ ( 1,64 )
0130  66    FORMAT (1X)
0131  C     2)    NEXT CARD IS NEXT PLAYER'S HEADER (OR EOF )
0132
0133        GO TO 30
0134
0135  C     ALL THE DATA HAS BEEN READ IN , SO NOW CALCULATE , FOR EACH
0136  C     PLAYER AND FOR EACH PROCESS , THE WEEK'S PROGRESS
0137  99    DO 300 I=1,NPLAYR
0138  C        HAS PLAYER(I) PRESENTED A PLY ?
0139        IF ( .NOT.MSEEN(I) ) GO TO 300
0140  C        WRITE IDENTIFICATION HEADING FOR EACH PLAYER
0141
0142        WRITE (2,69) I , IWEEK(I)
0143  69    FORMAT('1',12X,'----'/3X,'PLAYER NO.',I12,I.I/13X,'----'/
0144      &  '0 WEEK NO.',I12/30X,'PRODUCTION UNITS',14X,
0145      &  'LENGTH COMPLETED',22X,'TOTAL COST TO DATE'/
0146      &  12X,'PROCESS',15X,'EMPLOYED',6X,
0147      &  'HOURS',11X,'METRES'/8X,'COST',13X,'ACTUAL',7X,'PLANNED'/)
0148  C        INITIALISE COST COUNTER
0149  C        ( WCOST IS TOTAL COST FOR PLAYER I   THIS WEEK )
0150
0151        WCOST = 0.0
0152  C        ...AND PLANNED COST ACCUMULATOR
0153        TOTCPL = 0.0
0154        JFIRST = 0
0155  C        FOR EACH PROCESS
0156
0157        DO 290 J=1,7
0158  C        IS PROCESS MENTIONED THIS WEEK ?
0159        IF ( .NOT.TO WORK(J,I) ) GO TO 260
0160  C        REMEMBER FIRST PROCESS
0161        IF ( JFIRST.EQ.0 ) JFIRST = J
0162  C        DOES PLAYER WISH THIS PROCESS TO WORK THIS WEEK ?
0163        IF ( IPROC( J,I ).EQ.0 .OR. NPROD(J,I) .LE. 0
0164      &        .OR. HOURS (J,I) .LE. 0 ) GO TO 130
0165
0166  C        FIRST CALCULATE WEEK'S PRODUCTION
0167
0168  C        FIND INCREASE IN NO. OF PRODUCTION
0169  C           UNITS OVER PREVIOUS WEEK
0170        INCREA = NPROD (J,I) - IUNIPQ (J,I)
0171        IF ( INCREA.LT.0 ) INCREA =0
           C     ... CALCULATE PRODUCTIVITY FACTOR ACCORDING TO TYPE
           JUMPTY = IPRTYP (J)
           GO TO ( 112,112,134,134 ) ,JUMPTY
      C     TYPE L =LABOURES    AND TYPE G =GANGS
      112   PRODTY = ( IUNIPQ(J,I) + 0.5 * INCREA ) / IUNITP (J)
           GO TO 120
```

Fig. 18.2 – *continued*

```
0172  C              TYPE M =MACHINES   AND TYPE C =CONTINUOUS MACHINES
0173  134    PRODTY = FLOAT ( NPROD(J,I) ) / IUNITP (J)
0174  C
0175  C              PROTO=PRODUCTION (METRES) = PRODUCTIVITY FACTOR
0176  C                        * TIME FACTOR * PROGRESS FACTOR
0177  C              * RANDOM PRODUCTIVITY FACTOR (OVERALL * THIS WEEK)
0178  C
0179  120    PROTOP = PRODTY * ( HOURS (J,I) / STDHRS ) * TARGET *5
0180         * STDPRD (J) * GOSABF (0.75,1.25)
0181  C              FOR TYPES M AND C RATE OF WORK MUST NOT EXCEED
0182  C              MAX. RATE OF MACHINE
0183         IF ((IPRTYP (J) .EQ. 3 .OR. IPRTYP (J) .EQ.4)
0184       & .AND. PROTOP / HOURS (J,I) .GT. RATWRK )
0185       & PROTOP = RATWRK * HOURS (J,I)
0186  C
0187         GO TO 140
0188  C              PROTO PRODUCTION ZERO FOR OMITTED PROCESSES
0189  130    PROTOP = 0.0
0190  C              CALCULATE ACTUAL PRODUCTION FROM PROTOP PRODUCTION
0191  C              BY KEEPING PROCESSES AT LEAST 'OPRWID' APART
0192  140    ACLENG (J) = START (J,I) * PROTOP
0193  C              NO BUFFERING APPLIES TO FIRST PROCESS OF PLY
0194         IF ( J.EQ.JFIRST ) GO TO 170
0195         IF ( ACLENG ( J-1 ) .GE. PROJLN * 1000 - 0.5 ) GO TO 170
0196  C              PROCESSES MUST KEEP AT LEAST OPRWID M APART
0197         IF ( ACLENG(J-1) - ACLENG(J) .LT. OPRWID )
0198       & ACLENG (J) = ACLENG (J-1) - OPRWID
0199  C              MAXM PRODUCTION DOESN'T EXCEED PROJECTED LENGTH
0200         IF ( ACLENG(J) .GT. PROJLN * 1000 )
0201       & ACLENG (J) = PROJLN * 1000
0202  C
0203  C              NOW CALCULATE PRODUCTION COSTS
0204  C
0205  C              OVERTIME HOURS
0206         OVER = HOURS (J,I) - STDHRS
0207         IF ( OVER.LT.0.0 ) OVER = 0.0
0208  C              CALCULATE COSTS ACCORDING TO TYPE
0209  200    JUMPTY = IPRTYP (J)
0210         GO TO ( 210,220,230,260 ),JUMPTY
0211  C              TYPE L NPROD IS MEN
0212  210    COST = NPROD (J,I) * PAYRAT * ( STDHRS + OVRRAT*OVER )
0213         GO TO 250
0214  C              TYPE G : NPROD IS GANGS ( 3 MEN / GANG )
0215  220    COST = NPROD (J,I) * PAYRAT * ( STDHRS + OVRRAT*OVER ) * 3
0216         GO TO 250
0217  C              TYPE M : NPROD IS ( DOZER + SCRAPER ) UNITS
```

```
      C          TYPE C , COST OF MACHINE + LORRIES + DRIVERS
0221
0222  260   COST = HIRECO +
0223     &         NPROD (J,I) * ( WAGHIR * ( 1.0 + OVER / STDHRS ) +
0224     &                         PAYRAT * ( STDHRS + OVRRAT * OVER ) )
0225
0226        GO TO 250
0227  C          ACCUMULATE TOTAL EXPENDITURE FOR PLAYER( I )
0228  250   WCOST = WCOST + COST
0229  C          ACCUMULATE PROCESS EXPENDITURES
0230        PRCOST (J,I) = PRCOST (J,I) + COST
0231  C          STORE CURRENT PRODUCTION DETAILS
0232        START (J,I) = ACLENG (J)
0233  C          STORE PRODUCTION UNITS IN USE
0234        IUNIPQ (J,I) = NPROD (J,I)
0235  C          CALCULATE PLANNED COST FOR PROCESS GIVEN THAT
0236  C             'START' METRES ARE COMPLETE
0237  260   COSTPL = START (J,I) / PROJLN / 1000 * PLCOST (J)
0238  C             AND PLANNED COST TO DATE, OVER ALL PROCESSES
0239        TOTCPL = TOTCPL + COSTPL
0240  C          NO OUTPUT FOR PROCESSES NOT WORKED
0241        IF ( .NOT. TO WORK(J,I) ) GO TO 290
0242  C          WRITE OUT RESULTS FOR PROCESS J
0243        WRITE (2,270) J,(IPRNAM(K,J),K=1,4),NPROD (J,I),HOURS (J,I),
0244     &        ACLENG (J) , COST , PRCOST (J,I) , COSTPL
0245  270   FORMAT ( 5X,I2,' ',4A4,10X,I3,10X,I3,12X,F8.2,
0246     &        4X,'£',F8.2,11X,'£',F8.2,4X,'£',F8.2 )
0247  C          NEXT PROCESS
0248  290   CONTINUE
0249        IWKPLR(I) = IWEEK (I)
0250  C          THIS WEEK'S COSTS
0251        TOTAL = WCOST + OHCOST
0252        WRITE (2,298) IWKPLR (I) , WCOST , OHCOST , TOTAL
0253  298   FORMAT ( //10X,'COSTS FOR WEEK',I3
0254     &        /12X,'ACTUAL  £',F10.2
0255     &        /12X,'OVERHEAD £',F10.2
0256     &        /12X,'TOTAL   £',F10.2 )
0257  C          ACCUMULATE COST OVER ALL PREVIOUS WEEKS
0258        EXPEND (I) = EXPEND (I) + TOTAL
0259  C          ADD OVERHEADS TO TOTAL PLANNED COSTS
0260        OVHWKS = IWKPLR (I)
0261        IF ( IWKPLR (I) .GT. PLNDUR ) OVHWKS = PLNDUR
0262        TOTCPL = TOTCPL + OVHWKS * OHCOST
0263        WRITE (2,299) TOTCPL
0264  299   FORMAT ( // 10X,'TOTAL COSTS TO DATE '' ACTUAL : £',F12.2/
0265     &                    31X,'PLANNED : £',F12.2 )
0266  C          NEXT PLAYER
      300   CONTINUE
```

Fig. 18.2 – *continued*

```
0267    C                       AFTER PLY-PROCESSING , WRITE PRODUCTION DETAILS TO 5'
0268            DO 350 I=1,NPLAYR
0269            WRITE (5,17) ( START(J,I),J=1,7 ) , (IUNIPQ(J,I),J=1,7) ,
0270          &              ( PRCOST (J,I),J = 1,7 ) ,
0271          &              IWKPLR(I) , EXPEND (I) )
0272    350 CONTINUE       END=OF=JOB MESSAGE
0273    C
0274            WRITE (2,351) NPLIES
0275    351 FORMAT('1 NUMBER OF PLIES PROCESSED =',I3 )
0276            STOP
0277            END

END OF SEGMENT, LENGTH  1315, NAME  PLAY

0278            LOGICAL FUNCTION EQUAL ( WORD , MSTART , NLONG , TEST )
0279    C                  TESTS THE EQUALITY OF THE FIRST NLONG CHARS OF TEST
0280    C                  ( NLONG.LE.8 ) AND NLONG CHARS OF WORD STARTING FROM
0281    C                  CHARACTER=POSITION MSTART
0282            NN = NLONG
0283            CALL COMP ( NN,WORD,MSTART,TEST,1 )
0284    C             IF THEY ARE EQUAL
0285            EQUAL = NLONG .EQ. NN
0286            RETURN

0287            END

END OF SEGMENT, LENGTH   59, NAME  EQUAL

0288    FINISH

END OF COMPILATION = NO ERRORS
```

ROAD WAY CONSTRUCTION GAME - INITIALISATION DATA INCLUDING STANDARD PROCESS PRODUCTIVITIES

PAYRAT £	STDHRS	OVRRAT £	COSTIN £	HIRECO £/WK	RATWRK M/HR	WAGHIR £/WK	TARGET M/DAY	PROJLN KM	NPLAYR	OHRATE	OPRWID M
4.00	40.	1.5000	250.	500.	100.	150.	200.	10.	15	0.20	1000.

PROCESS NO. AND NAME	IPRTYP	IUNITP	STDPRD	PLCOST
1)SURFACE TRIM	M	3	0.893	36300.00
2)LAY SUB-BASE	C	20	1.237	51250.00
3)FRENCH DRAINS	G	10	0.942	24000.00
4)KERB LAYING	L	10	0.888	8000.00
5)LEAN MIX PAVER	C	10	1.237	28250.00
6)WEARING SURFACE	C	5	1.022	16750.00
7)FINISHING	L	10	1.229	8000.00

PLANNED DURATION IS : 16.0 WEEKS

OVERHEAD COST IS : £ 2156.87 PER WEEK

PLANNED DIRECT COST IS : £ 172550.00

PLANNED TOTAL COST IS : £ 207060.00 (INCLUDING OVERHEADS)

INITIALISATION COMPLETE

Fig. 18.3 Example of data input by the game supervisor.

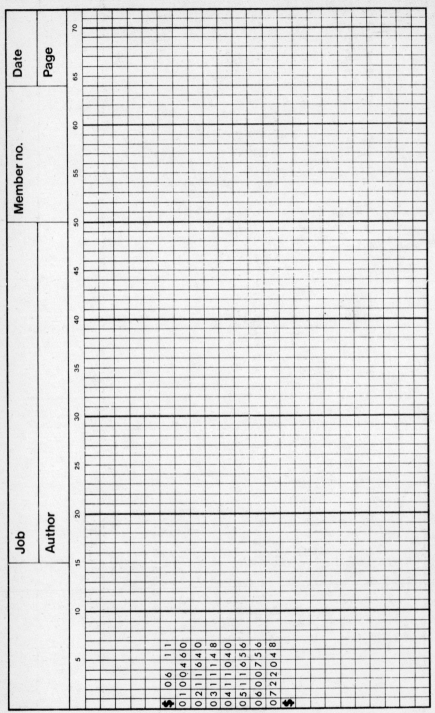

Fig. 18.4 Example of data input by a player.

```
PLAYER NO. +11+

WEEK NO. 7

                              PRODUCTION UNITS        LENGTH COMPLETED                    TOTAL COST TO DATE
         PROCESS              EMPLOYED   HOURS         (METRES)        COST               ACTUAL        PLANNED

1 )  SURFACE TRIM                2        40          10000.00     £ 2320.00             £37980.00     £36300.00
2 )  LAY SUB-BASE               20        55           9798.31     £ 7125.00             £42075.00     £50216.32
3 )  FRENCH DRAINS              13        60           7497.33     £ 5460.00             £22260.00     £17993.59
4 )  KERB LAYING                12        60           6497.33     £ 1680.00             £ 7420.00     £ 5197.86
5 )  LEAN MIX PAVER             10        50           5478.16     £ 3475.00             £11100.00     £15475.80
6 )  WEARING SURFACE             5        60           2833.42     £ 2325.00             £ 448.25      £ 4745.98
7 )  FINISHING                  10        60           1072.84     £ 1400.00             £ 1400.00     £ 858.27


     COSTS FOR WEEK 7
       ACTUAL   £ 23785.00
       OVERHEAD £  2156.87
       TOTAL    £ 25941.87


     TOTAL COSTS TO DATE , ACTUAL : £  141814.34
                           PLANNED : £  145885.91
```

Fig. 18.5 Progress information from computer.

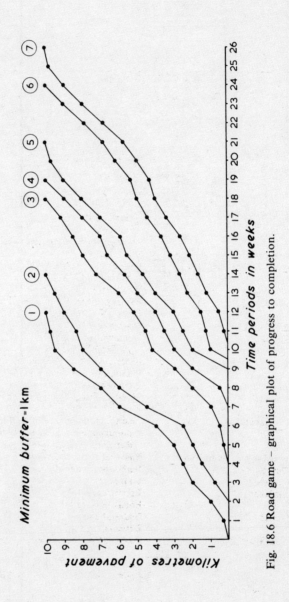

Fig. 18.6 Road game – graphical plot of progress to completion.